·S̲TAR· ·
W̲A̲L̲K

Grateful acknowledgment is made to the following publishers, authors, and agents for their permission to reprint copyrighted material. Any adaptations are noted in the individual acknowledgments and are made with the full knowledge and approval of the authors or their representatives. Every effort has been made to locate all copyright proprietors; any errors or omissions in copyright notice are inadvertent and will be corrected in future printings as they are discovered.

"Airy-Go-Round" adapted from *The Twenty-One Balloons* written and illustrated by William Pène du Bois. Copyright © 1947, renewed © 1975 by William Pène du Bois. Reprinted by permission of Viking Penguin Inc.

"Animal Language" excerpt adapted by permission of the American publisher, Pantheon Books, a Division of Random House, Inc., and of the British publisher, Angus & Robertson (UK), from *How Animals Communicate* by Bil Gilbert. Copyright © 1966 by Bil Gilbert.

"Another April" by Jesse Stuart. Copyright 1942, 1946, copyright © 1970, 1974 renewed Jesse Stuart. Adapted and used by permission of Marian Reiner for The Jesse Stuart Foundation, P. O. Box 391, Ashland, KY 41114.

"A Blessing" by James Wright. Copyright © 1961 by James Wright. This poem first appeared in *Poetry* magazine. Reprinted from *The Branch Will Not Break* by permission of Wesleyan University Press.

Acknowledgments continue on pages 638–640, which constitute an extension of this copyright page.

WORLD OF READING

·STAR· WALK

P. DAVID PEARSON   DALE D. JOHNSON

THEODORE CLYMER   ROSELMINA INDRISANO   RICHARD L. VENEZKY

JAMES F. BAUMANN   ELFRIEDA HIEBERT   MARIAN TOTH

Consulting Authors

CARL GRANT   JEANNE PARATORE

SILVER BURDETT & GINN

NEEDHAM, MA • MORRISTOWN, NJ
ATLANTA, GA • CINCINNATI, OH • DALLAS, TX
MENLO PARK, CA • NORTHFIELD, IL

TURNING POINTS

UNIT
ONE

5

Making Connections

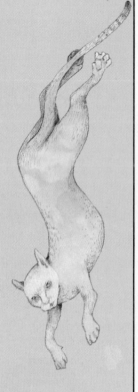

7

On Dreamers' Wings

UNIT
· THREE ·

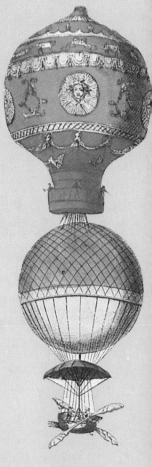

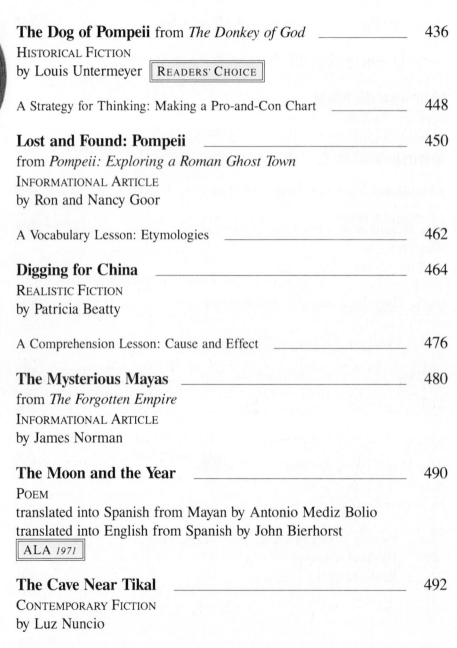

WHISPERS FROM THE PAST — 434

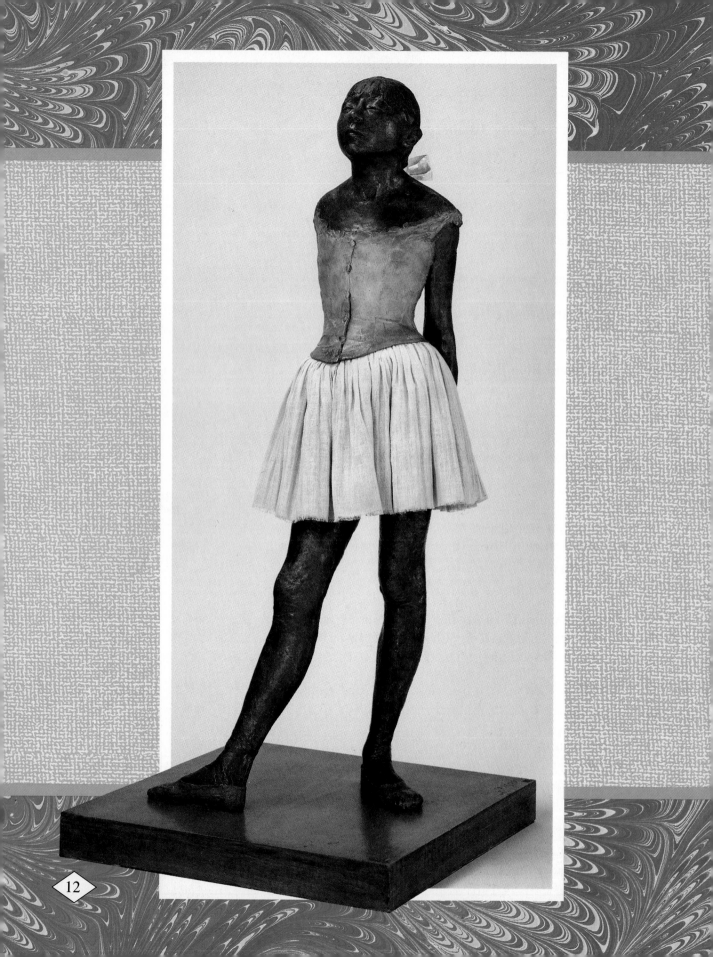

TURNING POINTS

*E*ach person is a truth," a wise person once said.

How do stories help you know what is true for you?

LITTLE FOURTEEN-YEAR-OLD DANCER,
bronze sculpture by Hilaire Germain Edgar Degas, French, 1922

Playing in a band takes cooperation as well as skill; but when a talented and mysterious bass player joins Eddie's band, he doesn't quite seem to be the cooperative type.

Blues Busters

by Judie Angell

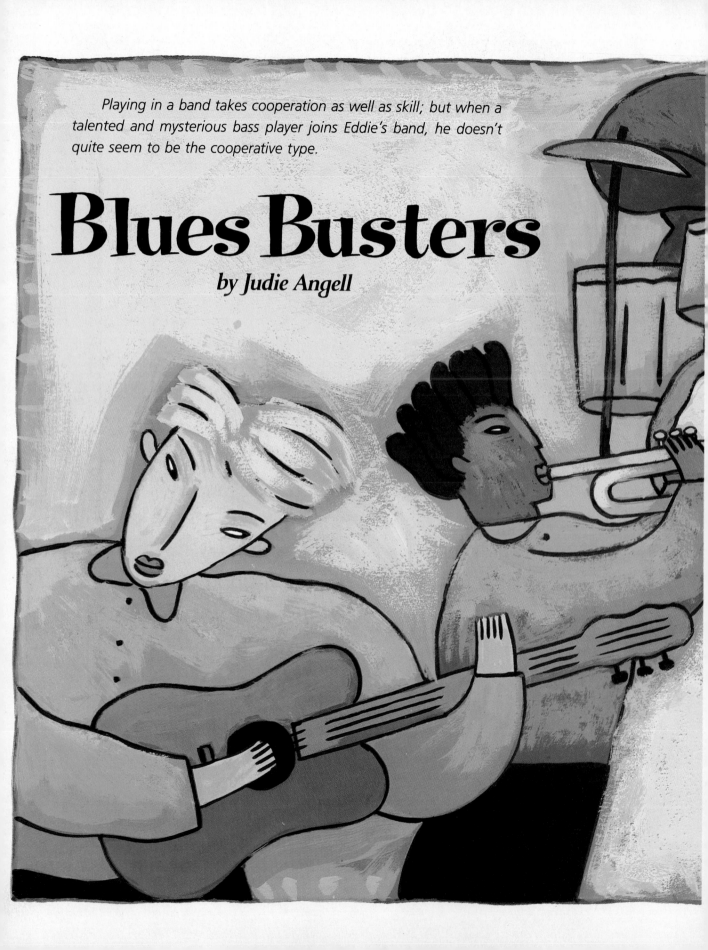

With Ivy on drums, Georgie on guitar, and Eddie on keyboards, the Centerin City Blues Trio was a big hit at the neighborhood picnic. On the advice of an experienced musician, they decided to develop their own "blues" sound. They added Shelby—a brilliant trumpet player— to the group. Now they need a good bass player. They've tacked up notices all over town: "Wanted: Bass guitar player for blues band. Must be fourteen or under. Call Eddie: 555-4234."

"Eddie."

"Yes, Pop?"

"Your music is going well? You've added a horn now?"

"A trumpet. Shelby Powell. You'll meet him soon, Pop, he's really good, but he can never stay past about quarter-to-five."

"Your mother says it sounds loud in there. In the garage."

"She doesn't like it?"

"No, no, you know your mother, she loves that you're making music. I was thinking about Dr. Broigen."

"No problem! Shelby's been with us a couple of weeks now and we haven't heard a word from Broigen. What is he, anyway?"

"He's a plant pathologist."

"Oh."

"Haven't you been wondering why you haven't heard him complain lately?"

"No . . ."

"Well, I'll tell you the reason. It's because he's not home. Your sister's been watering his plants and feeding his cats."

"She has?"

"You've been very busy, Eddie, you haven't noticed. Dr. Broigen is in Michigan."

"What's he doing there?"

"There are eight groves of trees in Michigan that have survived the blight. He's out there studying them."

"Oh. Great!"

"Not great. He's coming back soon and now that you're adding musicians to your group you might be in for some trouble. From him. You'd better think about that."

"But Pop, we only practice in the afternoons after school. It's not as if we play loud at night or anything . . ."

"I'm just telling you."

"Yeah, okay, Pop, thanks."

I couldn't worry about Mr. Broigen and his chestnut trees. I had much more important things to think about like where we were going to get our bass player. Every night I sat by the phone hoping someone would call about our ad, but nothing happened.

As it turned out, our bass player didn't phone. He kind of hunched up to me on my way out of school one afternoon in late October. Just as we had begun to think there were no bass players anywhere near Centerin City!

"Are you Eddie?"

"Yeah . . ."

"I want to talk to you."

"I'm in a hurry," I said. I was. We had to get to practice before Shelby the Mystery Man had to go home.

"Do you want a bass player or not?"

I stopped and looked him over. He was kind of mangy-looking and he had his hair all slicked back except for one curl that hung down over his forehead.

"You mean you?" I asked stupidly.

"Yeah, me, what's wrong with that?"

"Nothing. Nothing. You have to audition, though."

"Yeah, okay. When, now?"

"Now is fine. We're rehearsing at my house. Out in back, in the garage. Where's your bass?"

"I'll get it. Where do you live?"

"24 Coral."

"I'll be there."

"You have to be there soon. We quit at four-forty-five."

"Do you punch a clock?"

"It's a long story. What's your name?"

"Reese."

"First or last?"

"Both."

I barely had enough time to explain about Reese to the others before he showed up. He was carrying a burlap bag and the smallest amp I'd ever seen.

I introduced him to Ivy and Shelby and Georgie, whose eyebrows went through his hairline as Reese pulled his guitar out of the bag.

"Where do I plug in?" Reese asked, holding the power cord from his amp and looking around.

"You're not going to get any power out of that thing," Georgie wailed. "When was it made, 1909? That's no bass amp, that toy'll never give you any bottom!"

"Oh, yeah?" Reese snarled.

Things were getting off to a flying start. I elbowed Georgie who decided that amends were in order.

"Hey. I'm sorry. Look, the outlet's over there, but why don't you plug into my amp, okay?" And then he added, "I didn't mean anything . . ."

Reese accepted the apology by plugging into Georgie's amp.

"What'll you have?" I asked Reese.

"Crossroads," he answered, and then it was my turn for raised eyebrows.

"Really?" I asked.

"You're a blues band, aren't you? That's what the sign said."

"Yeah, we sure are!" I cried. "Crossroads is a great number! Shelby does a terrific wah-wah trumpet in that, don't you, Shel? Hey, you like Eric Clapton?"

"My brother says Eric Clapton is the best guitarist in the world."

"What's your brother play?" Ivy asked.

"Bass. Just like me. He taught me."

"How come he didn't come around to audition?"

Reese laughed.

"What's so funny?"

"He's twenty-eight years old. Anyway, he doesn't have time for band-playin'."

"All right," I said, sitting down at my keyboard, "let's do it, one . . . two . . . one, two, three, four—"

When the song was over, we chewed our lips and nodded our heads at each other.

"He sure was right on top of the beat," Ivy said.

"Whatever changes I played, he heard," I added.

"Good beat," Georgie said. "Very nice."

Shelby smiled. "He seems real good," he said.

"You've got a job with us if you want it, Reese," I said.

"Do you guys make any money?" he asked.

"Not yet. We just completed our band. Now we have to go to work, build up a repertoire, learn to work together. Then we can advertise and stuff."

Ivy said, "If we try really hard, maybe we can be ready by Christmas and pick up

17

on all the holiday parties!"

"Yeah! Well, let's start right now! How about it?" I cried. "Let's do *Crossroads* again. Let's see what we can do this time."

We were halfway through it when the garage door burst open.

We stopped instantly. Ivy muttered, "Uh oh."

"Welcome home, Mr. Broigen," I sighed.

"*Doctor* Broigen. And this is not what I consider a welcome. I thought you said this wasn't going to continue, Eddie."

I wanted to say "It's Edward," but I didn't. I said, "Well, I promised there wouldn't be any more firecrackers, Dr. Broigen, and there won't be."

"I can't work with this, Eddie. You're going to have to find another place to practice. Besides, it's getting cold now. Aren't you cold working in here?"

"No . . . we're not cold . . ."

"Listen, stay cool," Reese said, as Ivy covered her mouth to stifle a giggle. "We're not here to interfere with anyone's work, right?" Reese looked at the four of us but didn't wait for our answer. "Right," he said, "so don't worry about it. I'll take care of it."

Mr.—*Dr.* Broigen looked at me. I looked at Reese and shrugged. "He'll take care of it," I said and prayed silently.

"This is our only practice place," I said after Dr. Broigen left. "How are you going to take care of the sound? What can you do?"

Reese put up both his palms and closed his eyes. "I said I'd take care of it and I'll take care of it. You've got the word of Reese."

I decided to take the word of Reese. I still didn't want to worry about Broigen. Now, just when our band was complete I only wanted to think about that. I told Reese when we rehearsed and he said it was okay with him. He wouldn't tell us what grade he was in or even how old he was. He seemed mysterious, too, although not in the way Shelby was.

"It doesn't matter," Ivy said, as I walked her home that afternoon. "If he shows up and works hard and we have a good group with a new sound, that's what matters."

"But don't you wonder, though? Don't you wonder why shy ol' Shelby gets hyper if a tune runs over four-forty-five? Don't you wonder about Reese and why he won't say what grade he's in?"

"Yeah, I wonder," she said, "but I don't lose sleep over it. Neither should you."

"Oh, I don't, I don't. But . . . remember when we were talking about special friends and being up front and all that?"

"Uh huh . . ."

"Well, you're like that with me . . . and so is Ham, I guess, but Ham's pretty laid back most of the time . . ."

"But Shelby's not that kind of special friend. Is that what you mean? Because he doesn't talk about himself much, or Reese either?"

"Maybe," I answered. "But not exactly.

I mean, Georgie's pretty straight and I like him, it's just more than that. I tried to tell you before . . . You know, before we started working together last year—before all our free time was taken up practicing and stuff—I had a couple of friends, guys I used to hang out with—used to play D and D with them all the time . . ."

"Me, too," she said. "I mean, I had some girlfriends I just don't see any more."

"Yeah, same with me. But you know, I don't really mind it so much because I always have somebody to talk to about anything. You. I guess you're my best friend, Ivy." I wasn't sure if she knew, so I thought I'd better tell her.

"Does that bother you?" she asked after a minute. It wasn't the response I had expected.

"Bother me? No! What do you mean, *bother* me?"

"Well, for one thing, I'm a girl."

"No kidding."

"Usually twelve-year-old boys don't have best friends who are girls. Not to mention that I'm black and Presbyterian and you're white and Jewish, and—"

"Hey, Ivy, does it bother *you?*" I interrupted.

"Not at all," she said firmly. "You're my best friend now, too. Only sometimes I think about what other people think."

"What difference does that—"

"Not that what other people think is going to change me, no way," she said. "What I want is to play drums and be in

a blues band and have you for my best friend and I want all that to go on forever and ever. The thing is, though, I know that makes me different from other girls my age and sometimes I wonder about that and when you said just now that I was your best friend I knew you were wondering about it too. That's all."

"Oh. Well, yeah, I know what you mean. But our music for example— We want that to be different . . . to stand out from other groups, right?"

"Oh, sure, but there's 'different' and 'different'," she said. "You can stand out by wearing freaky clothes, too, y'know . . ." She laughed.

"Listen," I said, "even if some people think we're freaks right now, I don't even care. We'll show them when we start working. I've never seen such talented people, have you?"

"No, you're right," she said. "There never have been such talented people as we are."

The next afternoon when Ivy, Georgie, Shelby, and I arrived at the garage after school, Reese was standing in front of it, leaning against the door. My mother was standing next to him, smiling. Now what was this?

"Ma?"

"We have a surprise for you," she said.

"We?"

"Your friend Reese and I." She winked conspiratorially at Reese who winked back.

Talk about your odd couple!

"Well, . . . let's not keep them in suspense," my mother said and flung open the garage door.

The four of us stood there gawking. The walls of the garage were covered with—mattresses.

"Ma?" I said. Ivy's jaw was hanging down.

"Instant soundproofing!" my mother cried.

"And insulation!" Reese added. "Energy-saving, like the government wants." He folded his arms across his chest.

"Wha— Where did they come from?"

My mother spread her hands. "Listen," she said, "this morning, right after you left for school, there I was, scouring out the bathroom sink, when my eye catches on something crawling down the driveway toward the garage. I put down the scouring pad and go over to the window and I see what it is crawling. A mattress."

"Huh?"

"It's a mattress, only it isn't crawling by itself. Reese is under it. I go out there and stand in front of him as he's about to drop it on the ground here. 'Why are you dropping a mattress in front of my garage?' I say."

Reese opened his mouth then, but my mother said, "Sh! So he says, 'It isn't just one mattress I'm delivering, it's twelve.' I say, *Twelve mattresses?* I didn't even order one!' "

Reese and I both opened our mouths then, but my mother said, "Sh! So he explains how he got this idea to sound-proof the garage so Dr. Broigen can cure his chestnut tree blight in peace and you musicians can go on with your work uninterrupted. And he said how it would keep out the draft and wind. He said if he worked all day he could probably get five mattresses over here."

"Hey, Reese," I said, beginning to recover a little. "That was a great idea!"

"Yeah, but you got more than five here," Georgie said.

Reese turned to me. "Your mother," he said, "got her car and helped. We piled the mattresses on the roof and both of us put 'em up on the walls."

I looked around and shook my head. The mattresses sure didn't look like the kind you'd find on the beds at the Ritz Hotel. They were dirty and stained and stuffing popping out of them all over the place. Not that I cared about that because they sure would solve our problems, but I was curious.

"Where'd you get them, Reese?" I asked. "Twelve mattresses."

"From buildings," Reese answered with a shrug.

"He had them piled up on the street when I met him with the car," my mother said. "We made two trips."

"Buildings?" Ivy repeated. Shelby and Georgie went inside to inspect the nailing-up job.

"Yeah, you know, abandoned buildings. There's plenty of junk in those places—you'd be surprised. You could live for a long time in one of those. People do, y'know."

"Is that where you live?" I asked. "In one of those?"

Reese stiffened. "No! Of course not. But I know 'em. There's lots of things I know."

"*Nobody* has said 'thank you'," my mother said harshly.

I grinned. "Thank you," I said. "Thanks, Ma! Thanks, Reese! That's really terrific, really."

"It's great, Reese," Ivy said. "Thanks."

Shelby said, "Thanks, both of you," and Georgie cried, "Now we're really all set!"

Look, I'm not bragging. I don't brag. But we really *were* good. Somehow we lucked out in getting together and in all of us digging the same music. And even if two of us were a little mysterious, it didn't affect the way we played or got along . . . most of the time.

GEORGIE: Let's do this in E.

ME: E's too brittle, do it in E[flat].

GEORGIE: Yeah, but my voice squeaks on that top F.

IVY: Sing it in falsetto, then!

ME: Ivy, that's too loud. How about using brushes there instead of sticks? I can't even hear my own solo.

IVY: Loud: I'm never loud! Whaddya mean *loud?*

REESE: Shelby, that sounds like 'elevator music'! Can't you get a little *bite* in that horn?

SHELBY: Bite? Reese, did you ever hear the word 'subtle'?

Okay, nobody's perfect. Sure, we argued, but it was always about the music and all five of us really cared about how each song came across. We were five people all working toward making the Centerin City Blues Band something that people would enjoy and remember. And just keeping that in mind was what made us argue and what made us happy.

♦ LIBRARY LINK ♦

To find out more about Eddie and the band, read The Buffalo Nickel Blues Band *by Judie Angell, the book from which this excerpt was taken.*

Reader's Response

What was your opinion of Reese at the beginning of the story? Did it change by the end? Explain why.

Blues Busters

 ## Checking Your Comprehension

1. How did Reese come to join the band?
2. What kind of person do you think Dr. Broigen was? What makes you think so?
3. How did Dr. Broigen's problem create difficulties for the band?
4. Eddie and Ivy were best friends. Explain the personality traits they both had that made for a good friendship.
5. What made Reese seem to be such a mysterious character?
6. Can you find an alternative solution to the band's problem?

 ## Writing to Learn

THINK AND SYNTHESIZE Imagine that the band has made its first record album and you've been asked to write a brief description of one band member for the album cover. Collect information from the story about one of the band members.

WRITE Use the information that you have assembled and write your character sketch in a single paragraph.

A Strategy for Thinking:

Writing Discussion Questions

When you pick up a newspaper or watch the news on TV, you are reading and hearing about the most important issues of the day. When you read literature, especially nonfiction, you are also exposed to important issues. What are issues? An issue is a subject that people disagree about; it is a center of controversy, or a conflict of ideas. That is why issues make good discussion topics.

Important issues are rarely single-sided. Different people almost always have different viewpoints. In rare cases, people will disagree so strongly that they may never see eye-to-eye on an issue, but differences in viewpoint can often be resolved through discussion. As you read and discover important issues, it's a good idea to try to analyze the nature of the controversy and the arguments on either side of the issue.

Learning the Strategy

One way to identify and analyze an important issue in your reading is to imagine that you will lead a panel discussion about it. You would want to ask questions that focus on the most important issues of the selection. For example, read the following newspaper article.

Driving Age Increase Debated

The Commissioner of Motor Vehicles addressed a standing-room-only assembly at Johnson Regional High School yesterday on the subject of the proposed law that will raise the driving age to seventeen. The Commissioner pointed out to the packed assembly hall that the accident rate among teenagers has increased 20 percent over the past five years. He has urged state legislators to reduce the accident rate by passing the law.

Now think about the types of questions you would want to ask the Commissioner or questions you would want to raise with a group of your friends on the issue of the driving age. The following questions might be good ones for discussion.

◆ What are the causes of motor vehicle accidents among teenagers?
◆ Why has there been a recent increase in accidents?
◆ What other alternatives would decrease the number of accidents?

How would you answer these questions? Can you think of other questions to ask?

Using the Strategy

Imagine that you will be leading a discussion about the story "Blues Busters." Consider the topics below or any others that occur to you, and write three discussion questions about issues "Blues Busters" raised for you.

Neighbors   Friends
Common interests   Forming a band

Choose one of the three questions you wrote and answer it.

Applying the Strategy to the Next Selection

As you read the next article, "The Way It Was *And Is*," you will be asked at several points to think about possible discussion questions. Then you will be asked to write and answer one question.

◆◆◆ The writing connection can be found on page 71.

Have you ever heard the expression "the generation gap"? The phrase may be fairly modern, but the idea has been around ever since the first time a parent and child didn't see eye to eye or, as Bill Cosby might prefer to say, didn't hear ear to ear.

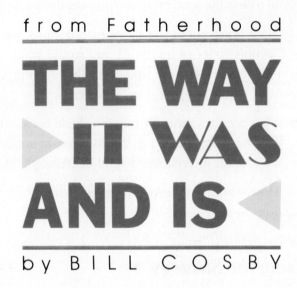

from Fatherhood

THE WAY IT WAS AND IS

by BILL COSBY

When I was thirteen, my father used to sit in our living room and listen on our Philco radio to strange music by people named Duke Ellington, Count Basie, and Jimmie Lunceford. Sometimes when I walked by, I saw him leaning back in his armchair and smiling blissfully. My mission was to sneak *past* that living room before he caught me and made me come inside for a music appreciation lesson on the old-timey music that I couldn't stand.

"Come here and sit down," he'd say. "Now this is Jimmie Lunceford." He pointed to the Philco and smiled, while I tried to adjust my ears to the low volume. And when the piece was over, he'd say, "Now *that's* music. I don't know what you call the noise you hear upstairs, but *that's* music."

During each of these command performances, I would smile respectfully and move my head back and forth in rhythm as if I really

enjoyed this junk; and after my own performance was over, I would pat my father on the knee, say, "Thank you, Dad," and tell him I had something important to do. That something important, of course, was to get away from that music. And then I would go upstairs and wonder how I could negotiate these walks past the living room and out of the house without having my father use his Philco to damage my brain. For a while, I considered putting a ladder against my window, but it also would have let a burglar in.

Had a burglar made it into my room, he would have had a wonderful time hearing Sonny Rollins, John Coltrane, Dizzy Gillespie, Miles Davis, Thelonious Monk, Bud Powell, and Philly Joe Jones. He would have been able to hear them right through any ski mask because I always played them at top volume. The greatest advantage of top volume was that I couldn't hear the grownups when they came in to tell me to turn that noise down.

From time to time my father would come by, kick the door open, and then stand there under the assault of the music. He had the look of a sailor standing on deck in a typhoon. And then his lips would start to move. I couldn't hear him, but I didn't have to, for he was sending an ancient message:

Turn that noise down.

I then would turn the sound down about halfway, moving him to say, "Turn it down, I said." I'd then turn the dial to the three-quarters point and he'd say, "More." Giving him more, I would say, "Dad, it's off."

"And that," he would say, "is what I want."

Music has changed so drastically since the days when I first heard the wonders of John Coltrane and Bud Powell. Today a guitar is a major appliance whose volume guarantees that the teenager playing it will never be aware of the start of World War III. This teenager will merely see the explosions and will probably think that they are a part of a publicity campaign for a new English group call the Armageddons.

I know I don't sound hip[1] talking like this, but no matter *how* he talks, a father cannot sound hip to his children. (I wonder if even the Duke sounded hip to Mercer Ellington, or if Mercer just humored the old man.) He can give high fives until his palms bleed; he can say "Chilly down" so much that he sounds like a short order cook; but the father will still be a man who lost all his hipness at the age of twenty-three.

The day he started paying rent.

Remember Cosby's First Law of Intergenerational Perversity? Well, it also applies to being hip. Anything that *you* like cannot possibly be something your kids like too, so it cannot possibly be hip. You know what would be the end of rock music? If enough parents suddenly started to like it. ◄◆►

What would be a good discussion question about Cosby's statement?

The volume of "that noise" is my own fault, of course. No one *made* me buy that complex stereo system for my decibel-hungry darlings. The day I went into the electronics store to see the equipment, those two BOX 95s and Bowie Twin Triple Hitter treble, woofer speakers, and double-headed action didn't *seem* too much for a twenty-by-fifteen bedroom, as long as there was no bed. I even failed to notice the gleam in my daughter's eye that resembled the gleam in Dr. Frankenstein's eye when he first decided to make a mobile. I had been busy falling into the great American trap: trying to make a child happy by buying something for her.

If the children's name for me is Dad-Can-I, then my name for them is Yes-You-May. (My response is weak but *grammatical*.) You may have the tuner, the amplifier, the tape deck, and those speakers that belong at a pregame rally at Grambling State. I must confess, however, that

[1]Hip (slang) (hip) adj: having up-to-date information

all this permissiveness was not entirely altruistic: I figured that whenever she wasn't home, I could rent her room as a recording studio.

And so I bought the stereo. The price was surrealistic, but what I got for my money was more than just equipment that belonged in Yankee Stadium: I got a smile that said that I was the greatest father in the world.

When I brought the equipment home, I simply opened the instruction book, which was slightly shorter than *Pride and Prejudice*, and flipped past the Chinese, Italian, French, and Turkish

until I got to the English, which had been written by a foreigner. Only two hours later, the unit was assembled and I was issuing wise paternal advice:

"Now the thing to know is you needn't turn this unit up so loud. Leave the volume control on two and a half and your ears will adjust to every little nuance."

"Yes, Dad," my daughter said, still feeling that I was a wonderful person; and going to the stereo, she put on a record that sounded like a train derailment, which I pretended to like. I was trying to reach out to her generation, to understand that there might be more to music than just melody, harmony, and rhythm. ◆◆◆

Then I went downstairs. A few minutes later, the doorbell rang (the first good music I had heard all day) and some of my daughter's friends came in. As I told them she was upstairs, I believe I heard one of them say that I was the greatest father since Abraham. And then, when they went upstairs, I sat down for lunch with my wife in the

◆◆◆

What would be a good discussion question about the issue of what happens when parents and children have different tastes?

dining room, which is just beneath my daughter's bedroom. Moments later, things began to move that ordinarily had no locomotion: the plates, the cups, the silverware, and the salt and pepper shakers.

"I was unaware," I told my wife, "that this house is sitting on a major geological fault."

When the chandelier began to swing and the chairs began to dance, I said, "If these are my last words, I want you to know only the greatest truth that is in my heart. I love you profoundly, and I never played halfback in that game against Penn."

While the glasses, plates, and utensils danced, my wife listened intently to a deep rhythmic thumping—two short thumps and one long one—that filled the house. And after listening to this extraterrestrial sound for about a minute, she turned to me and said, "That stereo is too loud."

You can see that I married above my IQ.

At once, I sprang into action. I rushed upstairs and kicked open the door to my daughter's bedroom like a man arriving at a fire. With the skin on my face feeling as though it were being pushed away from my skull, and with a vein struggling to free itself from the center of my forehead, the greatest father since Abraham cried the words that Abraham himself must have cried when Isaac brought home his new ram's horn:

"Turn that noise down!" ◄►

Write one more discussion question about "The Way It Was *and Is*" and supply your own answer.

Do you think writing discussion questions helps you focus on issues? How?

♦ LIBRARY LINK ♦

More of Bill Cosby's views on the generation gap can be found in his book, Fatherhood.

Reader's Response

How do you feel about Bill Cosby's view of the generation gap?

THE WAY
►IT WAS AND IS◄

Checking Your Comprehension

1. Did Bill Cosby react honestly when his father tried to introduce him to his kind of music?
2. Who were some of the musicians Cosby liked when he was young?
3. Bill Cosby said that he was "falling into the great American trap" by buying a stereo for his daughter. How did you know what he meant?
4. Why did Cosby pretend to like his daughter's music?
5. What was humorous about the way Cosby described the volume of his daughter's music?
6. Does Bill Cosby think the generation gap can be closed? Explain your answer.

Writing to Learn

THINK AND DEFINE You have read about how different generations struggle over the definition of good music. Copy the thought balloons below and complete them with each character's definition of music.

| Grandfather Cosby | Bill Cosby | Bill Cosby's daughter |

WRITE On your paper, add a thought balloon for yourself. In your thought balloon write a definition of music that meets your own standards.

31

To the Children

Do you remember the old song?
'This is the way he sows the seed,
So early in the morning.'

This is your world, your broad and furrowed fields,
Here what you plough will bear its fruit in time.
This friendly loam a richer garden yields
Than there, where the untended thistles climb.
Here are the roses for your hours of grace,
And there the stones to keep your meadows neat;
You shall declare the future of this place,
What shall be stone, what shall be flower and wheat—
What shall be love tomorrow when the spring
Returns across this winter and this land,
Bringing the dogwood and the robin's wing,
Bearing your own sweet summer in her hand.
That this may grow and ripen to your need,
Now mark the furrow well, and sow the seed.

'This is the way he sows the seed,
Sows the seed, sows the seed,
This is the way he sows the seed,
So early in the morning.'

Robert Nathan

Change

The summer
still hangs
heavy and sweet
with sunlight
as it did last year.

The autumn
still comes
showering gold and crimson
as it did last year.

The winter
still stings
clean and cold and white
as it did last year.
The spring
still comes
like a whisper in the dark night.

It is only I
who have changed.

Charlotte Zolotow

Jim Yoshida knows what his goals are, but to achieve them, he has some convincing to do.

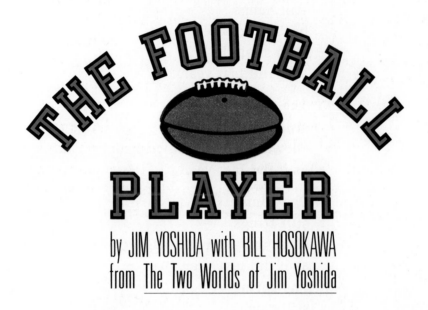

THE FOOTBALL PLAYER

by JIM YOSHIDA with BILL HOSOKAWA
from The Two Worlds of Jim Yoshida

My father was a sturdily built man, fairly tall for a Japanese, and he became heavier as he grew older. He sported a bristly Charlie Chaplin mustache and he never learned much English, so he always spoke to us in Japanese. I could understand him, but I couldn't express myself in Japanese so I replied in English. This is the way most Japanese-American families communicated, and we got along quite well.

I could never seem to penetrate my father's gruff exterior and I feared him as much as I loved him. I can't ever remember hearing him praise me. Whenever I did anything well, he simply said he expected me to do better next time, and eventually I came to understand that this was his way. When I was sixteen years old I picked a hundred-pound

sack of rice off the floor and held it up over my head, the
way a weight lifter lifts barbells. This was a feat of strength
recognized among Japanese families as a sign that a lad had
reached manhood. If Dad was proud, he didn't show any
sign. But later Mother told me how really happy he was.
About the same time I defeated my father for the first time
at arm wrestling. We sat at the kitchen table facing each
other. With elbows down on the table, we locked right
hands and each tried to force the other's arm down. I was
surprised at how easily I defeated him, for Dad had a reputation for physical strength. He was proud that I was growing strong and I felt sad that he was getting old, but neither
of us said anything. Our relationship was such that we seldom voiced our thoughts to each other,
and I suppose that's the way
he was brought up.

With my mother, the relationship was altogether different. She was a tiny woman, no more than five feet two inches tall, but she was blessed with enormous vitality. She had a beautiful heart-shaped face. She was gentle; not once did she ever strike me, although I deserved punishment frequently, and I don't recall that she ever raised her voice to me. But she had a way of talking to me when I did wrong; these talks usually left me weeping in remorse.

Mother had an understanding of young people that was extremely unusual in the Japanese immigrant generation. Dad was strict and stern. He wanted to rear his children the way he had been brought up. Mother was wise enough to know that American children could not be reared like Japanese children, that we were products of the new world and we required freedom. Eventually I came to realize she was a mellowing, liberalizing influence on my father. This does not mean she was entirely permissive. In her own way she kept a tight rein on her children. When I became old enough to go out at night, she insisted that I let her know when I came home. I would walk by her bedroom door and knock—*tum-ta-ta-tum-tum*. And she would knock back—*tum-tum*. If she slept while I was out, it was only lightly.

We lived an oddly mixed but pleasant life. We celebrated the Fourth of July, Thanksgiving, and Christmas as well as the Japanese festivals like Boys' Day and Girls' Day and the Festival of the Dead in late summer. As children we went to public schools and learned about George Washington at Valley Forge and the grand heritage of a people who were willing to revolt for liberty and freedom. And after school was dismissed at 3 P.M., we trudged on to the Japanese Language School to learn a little about that very difficult language of our parents. Although some resented the double dose of schooling, we did not think it strange, because many of our Jewish friends in Seattle attended Hebrew school.

Somehow this life must have agreed with me, for by the

time I was fifteen years old and a freshman at Broadway High School—in September of 1936—I stood five feet seven inches tall and weighed 168 pounds. Many of the other fellows signed up to try out for the freshman football team. I couldn't, because I had to go to Japanese school.

Still, it wouldn't hurt to watch for a little while. I sat on the sidelines, glancing at my Ingersoll watch frequently to make sure I would leave in time to get to Japanese school before the bell rang. About the third day the freshmen engaged in a scrimmage, and I couldn't tear myself away. I had played some sandlot football, and I figured I could do just as well as the boys in uniform. Before I knew it, it was too late to get to Japanese school on time. It didn't take me long to rationalize—being absent was only a little worse than being tardy. I was going to get a scolding if I showed up late without a good excuse, so I might just as well play hookey for the day. Before long, nothing seemed to be more important than playing football with the Broadway High School freshman team. I found myself walking over to the coach—his name was Bob Heaman—and telling him I wanted to try out.

Heaman looked up and down my stocky frame. "What's your name?" he asked.

"Katsumi Yoshida," I replied.

"That's no name for a kid who wants to play football," he said. "I'm going to call you Jim." He reached into a pocket and pulled out a mimeographed form. "You have to get your parents' permission," he said. "Take this home and get your father to sign it. Come down to the locker room after school tomorrow and check out a uniform."

My heart sank. Here I was being invited to try out for the team and parental permission—an impossible obstacle—blocked the way.

Full of apprehension, I went home at the normal time. Apparently my mother was unaware of my absence from Japanese school, and if my sister Betty had noticed, she hadn't said anything. I knew that my mother could sense when I had something on my mind. Besides, I wanted to talk to her before Dad came home, so I came straight to the point.

"Mom," I said, "I want to try out for the football team at school."

She scarcely looked up from her cooking, "Isn't it a very rough game?"

"Not really," I said.

After a moment she replied: "You are our only son, Katsumi, and I don't know what we would do if you were injured permanently playing football. Besides, what would you do about Japanese school? I think we had better forget about football."

I knew it was useless to try to change her mind, and even more useless to talk to Dad.

Next day, during a study period, I gave myself permission to play football. I carefully forged my father's signature on the slip. My hands were clammy when I gave the slip to Coach Heaman. I was sure he could hear the pounding of my heart and see the look of guilt that I knew was written on my face. But he failed to notice and routinely filed the permission form and issued me an ancient, hand-me-down uniform and a pair of ill-fitting shoes.

I made the team as a running guard. This meant I pulled out of the line and ran interference for the ball-carrier. If I did what I was supposed to do and threw a good block, the ball-carrier had a chance of making a good gain. The position required speed, agility, size, and the willingness to play the part of a human battering ram. I loved the body contact. At the end of the freshman season I was one of several boys invited to suit up with the varsity. In the season finale the varsity coach, Jerry Robinson, let me play half the game.

Meanwhile, for some reason I have never understood, my absence from Japanese school went unnoticed. Perhaps I

had dropped out before anyone became aware that I should have been attending classes. At any rate, three months had slipped by without my ever setting foot in Japanese school, and I all but forgot that I was really supposed to be studying the intricacies of the ancestral language rather than learning to block and tackle.

I was finally tripped up when Betty brought home her report card from Japanese school right after the football season ended. As usual she had done very well in her studies, and Dad nodded his approval as he examined her record. I knew what was coming next. He turned to me and asked to see my report card.

"Sir," I said, "I don't have one."

His eyebrows shot up. "Why not? Did you lose it?"

"No sir, I haven't been attending Japanese school."

He fixed me with a stare that bored right through me. We were at the dinner table and Mother had served all of us with hot boiled rice to eat with the cooked meat and vegetables. Steam rose from the bowl in front of my father as I could see his temper rising, too. Ordinarily, I was famished by mealtime and made quick work of my dinner, but now I had lost all interest in food.

"Explain yourself," Dad ordered.

So I told him the whole story, including the way I had forged his signature, and his frown grew darker and darker.

"Bakatare!" he finally shouted in fury. There is no precise English equivalent for that word. It means fool, or imbecile, but there is much more scorn, vitriol, and invective in the word than is indicated by direct translation.

Good old Mom. She averted a very explosive situation by suggesting that the dinner table was not the place for a scolding. She suggested we finish our dinner and then talk about the problem. I picked at my food while all the others seemed to eat with the usual relish. I wasn't too worried about what had happened—that was over the dam. My real concern was whether Dad would let me play football next season.

Sometime during the meal Dad must have seen the humor of my transgression. Perhaps he remembered pranks he had pulled as a boy. I was relieved to see his anger had given way to simply a serious mood when finally the dishes were cleared away.

First, he lectured me about how wrong it was to deceive one's parents, and I had to agree with him. Eventually he got around to football. "I can understand why you would want to play the game," he said. "It is a rough game and it is natural for boys to want to engage in rough sports. But you must remember you are the son of Japanese parents, and therefore you should take an interest in Japanese sports like *kendo* and judo."

Kendo is a form of fencing. The participants wear masks, helmets, and armor, and whale away at each other with split bamboo staves, which simulate the long, curved steel swords used by the samurai warriors of old. Judo is like wrestling, hand-to-hand combat, in which a smaller and weaker man learns to use his opponent's strength to defeat him. I wanted nothing to do with *kendo;* the prospect of fighting with sticks was too much. And I didn't have much enthusiasm for judo either, for I had heard that clever little fellows could whip big ones, and I was one of the "big" guys.

"Either sport is good," Dad was saying. "Either one will give you the discipline you need because they are Japanese sports. American life is too soft. You must learn to grow tougher, physically, mentally, and morally."

Football isn't tough? He had never played football. He didn't know what it was to get your brains jarred loose in a hard tackle and then come back for more.

Just then I saw an out. I apologized for what I had done. I was truly sorry. I agreed to go back to Japanese school and try my best to make up for what I had missed. And I said I would go to judo class—and here was the hooker—if I could play football again next year.

The smile that had started to take shape on Dad's face vanished.

"All right," he said with resignation. "Play football if you must, if it's that important to you. But remember there are things that are important to me, too. So go to Japanese school and try to learn a little about the language. And go to judo classes and learn a little about discipline." We shook hands and I think I gained a deeper understanding of Dad that night than ever before.

Several nights later when I came home from Japanese school Dad introduced me to a handsome, curly-haired fellow who was about eight or ten years older than I. His name was Kenny Kuniyuki; he was an instructor at the Tentoku-kwan Judo School and the son of one of Dad's best friends. Dad told me Kenny would be my judo teacher. Kenny was a little taller than I, powerfully built with broad, square shoulders that tapered down to slim hips and the muscular

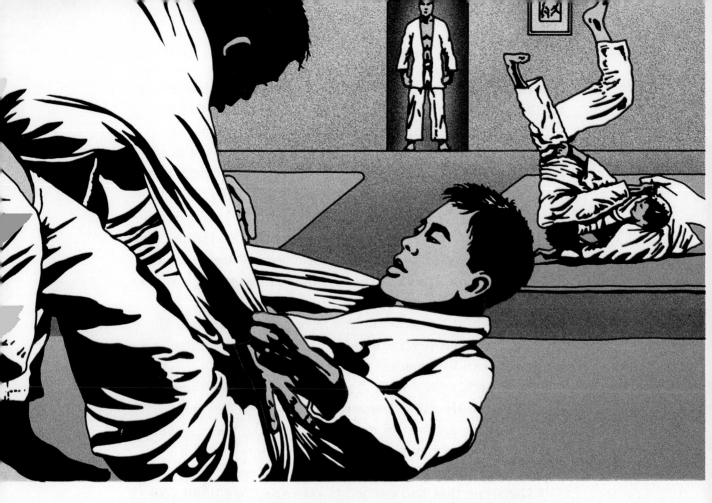

legs of an athlete. I liked him immediately. We had dinner together and then he drove me to the judo school.

There were perhaps two dozen boys, many of whom I knew, fooling around on the judo mats. All were wearing padded jackets and short trousers. When Kenny entered, their yelling and laughing stopped abruptly and they snapped to attention. Apparently he was a very important person at the school. Kenny led me to the framed portrait of a little, half-bald old man that hung on one wall and told me to bow before it each time I entered the hall. Later I learned he was Jigoro Kano, father of modern judo and regarded as a near-deity by devotees of the art.

For the next three weeks, every Monday, Wednesday, and Friday, I went to the school and learned to sit Japanese-style with my legs folded under me, and to fall. Falling without hurting yourself is an art in itself. Gradually I learned to roll to absorb the impact as I hit the mat, to break the momentum with my arms and legs and shoulders before I crashed to the floor. Then Kenny—I was supposed to call him Kuniyuki Sensei (Instructor Kuniyuki)—began on the holds and throws. He seemed to think the best way to teach was to demonstrate. From seven to nine-thirty I would practice with the other boys, throwing and being thrown almost without a break. Then the others were told to shower and change, but my evening was just starting.

"Come on, Yoshida," Kenny would say. He would let me throw him a few times, then *wham*, I would find myself thrown flat on the mat. "Get up," he would say. "We don't have time to sit around." *Wham*, I would go down again. Or he would say something like, "How would you like to see Tokyo?" I would drop my guard for the barest instant to reply, and *wham*, I would crash into the wall. He would pick me up, sweep my legs from under me and slam me to the mat, scolding me all the time for not taking the offensive. Once he put the choke hold on me and I was too exhausted to struggle. The bright lights overhead faded and I blacked out. Next thing I remember, I was sitting up with someone's knee in my back and arms across my chest. He jerked back on my shoulders while jabbing his knee into my spine and miraculously everything was in focus again.

Some of my friends felt that Kenny was picking on me unfairly. "Jim," one of them asked, "how come you take all that punishment? I'd quit if I were in your place." I must admit that I thought about quitting, especially on mornings after a particularly strenuous workout when I was so sore I could hardly crawl out of bed. But I knew that if I dropped judo I could forget about playing football. I also suspected that Dad had given Kenny orders to make it as rough as he could for me, and that only firmed up my determination to stick it out. Then one day it occurred to me that Kenny wouldn't be spending all that time with me if he didn't think a lot of me. And after that I vowed to take all the

punishment he dealt out and come back for more. When Mom asked how I was getting along, I assured her that Kuniyuki Sensei was being extra nice to me.

About six months after I began judo lessons, everything began to fall in place. I was tough physically, I had learned, finally, to take the hardest falls without hurting myself, and now I was able to coordinate my skill together with my strength and dish it out as well as take it. I found a new exhilaration in the combat of judo, and excitement in the smell of the judo mats. Judo was as much fun as football.

Once a month we would have an intra-club tournament. The boys at the Tentokukwan School would be divided into two teams; then we would engage in elimination matches starting with the youngest and newest students. If you threw an opponent, or won a decision over him, you took on the next man and remained in the ring until you were defeated. Although I was bigger than most of the fellows, I still wore the white belt of the novice and was about in the middle of our lineup. In my first tournament I threw seven boys in a row, including two wearing the black belt of experts. I was having the time of my life. A black-belter must throw a white-belter or lose face. I had nothing to lose

and could go all out. Kuniyuki Sensei gave me an approving look. Not long afterward I was jumped over all the intermediate steps—yellow, green, brown and purple—and given a black belt. It usually takes a student three or four years of hard work to win black-belt rating. I had done it in a fraction of that time. Dad beamed approval.

He raised no objection when I turned out for football in the fall of 1937, my sophomore year. I had kept my end of the bargain and he kept his. I made the team as running guard and was lucky enough to be an all-city selection even though we didn't win a single game. This was a busy time for I continued with judo after the daily football workouts. Still, I managed to keep my grades up. After football season I returned to Japanese school and made a valiant but futile effort to catch up with the other students trying to master an almost incomprehensible language.

I returned to Broadway High for my junior year with 190 muscular pounds on my five-foot nine-and-a-half-inch frame. We had a new coach and although I was a letterman, I had to start from scratch to earn my position. But I was bigger and stronger than most of the boys, and more experienced, and had no trouble keeping my job. Again we went through the season without a victory, and once more I was named all-city.

These were happy times. As a football star, I was a "big man" in school. My teammates were of many ethnic origins—Italians, Germans, Jews, Irish—but it never occurred to us that we were different. We were all Americans held together by a common love for football and loyalty to our school.

By the time my senior year rolled around, both my parents had become ardent football fans. Since someone had to stay at the barbershop, they alternated in coming out to watch me play. We had still another new coach, Al Lindquist. He figured that since I was fast enough to run in front of the ball-carrier, why couldn't I play in the backfield where my size would be useful? He shifted me to fullback and I guess the experiment was a success because, even though we still didn't win a game, we scored a touchdown—the first in three years. I took it over against Garfield High. We eventually lost the game 27 to 7. The crowd had overflowed from the stands onto the field and as I picked myself up after scoring I saw Dad standing just outside the end zone in his big brown overcoat, a big grin on his face. I think the sight of that grin made me happier than scoring the touchdown.

◆ LIBRARY LINK ◆

To find out more about Jim Yoshida, look for The Two Worlds of Jim Yoshida *by Jim Yoshida with Bill Hosokawa.*

Reader's Response

How do you feel about the way Jim Yoshida went about solving his problem?

THE FOOTBALL PLAYER

Checking Your Comprehension

1. How did Jim Yoshida's mother and father differ in their reactions to living in the United States?
2. Why was Jim's mother opposed to his playing football?
3. When did Jim's parents discover that he was on the football team?
4. If his mother had not delayed the scolding until after dinner, what might have happened to Jim Yoshida? What makes you think so?
5. Why was Jim's offer to his father an intelligent one?
6. What kind of teacher was Kuniyuki Sensei?
7. Why might his father's grin have been more important to Jim than the touchdown?

Writing to Learn

THINK AND PREDICT Will Japanese traditions continue to be important to Jim Yoshida in the future, when he has his own family? Copy the statements below and decide how you feel about them. Then write a number from the agreement scale next to each statement.

Agreement Scale:	Statements:
4 I agree strongly	_____ Jim Yoshida will encourage his children to play football.
3 I agree	_____ Jim Yoshida's children will attend the Japanese school.
2 I'm not sure	_____ The Yoshida family will discuss their disagreements.
1 I disagree	_____ Jim Yoshida will encourage his children to learn judo.

WRITE Select one of the statements from your chart and write a paragraph explaining why you agree or disagree with it.

47

READING
SOCIAL STUDIES TEXTBOOKS

Understanding Sequence

It is important to understand the order, or sequence, of events when you read a social studies text. This is especially true when reading about history. Unless you understand the sequence, you will not see how a historical event is connected to preceding events and to following events.

Social studies books usually describe historical events in the sequence in which they occurred. To understand the sequence, you need to think about how different events relate to one another. You should first pay attention to dates, such as *300 B.C.* and *1988*. Signal words, such as *first*, *then*, *during*, and *at this time*, can also help you to figure out the correct sequence. Finally, making a graphic aid, such as a time line, can help you determine the sequence of events in a historical text.

Following Events Presented in Sequence

Read the following paragraph and write down the signal words and dates you find on a separate piece of paper.

> By A.D. 300, Japan had begun to trade regularly with China. The Japanese studied the teachings of Confucius, a Chinese philosopher, and the Chinese system of government. As a result, they organized the Japanese government around a strong emperor. By A.D. 900, a university had been established in Kyōto, Japan's capital.

Early Japanese civilization was at a high point around A.D. 1000. By that time, Japan had developed a distinctly Japanese culture. Kyōto was a city with a half million people, whereas Paris and London were small towns with muddy streets and simple houses. The world's first full novel—*The Tale of Genji* by Lady Murasaki—was written at this time.

The dates and signal words in this paragraph show that the events are described in the order in which they occurred. The paragraph begins with the date A.D. 300. Then the events in Japan are described up to the year A.D. 1000.

Sometimes historical events are described without the use of dates or signal words. You can still follow the sequence of events by thinking logically about how one event leads to another.

For example, the paragraph on Japan begins by stating that Japan started to trade with China in A.D. 300. The next sentence says that the Japanese studied Chinese philosophy and government. Because trade—the first event—increased contact between the two countries, the Japanese were able to study China—the second event.

A time line is one of the best ways to help you understand the order of events. A time line is a diagram that shows the sequence of events over time. It is especially useful when events are not presented in sequence. For the passage about Japanese civilization, a time line might look like the one below. Finish the time line on your own paper.

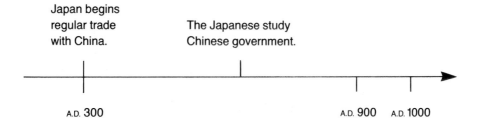

Understanding Events Not Presented in Sequence

Read the following paragraphs. Notice that the events in the paragraph that begins on the bottom of page 48 have been rearranged. The sequence of events has remained the same—only the order in which they are described is different.

> Early Japanese civilization was at a high point around A.D. 1000. At that time, Japan's capital, Kyōto, was a city of half a million people, whereas Paris and London were small towns with muddy streets and simple houses. A university in Kyōto was already one hundred years old. The world's first full novel—*The Tale of Genji* by Lady Murasaki—was written about A.D. 1000.
>
> Many aspects of Japanese civilization grew out of contact with China. Japan had begun to trade regularly with China around A.D. 300. The Japanese studied the teachings of Confucius and the Chinese government. As a result, they organized the Japanese system of government around a strong emperor. Although China's influence on Japan was great, by A.D. 1000 Japan had developed a distinct identity.

The writer has organized the paragraphs so that the emphasis is on Japan's advanced stage of development in the year A.D. 1000. The rest of the first paragraph gives details about Japanese civilization in A.D. 1000. The second paragraph describes the most important events that led to this stage of development.

In a passage organized as this one is, you must use dates, signal words, and logic to figure out the sequence of events. Some of the dates and signal words in the passage are *A.D. 1000, A.D. 300, at that time*, and *one hundred years old*. By using dates and signal words, you can see that the Japanese organized their government around a strong emperor *after* they had studied the Chinese government.

As You Read Read the following pages from a social studies textbook. Answer the questions on page 55.

A Very Old Country Moves into Modern Times

How did the Chinese Revolution change life for the average Chinese farmer?

Home of Early People   Scientists have discovered that people existed in China 500,000 years ago. Bones of humans who lived at that time were found in a cave near the city of Peking. Scientists know very little about these people. They do know that people who lived in China 50,000 years ago were hunters of elephant and rhinoceros. They also know that people who lived in China 5,000 years ago crafted pottery and made tools from stone. These people lived in villages and practiced slash-and-burn farming.

China is a very old civilization. There are written records of Chinese history beginning around 2000 B.C. They describe a series of **dynasties,** or families of rulers.

A Nation Develops   The dynasty that gave the country the name by which we know it was the Ch'in. In 221 B.C. a Ch'in emperor brought together several warring kingdoms into one strong, central government. The Chinese empire lasted in one form or another for the next 2,000 years. There were many dynasties. There were wars and famines. Even so, sometime during the period of the Sung dynasty (960–1279), China's population reached 100 million. In the early 1200s, China was invaded by outsiders. The Mongols, led by Genghis Khan, conquered the Chinese. Kublai Khan (kü′ blə kän′) was the grandson of Ghengis Khan. He was the emperor of China at the time of Marco Polo's visit.

Kublai Khan preferred the Chinese way of life to that of the Mongol. He chose Chinese officials to carry on the business of his empire. As a result, the rule of the Mongol emperor was much like that of the earlier Chinese emperors. The Mongols adopted the ways of the people they conquered. As a result, the Chinese civilization went on.

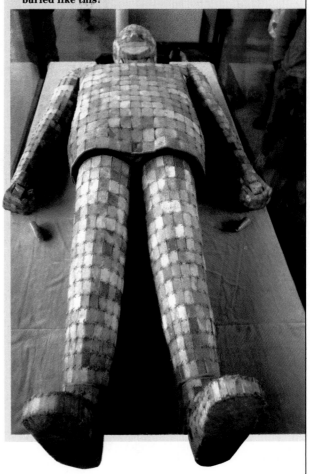

This jade shroud of a Han dynasty prince was found in an ancient tomb in 1970.
■ Do you think ordinary people were buried like this?

The Grand Canal, connecting Hangchow (30°N/120°E; map, p. 363) and Peking (39°N/116°E; map, p. 363), has been in use for over 1,000 years.
■ Why do the boats have numbers on them?

One reason for this was the development of two religions in China during the Chou dynasty (1100–250 B.C.). **Taoism** urges people to live in harmony with nature. It is based on the writings of the philosopher Lao-Tzu (lou′ dzů′). A **philosopher** is someone who searches for truth by reasoning or thinking. **Confucianism** is based on the ideas of Confucius (con fyü′ shəs). He felt that it was very important that society be well-ordered and that only superior people rule. Respect for the past and one's ancestors is also important in Confucianism. The philosophy of Confucius influenced the government of China even to modern times.

Chinese Contributions   The Chinese have made contributions to the rest of the world. They invented the compass. They were the first to weave silk into cloth, to make paper, and to turn clay into fine porcelain. The Chinese also developed the idea of printing. Carved wooden blocks were inked and then pressed on paper. This was at a time when books in Europe were still being copied by hand.

By the time that Marco Polo visited China in the thirteenth century, the Great Wall and the Grand Canal had been built. The Great Wall stretches 1,500 miles (2,400 km) across northern China. It has been called the largest structure ever built. If such a wall were built in the United States, it would reach halfway across the country. The Grand Canal is a series of waterways. By A.D. 605 it connected the Yangtze and Hwang rivers. The Grand Canal is still being used today. It is one of the longest waterways ever built. It extends for more than 1,000 miles (1,600 km). Find it on the map on page 363.

A Closed Country   When Europeans visited China, they saw a well-organized, self-sufficient, strong civilization. The Chinese viewed these quaint foreign visitors as **barbarians.** They thought their dress and habits were crude. They saw little value in the products that Europeans offered them in exchange for the silk, fine china, and tea that Europeans wanted from China. The Chinese insisted on being left to themselves. Foreigners could not go to any part of China except the port cities. This kept foreigners from being a bad influence on the Chinese.

Much later, after a series of wars in the 1800s, Europeans won trade agreements with China. By that time, Europe had grown in industry and wealth. China, which had closed its doors to Europe's inventions, had fallen behind in technology and military might. Foreign countries were able to influence the Chinese government.

Early in the twentieth century, China had about 40 years of civil war. Rival rulers struggled for power. Japan tried to take over China. In 1945, when the Japanese occupation ended, the once strong country of China was a war-torn shambles.

The Chinese Revolution   The Chinese farmer in the 1940s was one of the most unfortunate people in the world. All land was controlled by wealthy landowners who rented small parcels to farming families for high prices. The families also had to pay high taxes. There was no welfare system or social security for older people. When there was a bad harvest or a serious illness, the family had to borrow money or food at high interest rates. If they could not pay, their sons or daughters would become slaves to the landowner.

Two groups were struggling for power during this time, the Nationalists and the Communists. In 1949 the Communist Chinese defeated the Nationalist Chinese. They took control of the government. The Nationalists retreated to the island of Taiwan (tī wän′), off the southern coast of

In the 1940s these Chinese farmers worked much as their ancestors had for centuries. They are preparing the soil for rice planting.
■ What kind of animal is pulling the wooden plow?

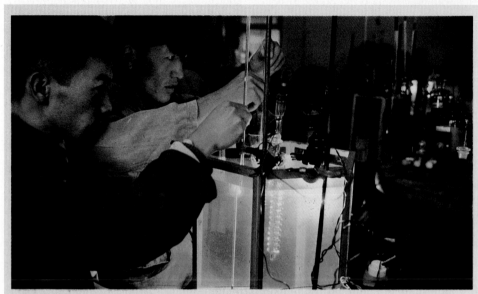

China's universities are training scientists for the country's rapidly developing industries. These students are working in a biochemistry laboratory at Peking University.
■ Is electricity part of this experiment?

China. Taiwan remains under a separate government today. It has been able to develop a strong trading partnership with the United States.

Revolutionary Changes   The new China, under Communist rule since 1949, is known as the People's Republic of China. There have been major changes in the way Chinese society is organized. The new government follows the Communist philosophy that all people should have a tolerable life before anybody has a better life. There are no wealthy landowners; their land was taken away. Farm families work together on shared land in a village system called a **commune.** People in the commune share in decision-making, work, and profit.

China is becoming a modern nation very rapidly. Modern industries are developing. New universities are training scientists, language specialists, and engineers. Farm production is large enough today to provide food for the people in the growing cities.

If China has a worry, it is that its population will grow too fast to be cared for properly. Limiting population growth is a serious concern for a country that already has over a billion people—roughly one fifth of the world's population.

CHECKUP

1. What is a dynasty?
2. What religions developed in China?
3. Name three Chinese inventions or discoveries.

4. **Thinking Critically**   In your opinion, why did the Chinese government organize villages into communes after the Chinese Revolution?

Using What You Have Learned

1. List the dates and signal words used in the first two paragraphs of "Home of Early People" on page 51. Are the events told in chronological order?

2. What major event occurred in the early 1200s? Did this event occur during the Chinese empire or after it had ended?

3. Look at the second paragraph of the section titled "A Closed Country" on page 53. What two developments occurred in the same time period?

4. What material and religious contributions has China made to the rest of the world? Why isn't the sequence of events emphasized in this section?

5. Look at the section titled "The Chinese Revolution" on page 53. What conditions led to the struggle for power between the nationalists and the Communists?

6. Use the events listed below and dates and signal words from page 51 to construct a time line.

◆ Marco Polo visits China.
◆ The Chinese make pottery and stone tools.
◆ Genghis Khan invades China.
◆ People occupy a cave near Peking.
◆ A Ch'in emperor unites warring kindgoms under a unified government.
◆ People living in China hunt elephants and rhinoceros.

The excerpt is from *A World View, Silver Burdett & Ginn Social Studies,* © 1988.

Rafael is moving to a new home and a new school. It sounds like it will be a long year . . . but maybe not.

THE OBSIDIAN RING

by Hilary Beckett

"Rafael," my mother kept saying, trying to make me see it her way, "we'll only be gone for a few months. And all that time your father's business will keep us on the move. How can you go to school over there in Europe with all that moving? Besides, you will improve your English here in New York."

It was September. The idea was that I would start in Miguel's school while my parents were gone. I would be living with him and his five-year-old brother, Francisco, at Aunt Teresa's house.

"I still want to go with you," I kept insisting.

"Rafael, it is impossible! You cannot," she said. "But tell me what you want for your birthday," she went on. "It is coming in December. Tell me what you want. Then we'll bring you back a present from Europe."

I guess this was supposed to make me feel better, her remembering my birthday. And I knew she and my father would buy me a fantastic birthday present. Almost anything I asked for.

But they wouldn't do this *one* thing for me, now—take me with them on their trip—so I said to my mother (to show her how angry I still felt), "Get me anything. You pick it out. Get what you like." I shrugged.

"Go on! Please tell me what you want, *mi hijo*,"[1] my mother said. "Tell me before our flight is called."

We were in this crowded passenger lounge at Kennedy Airport. I was standing with my mother near the exit door. My father was over by the checkout counter attending to last-minute details. Aunt Teresa and my cousins were looking out the big window at planes landing and taking off.

"Please, Rafael? Don't be childish about it. You're not a baby any more. You're almost thirteen, Rafael. Practically a man. Why, you are almost as tall as I am! If you grow any more while we are away, how will I recognize you when I come home?"

"You'll recognize me all right when you get home. But—" I was losing the fight. I looked down at the floor.

"Rafael, it's hard for us saying good-bye, too." My mother tilted my face up so that I would look at her. She stared straight into my eyes. "It's hard for you, I know—leaving Mexico and

[1]mi hijo (mē ē′ hō) my son

57

your friends."

"I wish at least I had something to give you to make you less homesick, a *recuerdo*[2] of Mexico." Her face brightened. She touched her middle right finger with the fingers of her left hand. "I know! Why don't you take the ring now, Rafaelito, the obsidian ring? Grandfather wanted you to have it some day. I think today is the perfect day!"

She pulled my grandfather's ring off her finger and folded it into my hand. "There. It's yours, Rafaelito. It will be a souvenir for you, a link to Mexico."

I looked at it. The shiny black stone was set in an old-fashioned silver band. Strong streaks of light ran through the dark obsidian as if the sun of Mexico was trapped in rich Mexican earth. Obsidian was "a jewel from a Mexican volcano." I remembered my grandfather telling me something like that when I was little.

"Take care of it, Rafael," said my mother. "And take care of yourself while we are away!" She hugged me.

I felt older because she'd given the ring to me, closer to being grown up. On the other hand, I knew I was still young enough to miss her very much while she was away. I rubbed the ring between my fingers.

"Thank you," I said. My eyes itched. But I didn't want her to think I was crying, so I didn't rub them.

Seconds later, it seemed, the plane departure was announced. The passengers in the lounge started collecting cameras, umbrellas, hand luggage, and began moving toward the exit. Friends and family saying good-bye to them pressed with them, as far as the gate and the big glass window. I held the ring tight as I kissed my parents good-bye. "*Adiós! Adiós!*"[3] we all said to each other.

The four of us (Aunt Teresa, my cousins, and I) stood waving at the big plane through the window after my parents boarded, although we couldn't really make out faces at the plane's tiny windows. It seemed to me that the smell of my mother's perfume still hung in the now almost empty passenger lounge.

"Come on, boys, let's go," said Aunt Teresa, gently putting an arm around my shoulders. "You won't be able to see the plane

[2]recuerdo (re kwer′ dō) momento; souvenir
[3]adiós (ä dyôs′) good-bye

once it's taxied down the field. Let's get the bus back home. You want sodas? Comic books?"

"I want a comic book!" Francisco jumped up and down with excitement.

"All right, *niños*.[4] Come on."

We picked out comic books and then climbed on a bus near the entrance to the airport. In the yellowish light inside the bus I showed my cousins the obsidian ring.

"Wow!" said Miguel. "The Aztecs used to have obsidian in ancient times in Mexico."

Francisco asked, "Is it worth a lot of money?"

"I don't think so."

"It's nice anyway," he told me. He touched the obsidian with his small finger. "Can I see Mexico some day, Mom?"

"You were born there, although you don't remember. Of course, you can see it again some day, Francisco," Aunt Teresa answered.

In half an hour we were in her neighborhood. She lived in Queens, and I knew it was not far from the airport. In fact, I'd been there earlier in the morning. But I didn't remember the neighborhood at all when we got off the bus.

How could I recognize anything I'd seen that day? We'd come in early, my parents and I, from Mexico—so early the sun hadn't yet risen. Then we'd dropped off my stuff at Aunt Teresa's. My parents wanted to sight-see in New York before they left for Europe, so the day (to me) was a jumble of Radio City, the Statue of Liberty, Central Park Zoo, the Empire State Building. It was like one of these round tubes you get for Christmas, that you look through and see the jagged patterns of colored glass.

Aunt Teresa pointed down her street. "There's the apartment."

She lived in what she called "garden apartments," low two-story buildings with shrubs and trees around them. Above the trees, I saw the moon in the clear autumn sky. Near the stars I could make out the flickering lights of a plane. I wondered how near my parents' plane was to Europe. Francisco looked up, too.

[4]*niños* (nē nyōs) children

59

"That plane Aunt Maria and Uncle Emilio went away in, how big was it, Miguel?"

"As big as the Empire State Building," said Miguel.

"That big?"

"Maybe not quite . . ."

"Mom, can I stay up and talk with Rafe and Miguel? Rafe, are you going to stay with us a long time?"

"Right," I said in answer to Francisco's second question. I lifted him up on my shoulders. He grabbed onto my hair.

"Rafe, do they have TV in Mexico?"

"Sure."

"Comic books?"

"Sure."

"Baseball? Bubble gum? Ice cream?"

"Sure, Francisco. It's just like here."

Only it wasn't, of course. Mexico was my home.

"Time for bed, Francisco!" Aunt Teresa called.

I hugged him and put him down.

"Come on into my room, Rafe," Miguel said. I was going to sleep in the other bed, the bed Francisco usually had. For the time I was staying there he had a cot in Aunt Teresa's bedroom.

That morning I'd thrown my suitcases on the bed without really looking at the room. So I wasn't prepared, when Miguel turned on his light, for the sight of so many familiar things. Miguel and I had a lot of the same posters, the same books, the same records. I walked around the room touching his stuff, telling him, "I've got that in Mexico. And that. And that."

He grinned. "Don't you remember that the aunts and uncles always said we were like twins? That we looked alike and acted alike? And we always liked the same things? Do you think we look like brothers, now?"

I stood near him and we looked in the closet mirror. Miguel was taller. His hair was longer. But our eyes were alike—gray-green and deep-set. And we both were on the skinny side.

I was born five days before Miguel, and we had the same sign of the zodiac—Sagittarius.

"Aunt Luisa said Sagittarians were always close. Especially when they were relatives. Remember?" Miguel said. "You'll be here for your birthday, won't you, Rafe? Wow, that's the first time since before I left Mexico!"

"Can we have a party?"

"A super-party! *Una fiesta fantástica!*[5] Like no other party in the world!"

Miguel settled himself on his bed and stretched out with his hands under his head. "Hey, Rafe, do you remember the jokes we used to save for each other?"

Before Miguel had moved up to New York after his father died, he'd lived in Guadalajara[6]—just far enough away from Mexico City to mean we couldn't see each other every day. Or even every week. We'd gone through a stage where we'd done nothing but store up jokes between visits. Even after he'd come up to the States, we'd written jokes to each other in letters.

"Hey, Miguel," I said, "Where does a sheep go to get a haircut?"

[5]Una fiesta fantástica ($\overline{oo}'$ nä fē es' tä fän täs' tē kä) a wonderful feast
[6]Guadalajara (gwä dä lä hä' rä)

"To the baa-baa shop!" He started to laugh. "That was the summer we went up to Disneyland. We weren't much older than Francisco is now. Hey, Rafe, how does an elephant get down from a tree?"

"He sits in a tree and waits until fall!"

Laughing hysterically, we threw ourselves on the beds and muffled our giggles in pillows. We heard Aunt Teresa call to us. "Quiet, boys! Not so much noise. It's after Francisco's bedtime. You can laugh tomorrow."

"Tomorrow we'll explore the neighborhood!" Miguel whispered. "I'll take you to meet my friends."

That scared me. I wanted to think Miguel had no other friends but me in this strange neighborhood where everyone spoke English, where I was going to have to start a new school. I wanted to be his only friend, the way it had been when we'd been together during vacations when we were little kids.

We undressed and got ready for bed. After Miguel switched off the light, I reached back up to the table for my ring, my obsidian ring. I thought about Mexico. I'd be away from home, and from my own friends, for a long time. Suppose they forgot me? I decided to send them all post cards the next day.

But the next day Miguel had big plans. He was on the phone calling his friends before breakfast. "We've only got Saturday and Sunday before school starts. A lot of people to see."

Aunt Teresa and Francisco and I sat at the table in the dinette. She offered to put bread in the toaster for me. I said, "No thanks, Aunt Teresa. I'm not hungry."

She laughed. It was a nice laugh, not a teasing one.

"Thinking about Monday, about a new school and about meeting new people, Rafael?"

I shrugged. "I guess they'll laugh at my English."

I figured the English I'd learned as a kid growing up in Mexico was going to turn out to be about as much like the English kids spoke in Queens as apples are like oranges.

"Try speaking it more with us," she said. "You speak it already with Francisco."

It was true. He knew hardly any Spanish. I'd used English with him all the time. I guess I wasn't scared because he was so young. I didn't expect a *little* kid to laugh at me.

"I know how you feel about school, Rafael. I remember how I felt when we moved to a new city when I was a girl. Nobody disliked school like I did, for a while. It was because I was afraid I'd be laughed at."

"How come, Aunt Teresa?"

"Would you believe it was because of a jar of preserves? Of jam? The lunch I took to the new school wasn't exactly like the other kids'." She laughed again. "It was—well, a little unusual. A little funny. All because *mamacita*[7] used to put in a little jar of jam my grandmother made. As a treat. None of the children had ever heard of taking jam to school in their lunch in a jar. They thought it was funny. They all enjoyed something to laugh at. *Me*. For a while I was the saddest child in the new school."

"What could you do about it, Aunt Teresa?"

"I came home in tears to my mother. And she told me that of course if I didn't want to take the jam, I didn't have to. But if I wanted it, I would have to stand up to the other children."

"What did you decide?"

"I decided there was a day now and then when I liked the jam and that I wouldn't be bullied into leaving it at home. I told the children to stop laughing."

"Did they?"

"Some did. Some didn't. But I didn't give anyone the satisfaction of seeing me cry any more. And after a while, the children respected me. Some of them even asked for a taste of the jam.

"It sounds scary."

"Oh, it was. But, you see, it was the only thing to do. Want some toast now, Rafael?"

"OK."

Miguel was still on the phone, his feet up and over one end of the sofa. How was he dressed? I looked carefully to see.

It was OK to listen to a grown-up person like Aunt Teresa tell me how brave she'd been about a jar of jam, but I still didn't

[7]mamacita (mä mä sē′ tä)

63

intend to make any more mistakes than I had to, to stand out any more than I had to, in Queens.

I especially didn't intend to *look* funny. Whatever Miguel had on, I'd wear it, too.

Jeans?

I checked out mine.

He had on sneakers.

Right. I had mine on, too.

"What do you want to eat tonight, Rafael? *Comida mexicana*?"[8] Aunt Teresa asked. She was on her way to the shopping center.

"Something American . . ." I kept looking at Miguel's clothes.

"All right. American food it will be. So long, kids!"

She took Francisco with her, even though he wanted to stay with us, wanting to be in on any fun we might be having. "Have a good day!"

Miguel got off the phone. "What do you do in Mexico these days, on a Saturday? Or on a vacation day? I forget. It's been such a long time."

"See friends. Play ball."

Miguel grinned. "Exactly the same as in Queens! Let's go."

To look at, Queens wasn't too different from the part of Mexico City I lived in. I lived in a taller apartment building (we had an elevator). And we had a balcony, not a small backyard. Also, the trees are different in Mexico City (more tropical). But the highways, the traffic, the parks reminded me of home. Except that the signs here were all in English, not in Spanish.

"Any other new kids going to start school Monday besides me?" I asked. "Will I be the only one?"

"There are always a lot of kids coming and going." Miguel sighed. "Hey, I wish you'd stay the whole year, Rafe, not just one semester. Any chance? It would really be great to have you around!"

Wow, he was planning my entire year, and I wasn't even eager for the first day of school.

64   [8]comida mexicana (kô mē′ dä me hē kä′ nä) Mexican food

"Thanks," I said, and meant it. As I said, Miguel was my favorite cousin.

Which made it all the harder meeting his friends.

Not only did I want him not to *have* friends—except for me—but I wanted to be cool. I wanted to be friendly, but I didn't want to open my mouth and sound foolish. Don't think it wasn't a strain.

Yet I really liked his friends, I decided, after we'd gone to visit some. We ended up in Josh's backyard. He was Miguel's closest friend. Josh, Karen (another friend), and Miguel and I sat in the sun on the edge of Josh's kid brother's sandbox. Like kids, we played with the sand while we talked.

"Hey, Rafe, are you hungry?" Miguel asked when the sun was directly over our heads.

"Let's go to Louie's for lunch," Josh suggested.

We called Aunt Teresa and told her we'd eat lunch out. Then we went to this special hamburger place.

Now, we have big fancy hamburger stands in Mexico, but I'd never seen one as big as this one. It had an arch over it that made it look about a mile high. And the big glass front looked about a mile wide. A million people seemed to be inching in, then inching out, with their arms full of paper bags.

"They've got thirty-one kinds of hamburgers," Miguel boasted. "Anything you want!"

I looked at the giant menu over the counter while we waited in line. "Hey, what's a Luau Burger?" I spelled it out.

"Hawaiian. It's got pineapple," Karen said.

"And a True Blue Burger?"

"Blue cheese on top," Josh said.

That was great. But why, oh, why, didn't I keep my mouth shut after that? The kids kept nudging me, asking me if I wanted potatoes, relish, catsup—

To be polite, the other kids pushed me ahead of them in the line. I was the visitor, the guest. It was hard making my mind up. I finally settled on a Chili Burger.

So I finally asked for "potato ships."

Or maybe I said "potato sheeps."

Whatever it was, the kids cracked up, laughing. I knew they didn't want to hurt my feelings, but they thought what I said was funny. And it really upset me. I hate being laughed at.

Which is why I spent the rest of the weekend dreaming of every possible way I could think of to make my parents come back and get me. Could I tell them I was dying of a mysterious disease, that they'd have to hurry back if they wanted to see me alive? No, they wouldn't really believe that. Nor would they believe the other phony excuses I thought up.

There really wasn't any reason, any way, I could get out of staying at Aunt Teresa's, and I knew it.

Sunday I was a miserable blob of homesickness. Only I didn't want Miguel to know that was the reason I was refusing to go out with him.

He knew, anyway. "Listen, Rafe, they laughed at my English too when I first came to Queens. There's no way to keep kids from laughing. But that doesn't mean they don't like you. Come on, let's go see Karen and Josh."

I let him drag me out of the house. But I didn't feel like talking much that day. I went to bed early, worrying about the next day.

"Are you sure school really starts today?" I asked Miguel in the morning.

"Sure. Come on and eat breakfast, Rafe."

Miguel sat there and calmly buttered his second piece of toast while elephants played soccer in my stomach. As much alike as we were, I remembered one of the main differences between Miguel and me.

When we were kids the relatives always called him "daring" and me "thoughtful." I think they meant I would think of all the scary sides to everything.

"Are you positive this isn't the wrong day?" I asked again.

"Today," Miguel insisted.

"Yeah, today." Francisco nodded vigorously. He stopped

listening to his cereal crackle in the milk long enough to say, "It's the first day of kindergarten, too. Maybe I can be milk monitor, like I was in nursery school." His brown eyes widened at the happy thought.

"Maybe this year you'll be late. Hurry up, Francisco!"

Aunt Teresa had to leave him at his school before she went to the office where she worked. "*Andale*,[9] Francisco!"

Miguel and I were the first ones out the door. Francisco and Aunt Teresa waved good-bye.

"Smell the fall leaves, Rafe!" Miguel said, happily shuffling his way to school through them.

"I don't feel like it," I said. The nearer we got to school the slower my steps got. Like I was walking through warm tar instead of through crisp leaves.

"I keep telling you, Rafe, you won't be the only new kid." Miguel dragged me up the front steps of the school.

"You naturally like people!" I said. "I'm afraid of them."

"But people like *you*, Rafe."

Everyone said hello to Miguel. He tried to introduce me to kids but I was afraid to start talking. I stood alone. Everyone else but me had someone to talk over the good times of summer with. I deliberately stood alone. I felt like I was watching a foreign movie with fuzzy subtitles.

When a bell rang, we pushed in. Miguel pointed out a line to me, a line in the front hall where new kids waited for their home-room assignments. I got in it automatically, like I was sleep-walking.

I began writing a letter (in my head) to my parents. "Dear Mother and Father, come to my rescue!" Then before I wrote much more, I found myself at the front of the line and I froze, remembering the "potato ships."

"Your name, please."

"Ortiz. Rafael Ortiz," I managed to say.

"Are you new?"

"Y-yes. My aunt t-telephoned about me." I took a deep breath and spoke slowly.

[9]*ándale* (än′ dä le) walk

"Do you have a passport? Or other identification?"

Aunt Teresa had told me to bring my birth certificate. I handed it to the lady behind the desk.

She looked at it. Then she filled out a card with my name, a room number, the name of a teacher.

"Out that way." She pointed.

I found myself in the hall again. Every doorway looked exactly alike. There were miles of steel lockers. The number on the card was 243. Where was 243?

"You lost, kid?"

A huge guy with a tag saying STUDENT GUIDE stopped me. I handed him my card without speaking.

"Down the hall, then go upstairs, but be sure you take the steps marked UP not DOWN."

My feet echoed on the steps.

I found 241, 242, 243 . . .

And I didn't want to go in.

Through the little window in the door I could see kids laughing and joking. No doubt, in *English*. No doubt, they already all knew each other. I went in.

The teacher was just inside, sitting at his desk. He took my white card. "Welcome," he said, and shook my hand. "My name is Schwartz. Let's see what yours is." He looked at the card.

"Nice to have you—" he started to say, when a familiar voice said, "Hey, Rafe! You in my homeroom? Hey, great!"

"Wow, Josh!"

"Well, I guess the two of you already know each other." The teacher grinned. Then he called the class to order. And he sat us next to each other.

It was one of the longest days in my life, but it turned out not to be quite the worst. Not only was Josh in my homeroom, but Miguel was in my social studies class. Twice I saw Karen in the hall. I felt—a little—like I belonged in the new school.

That night after dinner I decided to write a real letter to my parents. Miguel lay on his bed reading while I propped up my notebook (it had the name of the school on it and the school seal) and put a clean sheet of paper on top of it. I wanted my parents to miss me. But I also wanted them to know things were really going all right with me. I wrote:

Dear Mother and Father:
I am well and I hope you are, too. School has started now and I have made some new friends. I hope you are enjoying London and Paris and Zurich. I mean I hope you are enjoying Europe but not too much, because I hope you are homesick—a little—for Mexico. Like I am. I don't like school as much as my school in Mexico. But I guess I can stand it. Miguel wants to know if I can stay all year. I told him I would let him know. Aunt Teresa sends love and kisses. So do Miguel and Francisco.
Love from your son,
Rafael
P.S. I still have the obsidian ring.

♦ LIBRARY LINK ♦

This excerpt is from the book Rafael and the Raiders *by Hilary Beckett. Read it to find out more about Rafael's adventures in New York.*

Reader's Response

Do you think Rafael will look back on his time in New York as a bitter or a sweet experience?

THE OBSIDIAN RING

Checking Your Comprehension

1. Is "The Obsidian Ring" a good title for this story? What makes you think it is or is not?
2. In what ways were Rafael and Miguel alike, and in what ways were they different?
3. Why do you think Rafael wanted to be Miguel's only friend?
4. What was Rafael's greatest fear?
5. How was Rafael affected by Aunt Teresa's story about the jam?
6. Were Miguel's friends kind to Rafael?
7. What kind of letter would Rafael have written to his parents if the "potato ships" incident had never taken place?

Writing to Learn

THINK AND QUESTION "The Obsidian Ring" reveals difficult issues about moving from one area to another. If you were going to lead a discussion of this topic, what questions would you ask? Read the sample question below. Then write five additional questions you would like to discuss about living in a new place.

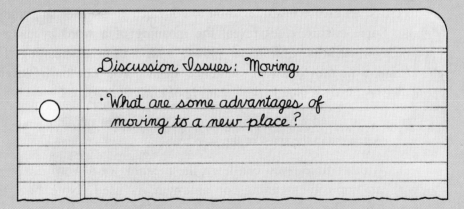

Discussion Issues: Moving

• What are some advantages of moving to a new place?

WRITE Try to put yourself in Rafael's shoes. Choose one of the questions you wrote, and write the answer you think Rafael would give.

READING NON-FICTION

Vocabulary:

Context Clues

When you read, you may discover that you can figure out the meaning of a word you do not know simply by looking at the words around it. For example, when you read the story "The Football Player," you might not have known the meaning of the word *rationalize*, but you were probably able to get a sense of the meaning of the word by looking at the words around it.

> Before I knew it, it was too late to get to Japanese school on time. It didn't take me long to rationalize—being absent was only a little worse than being tardy.

These sentences contain *context clues*—words and phrases around an unfamiliar word that help you to understand its meaning. The context clues in the example tell you that "to rationalize" means to create an excuse or explanation to convince yourself of something.

Some context clues reveal the meaning of a word by using a synonym—that is, a word or phrase with a similar meaning. For example, in the following sentence from "The Football Player," *excitement* gives a clue to the meaning of *exhilaration*:

> I found a new exhilaration in the combat of judo, and excitement in the smell of the judo mats.

At other times, you can learn the meaning of a word if a word with an opposite meaning, or antonym, is used. Note how the meaning of the word *tranquility* is revealed by using *violent*, a word with the opposite meaning:

> Although judo seemed violent, he often felt a deep tranquility during practice.

Where you don't have a synonym or antonym to help you understand the meaning of a word, you may have to use more subtle clues. Read the following sentence from Bill Cosby's "The Way It Was *And Is*"; he is trying to rationalize the purchase of a stereo system for his daughter.

> I must confess, however, that all this permissiveness was not entirely *altruistic:* I figured that whenever she wasn't home, I could rent her room as a recording studio.

In this sentence, you do not have an easy context clue for the word *altruistic*. Instead you must use the sense of the passage to help you understand what *altruistic* means. Think for a moment. Buying his daughter the stereo was not completely altruistic because Bill Cosby jokes that he did it partly for personal gain. Therefore, *altruistic* must mean "not for personal gain."

Using What You Have Learned

Write the context clues for the meanings of the words in italics. Using the clues, define the italicized words. Finally, write a new sentence for each italicized word that demonstrates its meaning.

1. I *loathe* washing dishes, but I hate drying them just as much.
2. *Pandemonium* broke out when we won the game. Students ran around shouting and hugging each other and throwing their hats into the air.
3. Daniel really stood out from the crowd in his *conspicuous* yellow and purple jacket.

As You Read

The play you are about to read, "The Diary of Anne Frank," may contain some words that are new to you. Look for context clues to help you figure out their meanings.

THE DIARY OF ANNE FRANK

by Frances Goodrich & Albert Hackett

CHARACTERS

Mr. Frank	Mrs. Frank
Miep Gies	Margot Frank
Mrs. Van Daan	Anne Frank
Mr. Van Daan	Mr. Kraler
Peter Van Daan	Mr. Dussel

During World War II, when the Jews of Europe were being sent to concentration and death camps, many families hid for months and years in secret rooms. In such a place, a young girl named Anne Frank wrote the diary on which this play is based.

ACT ONE

Scene I

The scene remains the same throughout the play. It is the top floor of a warehouse and office building in Amsterdam, Holland. The sharply peaked roof of the building is outlined against a sea of other rooftops, stretching away into the distance. Nearby is the belfry of a church tower, the Westertoren, whose carillon rings out the hours. Occasionally faint sounds float up from below: the voices of children playing in the street, the tramp of marching feet, a boat whistle from the canal.

74

The three rooms of the top floor and a small attic space above are exposed to our view. The largest of the rooms is in the center, with two small rooms, slightly raised, on either side. On the right is a bathroom, out of sight. A narrow steep flight of stairs at the back leads up to the attic. The rooms are sparsely furnished with a few chairs, cots, a table or two. The windows are painted over, or covered with makeshift blackout curtains. In the main room there is a sink, a gas ring for cooking and a wood-burning stove for warmth.

The room on the left is hardly more than a closet. There is a skylight in the sloping ceiling. Directly under this room is a small steep stairwell, with steps leading down to a door. This is the only entrance from the building below. When the door is opened we see that it has been concealed on the outer side by a bookcase attached to it.

The curtain rises on an empty stage. It is late afternoon November, 1945.

The rooms are dusty, the curtains in rags. Chairs and tables are overturned.

The door at the foot of the small stairwell swings open. Mr. Frank comes up the steps into view. He is a gentle, cultured European in his middle years. There is still a trace of a German accent in his speech.

He stands looking slowly around, making a supreme effort at self-control.

He is weak, ill. His clothes are threadbare.

After a second he drops his ruck-sack on the couch and moves slowly about. There is a many-colored scarf hanging from a nail. Mr. Frank takes it, putting it around his neck. As he starts back for his rucksack, his eye is caught by something lying on the floor. It is a woman's white glove. He holds it in his hand and suddenly all of his self-control is gone. He breaks down, crying.

We hear footsteps on the stairs. Miep Gies *comes up, looking for* Mr. Frank. Miep *is a Dutch girl of about twenty-two. She wears a coat and hat, ready to go home. She is pregnant. Her attitude toward* Mr. Frank *is protective, compassionate.*

Miep: Are you all right, Mr. Frank?

Mr. Frank: (*Quickly controlling himself*) Yes, Miep, yes.

Miep: Everyone in the office has gone home . . . It's after six. (*Then pleading*) Don't stay up here, Mr. Frank. What's the use of torturing yourself like this?

Mr. Frank: I've come to say good-bye . . . I'm leaving here, Miep.

Miep: What do you mean? Where are you going? Where?

Mr. Frank: I don't know yet. I haven't decided.

Miep: Mr. Frank, you can't leave here! This is your home! Amsterdam is your home. Your business is here, waiting for you . . . You're needed here . . . Now that the war is over, there are things that . . .

Mr. Frank: I can't stay in Amsterdam, Miep. It has too many memories for me. Everywhere there's something . . . the house we lived in . . . the school . . . that street organ playing out there . . . I'm not the person you used to know, Miep. I'm a bitter old man. (*Breaking off*) Forgive me. I shouldn't speak to you like this . . . after all that you did for us . . . the suffering . . .

Miep: No. No. It wasn't suffering. You can't say we suffered. (*As she speaks, she straightens a chair which is overturned.*)

Mr. Frank: I know what you went through, you and Mr. Kraler. I'll remember it as long as I live. (*He gives one last look around.*) Come, Miep.

Miep: (*Hurrying up to a cupboard*) Mr. Frank, did you see? There are some of your papers here. (*She brings a bundle of papers to him.*) We found them in a heap of rubbish on the floor after . . . after you left.

Mr. Frank: Burn them.

Miep: But, Mr. Frank, there are letters, notes . . .

Mr. Frank: Burn them. All of them.

Miep: Burn *this?* (*She hands him a paperbound notebook.*)

Mr. Frank: (*Quietly*) Anne's diary. (*He opens the diary and begins to read.*) Monday, the sixth of July, nineteen forty-two. (*To* Miep) Nineteen forty-two. Is it possible, Miep? . . . Only three years ago. (*As he continues his reading, he sits down on the couch.*) "Dear Diary, since you and I are going to be great friends, I will start by telling you about myself. My name is Anne Frank. I am thirteen years old. I was born in Germany the twelfth of June, nineteen twenty-nine. As my family is Jewish, we emigrated to Holland when Hitler came to power."

(*As* Mr. Frank *reads on, another voice joins his, as if coming from the air. It is* Anne's Voice.)

Mr. Frank and Anne: "My father started a business, importing spice and herbs. Things went well for us until nineteen forty. Then the war came, and the Dutch capitulation, followed by the arrival of the Germans. Then things got very bad for the Jews."

(Mr. Frank's Voice *dies out.* Anne's Voice *continues alone. The lights dim slowly to darkness. The curtain falls on the scene.*)

Anne's Voice: You could not do this and you could not do that. They forced Father out of his business. We had to wear yellow stars. I had to turn in my bike. I couldn't go to a Dutch school any more. I couldn't go to the movies, or ride in an automobile, or even on a streetcar, and a million other things. But somehow we children still managed to have fun. Yesterday Father told me we were going into hiding. Where, he wouldn't say. At five o'clock this morning, Mother woke me and told me to hurry and get dressed. I was to put on as many clothes as I could. It would look too suspicious if we walked along carrying suitcases. It wasn't until we were on our way that I learned where we were going. Our hiding place was to be upstairs in the building where Father used to have his business. Three other people were coming in with us . . . the Van Daans and their son Peter . . . Father knew the Van Daans but we had never met them . . .

(*During the last lines the curtain rises on the scene. The lights dim on.* Anne's Voice *fades out.*)

Scene II

It is early morning, July 1942. The rooms are bare, as before, but they are now clean and orderly.

Mr. Van Daan, *a tall, portly man in his late forties, is in the main room, pacing up and down, nervously. His clothes and overcoat are expensive and well cut.*

Mrs. Van Daan *sits on the couch, clutching her possessions, a hatbox, bags, etc. She is a pretty woman in her early forties. She wears a fur coat over her other clothes.*

Peter Van Daan *is standing at the window of the room on the right, looking down at the street below. He is a shy, awkward boy of sixteen. He wears a cap, a raincoat, and long Dutch trousers, like "plus fours." At his feet is a black case, a carrier for his cat.*

The yellow Star of David is conspicuous on all of their clothes.

Mrs. Van Daan: (*Rising, nervous, excited*) Something's happened to them! I know it!

Mr. Van Daan: Now, Kerli!

Mrs. Van Daan: Mr. Frank said they'd be here at seven o'clock. He said . . .

Mr. Van Daan: They have two miles to walk. You can't expect . . .

Mrs. Van Daan: They've been picked up. That's what's happened. They've been taken . . .

(Mr. Van Daan *indicates that he hears someone coming.*)

Mr. Van Daan: You see?

(Peter *takes up his carrier and his schoolbag, etc., and goes into the main room as* Mr. Frank *comes up the stairwell from below.* Mr. Frank *looks much younger now. His*

Above, front view of the Annex, or hiding place; *top left,* Margot Frank; *bottom left,* Mr. Frank and Miep

movements are brisk, his manner confident. He wears an overcoat and carries his hat and a small cardboard box. He crosses to the Van Daans, *shaking hands with each of them.*)

Mr. Frank: Mrs. Van Daan, Mr. Van Daan, Peter. (*Then, in explanation of their lateness*) There were too many of the Green Police[1] on the streets . . . we had to take the long way around.

(*Up the steps come* Margot Frank, Mrs. Frank, Miep [*not pregnant now*] *and* Mr. Kraler. *All of them carry bags, packages, and so forth. The*

Star of David is conspicuous on all of the Franks' *clothing.* Margot *is eighteen, beautiful, quiet, shy.* Mrs. Frank *is a young mother, gently bred, reserved. She, like* Mr. Frank, *has a slight German accent.* Mr. Kraler *is a Dutchman, dependable, kindly.*

As Mr. Kraler *and* Miep *go upstage to put down their parcels,* Mrs. Frank *turns back to call* Anne.)

Mrs. Frank: Anne?

(Anne *comes running up the stairs. She is thirteen, quick in her movements, interested in everything, mercurial in her emotions. She wears a cape, long wool socks and carries a schoolbag.*)

---

[1]Green Police: special forces police in Nazi Germany

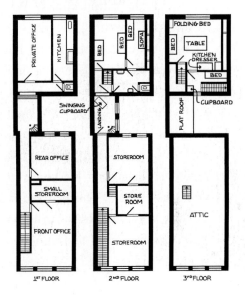

Above, rear view of the Annex; *top right,* the yellow star that Dutch Jews were ordered to wear; *bottom right,* floor plan of the Annex

Mr. Frank: (*Introducing them*) My wife, Edith. Mr. and Mrs. Van Daan (Mrs. Frank *hurries over, shaking hands with them*) . . . their son, Peter . . . my daughters, Margot and Anne.

(Anne *gives a polite little curtsy as she shakes* Mr. Van Daan's *hand. Then she immediately starts off on a tour of investigation of her new home, going upstairs to the attic room.*

Miep *and* Mr. Kraler *are putting the various things they have brought on the shelves.*)

Mr. Kraler: I'm sorry there is still so much confusion.

Mr. Frank: Please. Don't think of it. After all, we'll have plenty of leisure to arrange everything ourselves.

Miep: (*To* Mrs. Frank) We put the stores of food you sent in here. Your medicines are here . . . soap, linen here.

Mrs. Frank: Thank you, Miep.

Miep: I made up the beds . . . the way Mr. Frank and Mr. Kraler said. (*She starts out.*) Forgive me. I have to hurry. I've got to go to the other side of town to get some ration books for you.

Mrs. Van Daan: Ration books? If they see our names on ration books, they'll know we're here.

Mr. Kraler: There isn't anything . . .

Miep: Don't worry. Your names won't

79

be on them. (*As she hurries out*) I'll be up later.

Mr. Frank: Thank you, Miep.

Mrs. Frank: (*To* Mr. Kraler) It's illegal, then, the ration books? We've never done anything illegal.

Mr. Frank: We won't be living here exactly according to regulations.

(*As* Mr. Kraler *reassures* Mrs. Frank, *he takes various small things, such as matches, soap, etc., from his pockets, handing them to her.*)

Mr. Kraler: This isn't the black market, Mrs. Frank. This is what we call the white market . . . helping all of the hundreds and hundreds who are hiding out in Amsterdam.

(*The carillon is heard playing the quarter-hour before eight.* Mr. Kraler *looks at his watch.* Anne *stops at the window as she comes down the stairs.*)

Anne: It's the Westertoren!

Mr. Kraler: I must go. I must be out of here and downstairs in the office before the workmen get here. (*He starts for the stairs leading out.*) Miep or I, or both of us, will be up each day to bring you food and news and find out what your needs are. Tomorrow I'll get you a better bolt for the door at the foot of the stairs. It needs a bolt that you can throw yourself and open only at our signal. (*To* Mr. Frank) Oh . . . You'll tell them about the noise?

Mr. Frank: I'll tell them.

Mr. Kraler: Good-bye then for the moment. I'll come up again, after the workmen leave.

Mr. Frank: Good-bye, Mr. Kraler.

Mrs. Frank: (*Shaking his hand*) How can we thank you? (*The others murmur their good-byes.*)

Mr. Kraler: I never thought I'd live to see the day when a man like Mr. Frank would have to go into hiding. When you think—

(*He breaks off, going out.* Mr. Frank *follows him down the steps, bolting the door after him. As* Mr. Frank *comes back up the steps,* Mrs. Frank *questions him anxiously.*)

Mrs. Frank: What did he mean, about the noise?

Mr. Frank: First let us take off some of these clothes.

(*They all start to take off garment after garment. On each of their coats, sweaters, blouses, suits, dresses, is another yellow Star of David.* Mr. *and* Mrs. Frank *are dressed quite simply. The others wear several things, sweaters, extra dresses, bathrobes, aprons, nightgowns, etc.*)

Mr. Van Daan: It's a wonder we weren't arrested, walking along the streets . . . Petronella with a fur coat in July . . . and that cat of Peter's crying all the way.

Anne: A cat?

(*Finally they have all removed their surplus clothes.*)

Mr. Frank: Now. About the noise.

While the men are in the building below, we must have complete quiet. Every sound can be heard down there, not only in the workrooms, but in the offices too. The men come at about eight-thirty, and leave at about five-thirty. So, to be perfectly safe, from eight in the morning until six in the evening we must move only when it is necessary, and then in stockinged feet. We must not speak above a whisper. We must not run any water. We cannot use the sink, or even, forgive me, the w.c.[2] The pipes go down through the workrooms. It would be heard. No trash . . . (Mr. Frank *stops abruptly as he hears the sound of marching feet from the street below. Everyone is motionless, paralyzed with fear.* Mr. Frank *goes quietly into the room on the right to look down out of the window.* Anne *runs after him, peering out with him. The tramping feet pass without stopping. The tension is relieved.* Mr. Frank, *followed by* Anne, *returns to the main room and resumes his instructions to the group.*) . . . No trash must ever be thrown out which might reveal that someone is living up here . . . not even a potato paring. We must burn everything in the stove at night. This is the way we must live until it is over, if we are to survive. (*There is silence for a second.*)

Mrs. Frank: Until it is over.

Mr. Frank: (*Reassuringly*) After six we can move about . . . we can talk and laugh and have our supper and read and play games . . . just as we would at home. (*He looks at his watch.*) And now I think it would be wise if we all went to our rooms, and were settled before eight o'clock. Mrs. Van Daan, you and your husband will be upstairs. I regret that there's no place up there for Peter. But he will be here, near us. This will be our common room, where we'll meet to talk and eat and read, like one family.

Mr. Van Daan: And where do you and Mrs. Frank sleep?

Mr. Frank: This room is also our bedroom.

Mrs. Van Daan: That isn't right. We'll sleep here and you take the room upstairs.

Mr. Van Daan: It's your place.

Mr. Frank: Please. I've thought this out for weeks. It's the best arrangement. The only arrangement.

Mrs. Van Daan: (*To* Mr. Frank) Never, never can we thank you. (*Then to* Mrs. Frank) I don't know what would have happened to us, if it hadn't been for Mr. Frank.

Mr. Frank: You don't know how your husband helped me when I came to this country . . . knowing no one

---

[2]w.c.: water closet; a room containing a toilet

. . . not able to speak the language.
I can never repay him for that.
(*Going to* Van Daan) May I help
you with your things?

Mr. Van Daan: No. No. (*To* Mrs. Van
Daan) Come along.

Mrs. Van Daan: You'll be all right,
Peter? You're not afraid?

Peter: (*Embarrassed*) Please, Mother.

(*They start up the stairs to the attic
room above.* Mr. Frank *turns to*
Mrs. Frank.)

Mr. Frank: You too must have some
rest, Edith. You didn't close your
eyes last night. Nor you, Margot.

Anne: I slept, Father. Wasn't that
funny? I knew it was the last night
in my own bed, and yet I slept
soundly.

Mr. Frank: I'm glad, Anne. Now
you'll be able to help me straighten
things in here. (*To* Mrs. Frank *and*
Margot) Come with me . . . You
and Margot rest in this room for the
time being.

Mrs. Frank: You're sure . . . ? I
could help . . . And Anne hasn't
had her milk . . .

Mr. Frank: I'll give it to her. (*To*
Anne *and* Peter) Anne, Peter . . .
it's best that you take off your shoes
now, before you forget.

(*He leads the way to the room, followed
by* Margot.)

Mrs. Frank: You're sure you're not
tired, Anne?

Anne: I feel fine. I'm going to help
Father.

Mrs. Frank: Peter, I'm glad you are
to be with us.

Peter: Yes, Mrs. Frank.

(Mrs. Frank *goes to join* Mr. Frank *and*
Margot.)

(*During the following scene* Mr. Frank
helps Margot *and* Mrs. Frank *to
hang up their clothes. The* Van
Daans *in their room above settle
themselves. In the main room* Anne
and Peter *remove their shoes.* Peter
takes his cat out of the carrier.)

Anne: What's your cat's name?

Peter: Mouschi.[3]

Anne: Mouschi! Mouschi! Mouschi!
(*She picks up the cat, walking away
with it. To* Peter) I love cats. I have
one . . . a darling little cat. But
they made me leave her behind. I
left some food and a note for the
neighbors to take care of her . . .
I'm going to miss her terribly. What
is yours? A him or a her?

Peter: He's a tom. He doesn't like
strangers.

(*He takes the cat from her, putting it
back in its carrier.*)

Anne: (*Unabashed*) Then I'll have to
stop being a stranger, won't I?
Where did you go to school?

Peter: Jewish Secondary.

Anne: But that's where Margot and I

---

[3]Mouschi (mōō′ shē)

Left, Peter Van Daan; *right,* Anne in 1942

Mr. and Mrs. Van Daan, and Victor Kraler

go! I never saw you around.

Peter: I used to see you . . . sometimes . . .

Anne: You did?

Peter: . . . in the school yard. You were always in the middle of a bunch of kids.

(*He takes a penknife from his pocket.*)

Anne: Why didn't you ever come over?

Peter: I'm sort of a lone wolf.

(*He starts to rip off his Star of David.*)

Anne: What are you doing?

Peter: Taking it off.

Anne: But you can't do that. They'll arrest you if you go out without your star.

(*He tosses his knife on the table.*)

Peter: Who's going out?

Anne: Why, of course! You're right! Of course we don't need them any more. (*She picks up his knife and starts to take her star off.*) I wonder what our friends will think when we don't show up today?

Peter: I didn't have any dates with anyone.

Anne: Oh, I did. I had a date with Jopie to go and play ping-pong at her house. Do you know Jopie de Waal?

Peter: No.

Anne: Jopie's my best friend. I wonder what she'll think when she telephones and there's no answer? . . . Probably she'll go over to the house

. . . I wonder what she'll think . . . we left everything as if we'd suddenly been called away . . . breakfast dishes in the sink . . . beds not made. . . (*As she pulls off her star, the cloth underneath shows clearly the color and form of the star.*) Look! It's still there! (Peter *goes over to the stove with his star.*) What're you going to do with yours?

Peter: Burn it.

Anne: (*She starts to throw hers in, and cannot.*) It's funny, I can't throw mine away. I don't know why.

Peter: You can't throw . . . ? Something they branded you with . . . ? That they made you wear so they could spit on you?

Anne: I know. I know. But after all, it *is* the Star of David, isn't it?

Peter: Maybe it's different for a girl.

(Mr. Frank *comes into the main room.*)

Mr. Frank: Forgive me, Peter. Now let me see. We must find a bed for your cat. (*He goes to a cupboard.*) I'm glad you brought your cat. Anne was feeling so badly about hers. (*Getting a used small washtub*) Here we are. Will it be comfortable in that?

Peter: Thanks.

Mr. Frank: (*Opening the door of the room on the left*) And here is your room. But I warn you, Peter, you can't grow any more. Not an inch, or you'll have to sleep with your feet out of the skylight. Are you hungry?

Peter: No.

Mr. Frank: We have some bread and butter.

Peter: No, thank you.

Mr. Frank: You can have it for luncheon then. And tonight we will have a real supper . . . our first supper together.

Peter: Thanks. Thanks.

(*He goes into his room.*)

Mr. Frank: That's a nice boy, Peter.

Anne: He's awfully shy, isn't he?

Mr. Frank: You'll like him, I know.

Anne: I certainly hope so, since he's the only boy I'm likely to see for months and months.

Mr. Frank: Anneke,[4] there's a box there. Will you open it?

(*He indicates a carton on the couch. Anne brings it to the center table.*)

Anne: (*As she opens the carton*) You know the way I'm going to think of it here? I'm going to think of it as a boarding house. A very peculiar summer boarding house, like the one that we—(*she breaks off as she pulls out some photographs*) Father! My movie stars! I was wondering where they were! I was looking for them this morning . . . and Queen

---

[4]Anneke (ä′ nə kə)

Wilhelmina! How wonderful!

Mr. Frank: There's something more. Go on. Look further.

Anne: (*Pulling out a pasteboard-bound book*) A diary! (*She throws her arms around her father.*) I've never had a diary. And I've always longed for one. (*She looks around the room.*) Pencil, pencil, pencil, pencil. (*She starts down the stairs.*) I'm going down to the office to get a pencil.

Mr. Frank: Anne! No!

(*He goes after her, catching her by the arm and pulling her back.*)

Anne: (*Startled*) But there's no one in the building now.

Mr. Frank: It doesn't matter. I don't want you ever to go beyond that door.

Anne: (*Sobered*) Never . . . ? Not even at nighttime, when everyone is gone? Or on Sundays? Can't I go down to listen to the radio?

Mr. Frank: Never. I am sorry, Anneke. It isn't safe. No, you must never go beyond that door.

(*For the first time Anne realizes what "going into hiding" means.*)

Anne: I see.

Mr. Frank: It'll be hard, I know. But always remember this, Anneke. There are no walls, there are no bolts, no locks that anyone can put on your mind. Miep will bring us books. We will read history, poetry, mythology. (*He gives her the glass of milk.*) Here's your milk. (*With his arm about her, they go over to the couch, sitting down side by side.*) As a matter of fact, between us, Anne, being here has certain advantages for you. For instance, you remember the battle you had with your mother the other day on the subject of overshoes? You said you'd rather die than wear overshoes? But in the end you had to wear them? Well now, you see, for as long as we are here you will never have to wear overshoes! Isn't that good? And the coat that you inherited from Margot, you won't have to wear that any more. And the piano! You won't have to practice on the piano. I tell you, this is going to be a fine life for you!

(Anne's *panic is gone.* Peter *appears in the doorway of his room. He is carrying his cat.*)

Peter: I . . . I . . . I thought I'd better get some water for Mouschi before . . .

Mr. Frank: Of course.

(*As he starts toward the sink the carillon begins to chime the hour of eight. He turns to* Peter, *indicating in pantomime that it is too late.* Peter *starts back for his room. He steps on a creaking board. The three of them are frozen for a minute in fear. As* Peter *starts away again,* Anne *tiptoes over to him and pours some of the milk from her glass into the saucer for the cat.* Peter *squats on the floor, putting the milk before the cat.* Mr. Frank *gives* Anne *his fountain pen, and then goes into the room at the right. For a second* Anne *watches the cat, then she goes over to the center table, and opens her diary.*)

Anne *starts to write in her diary. The lights dim out, the curtain falls.*

In the darkness Anne's Voice *comes to us again, faintly at first, and then with growing strength.*)

Anne's Voice: I expect I should be describing what it feels like to go into hiding. But I really don't know yet myself. I only know it's funny never to be able to go outdoors . . . never to breathe fresh air . . . never to run and shout and jump. It's the silence in the nights that frightens me most. Every time I hear a creak in the house or a step on the street outside, I'm sure they're coming for us. The days aren't so bad. At least we know that Miep and Mr. Kraler are down there below us in the office. Our protectors, we call them. I asked Father what would happen to them if the Nazis found out they were hiding us. Pim said that they would suffer the same fate that we would . . . Imagine! They know this and yet when they come

Anne (third from right), Mr. Frank (center), and friends on their way to a 1941 wedding

up here, they're always cheerful and gay as if there were nothing in the world to bother them . . . Friday, the twenty-first of August, nineteen forty-two. Today I'm going to tell you our general news. Mother is unbearable. She insists on treating me like a baby, which I loathe. Otherwise things are going better. The weather is . . .

(As Anne's Voice *is fading out, the curtain rises on the scene.*)

Above, Mrs. Frank; *right,* Mr. Dussell

ACT TWO
Scene I

It is two years later. Mr. Dussel, a dentist, has recently joined the Franks *and the* Van Daans *in hiding. It is nighttime and everyone is in bed. There is complete quiet. In the* Van Daans' *room a match flares up for a moment and then is quickly put out. Mr.* Van Daan, *in bare feet, dressed in an undershirt and trousers, is dimly seen coming stealthily down the stairs and into the main room, where* Mr. *and* Mrs. Frank *and* Margot *are sleeping. He goes to the food safe and again lights a match. Then he cautiously opens the safe, taking out a half loaf of bread. As he closes the safe, it creaks. He stands rigid.* Mrs. Frank *sits up in bed. She sees him.*

Mrs. Frank: (*Screaming*) Otto! Otto! *Komme schnell!*[5]

(*The rest of the people wake, hurriedly getting up.*)

---

[5]*Komme schnell!* (kō′mə shněl): German for "Come quickly!"

Mr. Frank: *Was ist los?*[6] *Was ist passiert?*[7]

(Dussel, *followed by* Anne, *comes into the room.*)

Mrs. Frank: (*As she rushes over to* Mr. Van Daan) *Er stiehlt das Essen!*[8]

Dussel: (*Grabbing* Mr. Van Daan) You! You! Give me that.

Mrs. Van Daan: (*Coming down the stairs*) Putti . . . Putti . . . what is it?

Dussel: (*His hands on* Van Daan's *neck*) You dirty thief . . . stealing food . . . you good-for-nothing. . .

Mr. Frank: Mr. Dussel! Help me, Peter!

(Peter *comes over, trying, with* Mr. Frank, *to separate the two struggling men.*)

Peter: Let him go! Let go!

(Dussel *drops* Mr. Van Daan, *pushing him away. He shows them the end of a loaf of bread that he has taken from* Van Daan.)

Dussel: You greedy, selfish . . . !

(Margot *turns on the lights.*)

Mrs. Van Daan: Putti . . . what is it?

(*All of* Mrs. Frank's *gentleness, her self-control, is gone. She is outraged, in a frenzy of indignation.*)

Mrs. Frank: The bread! He was stealing the bread!

Dussel: It was you, and all the time we thought it was the rats!

Mr. Frank: Mr. Van Daan, how could you!

Mr. Van Daan: I'm hungry.

Mrs. Frank: We're all of us hungry! I see the children getting thinner and thinner. Your own son Peter . . . I've heard him moan in his sleep, he's so hungry. And you come in the night and steal food that should go to them . . . to the children!

Mrs. Van Daan: (*Going to* Mr. Van Daan *protectively*) He needs more food than the rest of us. He's used to more. He's a big man.

Mrs. Frank: (*Turning on* Mrs. Van Daan) And you . . . you're worse than he is! You're a mother, and yet you sacrifice your child to this man . . . this . . .

Mr. Frank: Edith! Edith!

(Margot *picks up the pink woolen stole, putting it over her mother's shoulders.*)

Mrs. Frank: (*Paying no attention, going on to* Mrs. Van Daan) Don't think I haven't seen you! Always saving the choicest bits for him! I've watched you day after day and I've held my tongue. But not any longer! Not after this! Now I want him to go! I want him to get out of here!

Mr. Frank: Edith!

---

[6]Was ist los? (väs is lōs): German for "What is going on?"

[7]Was ist passiert? (väs is pa′ sī ārt): German for "What is happening?"

[8]Er stiehlt das Essen! (ār stēlt däs es′ ən): German for "He stole the food."

Mr. Van Daan: Get out of here?

Mrs. Van Daan: What do you mean?

Mrs. Frank: Just that! Take your things and get out!

Mr. Frank: (*To* Mrs. Frank) You're speaking in anger. You cannot mean what you are saying.

Mrs. Frank: I mean exactly that!

Mr. Frank: For two long years we have lived here, side by side. We have respected each other's rights . . . we have managed to live in peace. Are we now going to throw it all away? I know this will never happen again, will it, Mr. Van Daan?

Mr. Van Daan: No. No.

Mrs. Frank: He steals once! He'll steal again!

(Mr. Van Daan, *holding his stomach, starts for the bathroom.* Anne *puts her arms around him, helping him up the step.*)

Mr. Frank: Edith, please. Let us be calm. We'll all go to our rooms . . . and afterwards we'll sit down quietly and talk this out . . . we'll find some way . . .

Mrs. Frank: No! No! No more talk! I want them to leave!

Mrs. Van Daan: You'd put us out, on the streets?

Mrs. Frank: There are other hiding places.

Mrs. Van Daan: A cellar . . . a closet. I know. And we have no money left even to pay for that.

Mrs. Frank: I'll give you money. Out of my own pocket I'll give it gladly.

(*She gets her purse from a shelf and comes back with it.*)

Mrs. Van Daan: Mr. Frank, you told Putti you'd never forget what he'd done for you when you came to Amsterdam. You said you could never repay him, that you . . .

Mrs. Frank: (*Counting out money*) If my husband had any obligation to you, he's paid it, over and over.

Mr. Frank: Edith, I've never seen you like this before. I don't know you.

Mrs. Frank: I should have spoken out long ago.

Dussel: You can't be nice to some people.

Mrs. Van Daan: (*Turning on* Dussel) There would have been plenty for all of us, if *you* hadn't come in here!

Mr. Frank: We don't need the Nazis to destroy us. We're destroying ourselves.

(*He sits down, with his head in his hands.* Mrs. Frank *goes to* Mrs. Van Daan.)

Mrs. Frank: (*Giving* Mrs. Van Daan *some money*) Give this to Miep. She'll find you a place.

Anne: Mother, you're not putting Peter out. Peter hasn't done anything.

Mrs. Frank: He'll stay, of course.

When I say I must protect the children, I mean Peter too.

(Peter *rises from the steps where he has been sitting.*)

Peter: I'd have to go if Father goes.

(Mr. Van Daan *comes from the bathroom,* Mrs. Van Daan *hurries to him and takes him to the couch. Then she gets water from the sink to bathe his face.*)

Mrs. Frank: He's no father to you . . . that man! He doesn't know what it is to be a father!

Peter: (*Starting for his room*) I wouldn't feel right. I couldn't stay.

Mrs. Frank: Very well, then. I'm sorry.

Anne: (*Rushing over to* Peter) No, Peter! No! (Peter *goes into his room, closing the door after him.* Anne *turns back to her mother, crying.*) I don't care about the food. They can have mine! I don't want it! Only don't send them away. It'll be daylight soon. They'll be caught . . .

Margot: Please, Mother!

Mrs. Frank: They're not going now. They'll stay here until Miep finds them a place. (*To* Mrs. Van Daan) But one thing I insist on! He must never come down here again! He must never come to this room where the food is stored! We'll divide what we have . . . an equal share for each! (Dussel *hurries over to get a sack of potatoes from the food safe.*) You can cook it here and take it up to him.

(Dussel *brings the sack of potatoes back to the center table.*)

Margot: Oh, no. No. We haven't sunk so far that we're going to fight over a handful of rotten potatoes.

Dussel: (*Dividing the potatoes into piles*) Mrs. Frank, Mr. Frank, Margot, Anne, Peter, Mrs. Van Daan, Mr. Van Daan, myself . . . Mrs. Frank. . .

(*A buzzer sounds. It is* Miep's *signal.*)

Mr. Frank: It's Miep!

Margot: At this hour?

Mrs. Frank: It is trouble.

Mr. Frank: (*As he starts down to unbolt the door*) I beg you, don't let her see a thing like this!

(Dussel *continues on with his dividing.* Peter, *with his shirt and trousers on, comes from his room.*)

Margot: Stop it! Stop it!

(*We hear* Miep's *excited voice speaking to* Mr. Frank *below.*)

Miep: Mr. Frank . . . the most wonderful news! . . . The invasion has begun!

Mr. Frank: Go on, tell them! Tell them!

(Miep *comes running up the steps, ahead of* Mr. Frank. *She has a man's raincoat on over her nightclothes and a bunch of orange-colored flowers in her hand.*)

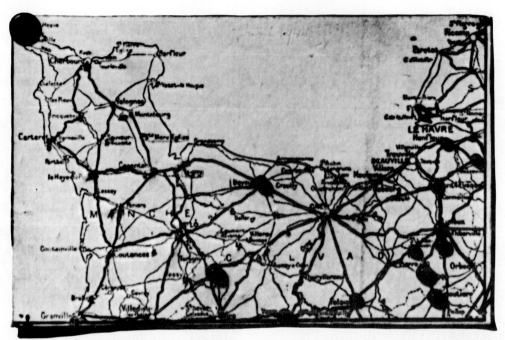

The map on the wall in the hiding place, showing the progress of the Allied troops

Miep: Did you hear that, everybody? Did you hear what I said? The invasion has begun! The invasion!

(*They all stare at* Miep, *unable to grasp what she is telling them.* Peter *is the first to recover his wits.*)

Peter: Where?

Mrs. Van Daan: When? When, Miep?

Miep: It began early this morning. . .

(*As she talks on, the realization of what she has said begins to dawn on them. Everyone goes crazy. A wild demonstration takes place.* Mrs. Frank *hugs* Mr. Van Daan.)

Mrs. Frank: Oh, Mr. Van Daan, did you hear that?

(Dussel *embraces* Mrs. Van Daan. Peter *grabs a frying pan and parades around the room, beating on it,* *singing the Dutch National Anthem.* Anne *and* Margot *follow him, singing, weaving in and out among the excited grownups.* Margot *breaks away to take the flowers from* Miep *and distribute them to everyone. While this pandemonium is going on* Mrs. Frank *tries to make herself heard above the excitement.*)

Mrs. Frank: (*To* Miep) How do you know?

Miep: The radio . . . The B.B.C.![9] They said they landed on the coast of Normandy!

Peter: The British?

Miep: British, Americans, French, Dutch, Poles, Norwegians . . . all

---

[9]B.B.C.: abbreviation for British Broadcasting Company

92

of them! More than four thousand ships! Churchill spoke, and General Eisenhower! D-Day they call it!

Mr. Frank: Thank goodness, it's come!

Mrs. Van Daan: At last!

Miep: (*Starting out*) I'm going to tell Mr. Kraler. This'll be better than any blood transfusion.

(*She goes hurriedly out.*)

Mr. Frank: (*To* Mrs. Frank) What did I tell you? What did I tell you?

(Mrs. Frank *indicates that he has forgotten to bolt the door after* Miep. *He hurries down the steps.* Mr. Van Daan, *sitting on the couch, suddenly breaks into a convulsive sob. Everybody looks at him, bewildered.*)

Mrs. Van Daan: (*Hurrying to him*) Putti! Putti! What is it? What happened?

Mr. Van Daan: Please. I'm so ashamed.

(Mr. Frank *comes back up the steps.*)

Dussel: Oh, for goodness sake!

Mrs. Van Daan: Don't, Putti.

Margot: It doesn't matter now!

Mr. Frank: (*Going to* Mr. Van Daan) Didn't you hear what Miep said? The invasion has come! We're going to be liberated! This is a time to celebrate!

(*He embraces* Mrs. Frank.)

Mr. Van Daan: To steal bread from children!

Mrs. Frank: We've all done things that we're ashamed of.

Anne: Look at me, the way I've treated Mother . . . so mean and horrid to her.

Mrs. Frank: No, Anneke, no.

(Anne *runs to her mother, putting her arms around her.*)

Anne: Oh, Mother, I was. I was awful.

Mr. Van Daan: Not like me. No one is as bad as me!

Dussel: (*To* Mr. Van Daan) Stop it now! Let's be happy!

Mr. Frank: (*Giving* Mr. Van Daan *a glass.*) Here! Here! Let's be friends.

(Van Daan *gives them a feeble smile.* Anne *puts up her fingers in a V-for-Victory sign. As* Van Daan *gives an answering V-sign, they are startled to hear a loud sob from behind them. It is* Mrs. Frank, *stricken with remorse. She is sitting on the other side of the room.*)

Mrs. Frank: (*Through her sobs*) When I think of the terrible things I said . . .

(Mr. Frank, Anne *and* Margot *hurry to her, trying to comfort her.* Mr. Van Daan *joins them.*)

Mr. Van Daan: No! No! You were right!

Mrs. Frank: That I should speak that way to you! . . . Our friends! . . . Our guests!

Dussel: Stop it, you're spoiling the whole invasion!

(*As they are comforting her, the lights dim out. The curtain falls.*)

Anne's Voice: (*Faintly at first and then with growing strength*) We're all in much better spirits these days. There's still excellent news of the invasion. The best part about it is that I have a feeling that friends are coming. Who knows? Maybe I'll be back in school by fall. Ha, ha! The joke is on us!

Wednesday, the second of July, nineteen forty-four. The invasion seems temporarily to be bogged down. Mr. Kraler has to have an operation, which looks bad. The Gestapo[10] have found the radio that was stolen from the office downstairs. Mr. Dussel says they'll trace it back and then, it's just a matter of time till they get to us. Everyone is low. I have often been downcast myself . . . but never in despair. I can shake off everything if I write. But . . . and that is the great question . . . will I ever be able to write well? I want to so much. I want to go on living even after my death. Another birthday has gone by, so now I am fifteen. Already I know what I want. I have a goal, an opinion.

(*As this is being said—the curtain rises on the scene, the lights dim on, and Anne's Voice fades out.*)

---

[10]Gestapo (gə stä′ pō) secret police of Nazi Germany

Scene II

It is an afternoon a few weeks later . . . Everyone but Margot *is in the main room. There is a sense of great tension.*

Both Mrs. Frank *and* Mr. Van Daan *are nervously pacing back and forth,* Dussel *is standing at the window, looking down fixedly at the street below.* Peter *is at the center table, trying to do his lessons.* Anne *sits opposite him, writing in her diary.* Mrs. Van Daan *is seated on the couch, her eyes on* Mr. Frank *as he sits reading.*

The sound of a telephone ringing comes from the office below. They all are rigid, listening tensely. Mr. Dussel *rushes down to* Mr. Frank.

Dussel: There it goes again, the telephone! Mr. Frank, do you hear?

Mr. Frank: (*Quietly*) Yes. I hear.

Dussel: (*Pleading, insistent*) But this is the third time, Mr. Frank! The third time in quick succession! It's a signal! I tell you it's Miep, trying to get us! For some reason she can't come to us and she's trying to warn us of something!

Mr. Frank: Please. Please.

Mr. Van Daan: (*To* Dussel) You're wasting your breath.

Dussel: Something has happened, Mr. Frank. For three days now Miep hasn't been to see us! And today not

94

The entrance to the hiding place, with the bookcase in front of the doorway *(left)*, and moved aside to show the doorway and stairs *(right)*

a man has come to work. There hasn't been a sound in the building!

Mrs. Frank: Perhaps it's Sunday. We may have lost track of the days.

Mr. Van Daan: (*To* Anne) You with the diary there. What day is it?

Dussel: (*Going to* Mrs. Frank) I don't lose track of the days! I know exactly what day it is! It's Friday, the fourth of August. Friday, and not a man at work. (*He rushes back to* Mr. Frank, *pleading with him, almost in tears.*) I tell you Mr. Kraler's dead. That's the only explanation. He's dead and they've closed down the building, and Miep's trying to tell us!

Mr. Frank: She'd never telephone us.

Dussel: (*Frantic*) Mr. Frank, answer that! I beg you, answer it!

Mr. Frank: No.

Mr. Van Daan: Just pick it up and listen. You don't have to speak. Just listen and see if it's Miep.

Dussel: (*Speaking at the same time*) For goodness sake . . . I ask you.

Mr. Frank: No. I've told you, no. I'll do nothing that might let anyone know we're in the building.

Peter: Mr. Frank's right.

Mr. Van Daan: There's no need to tell us what side you're on.

Mr. Frank: If we wait patiently, quietly, I believe that help will come.

(*There is silence for a minute as they all listen to the telephone ringing.*)

The church tower seen from the window of the attic in the hiding place

Dussel: I'm going down. (Dussel *runs to the lower door, unbolting it. The telephone stops ringing.* Dussel *bolts the door and comes slowly back up the steps.*) Too late. (Mr. Frank *goes to* Margot *in* Anne's *bedroom.*)

Mr. Van Daan: So we just wait here until we die.

(Mrs. Van Daan *hurries up the stairs, followed by* Mr. Van Daan. Peter, *unable to bear it, goes to his room.* Dussel *returns to his post at the window.* Mr. Frank *comes back into the main room and takes a book, trying to read.* Mrs. Frank *sits near the sink, starting to peel some potatoes.* Anne *quietly goes to* Peter's *room.* Peter *is lying face down on the cot.*)

Anne: Look, Peter, the sky. (*She looks up through the skylight.*) What a lovely, lovely day! Aren't the clouds beautiful? You know what I do when it seems as if I couldn't stand being cooped up for one more minute? I think myself out. I think myself on a walk in the park where I used to go. Where the jonquils and the crocus and the violets grow down the slopes. You know the most wonderful part about thinking yourself out? You can have it any way you like. You can have roses and violets and chrysanthemums all blooming at the same time . . . It's funny . . . I used to take it all for granted . . . and now I've gone crazy about everything to do with nature. Haven't you?

Peter: I've just gone crazy. I think if something doesn't happen soon . . . if we don't get out of here . . . I can't stand much more of it!

Anne: We're not the only people that've had to suffer. There've always been people that've had to . . . sometimes one race . . . sometimes another . . . and yet . . .

Peter: That doesn't make me feel any better!

Anne: (*Going to him*) You know what I sometimes think? I think the world may be going through a phase, the way I was with Mother. It'll pass, maybe not for hundreds of years, but some day . . . I still believe, in spite of everything, that people are really good at heart.

Peter: I want to see something now . . . Not a thousand years from now!

(*He goes over, sitting down again on the cot.*)

Anne: But, Peter, if you'd only look at it as part of a great pattern . . . that we're just a little minute in the life . . . (*She breaks off*) Listen to us, going at each other like a couple of stupid grownups! Look at the sky now. Isn't it lovely? (*She holds out her hand to him. Peter takes it and rises, standing with her at the window looking out.*) Some day, when we're outside again, I'm going to . . .

(*She breaks off as she hears the sound of a car, its brakes squealing as it comes to a sudden stop. The people in the other rooms also become aware of the sound. They listen tensely. Another car roars up to a screeching stop. Anne and Peter come from Peter's room. Mr. and Mrs. Van Daan creep down the stairs. Dussel comes out from his room. Everyone is listening, hardly breathing. A doorbell clangs again and again in the building below. Mr. Frank starts quietly down the steps to the door. Dussel and Peter follow him. The others stand rigid, waiting, terrified.*

In a few seconds Dussel comes stumbling back up the steps. He shakes off Peter's help and goes to his room. Mr. Frank bolts the door below, and comes slowly back up the steps. Their eyes are all on him as he stands there for a minute. They realize that what they feared has happened. Mrs. Van Daan starts to whimper. Mr. Van Daan puts her gently in a chair, and then hurries off up the stairs to their room to collect their things. Peter goes to comfort his mother. There is a sound of violent pounding on a door below.)

Mr. Frank: (*Quietly*) For the past two years we have lived in fear. Now we can live in hope.

(*The pounding below becomes more insistent. There are muffled sounds of voices, shouting commands.*)

Soldiers' Voices: Auf machen![11] Da drinnen![12] Auf machen! Schnell! Schnell! Schnell!

(*The street door below is forced open.*

---

[11]Auf machen! (ouf mä′ kən) German for "Open up!"
[12]Da drinnen! (də drī′ nən) "There, inside!"

We hear the heavy tread of footsteps coming up. Mr. Frank *gets two school bags from the shelves, and gives one to* Anne *and the other to* Margot. *He goes to get a bag for* Mrs. Frank. *The sound of feet coming up grows louder.* Peter *comes to* Anne, *then he goes to his room to collect his things. The buzzer of their door starts to ring.* Mr. Frank *brings* Mrs. Frank *a bag. They stand together, waiting. We hear pounding on the door, trying to break it down.*

Anne *stands, holding her school satchel, looking over at her father and mother with a soft, reassuring smile. She is no longer a child, but a woman with courage to meet whatever lies ahead.*

The lights dim out. The curtain falls on the scene. We hear a mighty crash as the door is shattered. After a second Anne's Voice *is heard.*)

Anne's Voice: And so it seems our stay here is over. They are waiting for us now. They've allowed us five minutes to get our things. We can each take a bag and whatever it will hold of clothing. Nothing else. So, dear Diary, that means I must leave you behind. Good-bye for a while. P.S. Please, please, Miep, or Mr. Kraler, or anyone else. If you should find this diary, will you please keep it safe for me, because some day I hope . . .

(*Her voice stops abruptly. There is silence. After a second the curtain rises.*)

 Reader's **R**esponse

What admirable qualities did you find in Anne Frank as you read this play?

THE DIARY OF
ANNE FRANK

Checking Your Comprehension

1. How was the time period of the opening scene of the play different from the time period of the rest of the play?
2. Why were Anne Frank and the others living in the attic of an old warehouse?
3. How were the relationships between the people in the attic made more difficult by the circumstances in which they lived? What clues in the play told you this?
4. What did you think of Mrs. Frank when she wanted to make the Van Daans leave?
5. What career did Anne seem to be thinking about?
6. How did Peter and Anne react differently to the hardships in their lives?

Writing to Learn

THINK AND ANALYZE The bravery of Anne Frank and her family has been an inspiration to readers. Find a quotation from this play that is meaningful to you. Copy it on your paper. Here is an example:

> "But always remember this, Anneke.
> There are no walls, there are no bolts,
> no locks that anyone can put on your mind."
> Mr. Frank

WRITE In your own words, explain the quotation above or the one that you chose. Tell why it is meaningful for today's world. Use details to support the ideas you express.

THE WORLD OF READING

A Diary Worth Saving

▲ Anne Frank in 1941

On Friday, June 12th, I woke up at six o'clock and no wonder; it was my birthday. But of course I was not allowed to get up at that hour. . . ." Those probably don't sound like words that would begin one of the most important books ever written. If you were told that a thirteen-year-old girl wrote them, you'd be even more surprised that the book was considered that important. But it was, because they were Anne Frank's words. The book, of course, was her diary.

Anne herself wondered whether the little red cloth diary she had received for her birthday would be worth keeping. No one, she felt, would be interested in what she had to say. She was wrong. Her book has been translated into every major language in the world and read by millions of people. Many have called it the most important book written about the Holocaust and the Second World War.

One of the most amazing things about the book, besides what it says, is that it ever got published in the first place. Nazi police were capturing Jews hiding in Holland and sending them to concentration camps. They had been instructed not to leave any records of what they were doing. The rest of the world was not to know about their deeds. A diary like Anne's would show the terrible things they had done, and they had it right in their hands.

►

The courtyard outside the Franks' hiding place as it appears today

100

The day the Nazi police followed an informer's tip to the Franks' hiding place and dragged the family away, they also took the few valuable items the Franks had brought into hiding—some silverware and a Hanukah candleholder. Then they saw Mr. Frank's briefcase. When Mr. Frank told them that it contained only some papers, they emptied the case onto the floor and left. Among those papers, which came so close to being destroyed, was Anne's diary. After the Nazis had left with their captives, the Dutch family who had hidden the Franks returned home and found the papers and Anne's diary. They gathered them up and put them away without reading them.

Everyone in the Frank family except Anne's father, Otto Frank, died in the concentration camps. He was released when the camp was liberated and later decided to return to Holland to see what had happened to the people who had hidden his family. When he got there, Miep von Santen, his old friend, remembered the diary and gave it to him. He read it and decided to show it to other people as a way of keeping the memory of Anne and the rest of his family alive. Fortunately, a Dutch professor who saw it realized what a wonderful book it was and convinced Mr. Frank to have it published.

▲
A 1933 photograph showing, from left, Anne, her mother, and her sister

▼ This diagram shows the Franks' hiding place. The secret entrance is circled in red.

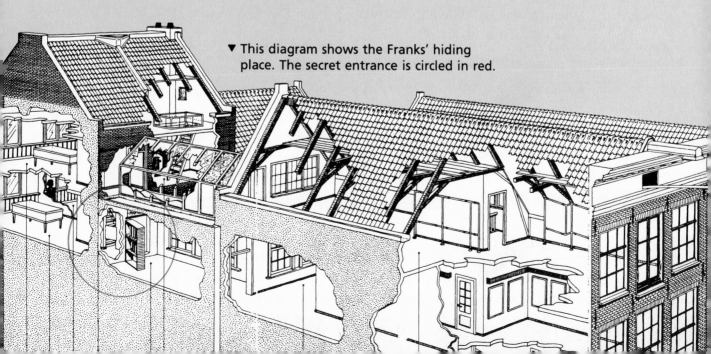

READING FICTION

Comprehension:

Making Comparisons

Have you ever moved to a new city? Or have you ever gone to a new school where you didn't know anyone else? If you have, you probably found yourself noting all the ways in which your new city or school was similar to, or different from, the one you knew previously. When it was similar in some way, you probably felt a bit more comfortable. When it was different, you might have decided it would be best to get used to the new experience.

In "The Obsidian Ring," Rafael finds himself in exactly that kind of situation. He has moved from his home in Mexico City to Queens, a section of New York City. He quickly realizes that this new life is very different from his old one, but he also discovers that a surprising number of things are the same. You may remember that it is Rafael who tells the story. In the following passage he is talking with a cousin, Francisco. Francisco is also interested in the similarities and differences between Mexico City and New York, and he asks Rafael about them:

> "Rafe, do they have TV in Mexico?"
> "Sure."
> "Comic books?"
> "Sure."
> "Baseball? Bubble gum? Ice cream?"
> "Sure, Francisco. It's just like here."
> Only it wasn't, of course. Mexico was my home.

There are many similarities between the two cities, such as TV and baseball. There is, however, one major difference: Mexico City is Rafael's home, and New York is not.

When you read the story, you may have found yourself making these comparisons along with Rafael—perhaps without even recognizing that this was what you were doing. A *comparison* states how two things are alike. It may also tell how they are different. Making comparisons can be a helpful tool for organizing information, for forming opinions, and for understanding the points that an author is making.

Making Comparisons

When you want to identify comparisons in a story, think about the characteristics of each thing that the author describes. Then decide which characteristics are shared by both (how they are similar), and which characteristics belong to only one of them (how they are different).

Sometimes you will notice word clues that will alert you to similarities and differences. Words and phrases such as "both," "alike," and "the same as" point to similarities. Words such as "different," "however," and "unlike" point to differences.

Authors do not always include word clues, but you can always find similarities and differences between two (or even more) things by asking yourself these questions: "How are these things alike? How are they different?"

If you were to compare Rafael's life in Mexico City with his life in New York, you might want to start with these aspects: the family he is living with, the apartment in which they live, his neighborhood, his school, his friends, and the language spoken in the area. Then you can ask yourself which features are the same in both cities, and which are different. You might even want to make a chart to show the similarities and differences.

Mexico City / New York	Similar	Different
Family Life	✓	
Apartment		✓
Neighborhood		✓
School		✓
Friends	✓	
Language		✓

Another selection you read, "The Football Player," is similar to "The Obsidian Ring" because it tells the story of a young man who is struggling with two different cultures. In this case, Jim Yoshida is living with both the Japanese culture of his parents and the American culture that is all around him. Like Rafael, Jim finds himself making comparisons between the two cultures. The following sentences are from "The Football Player":

> Judo is like wrestling, hand-to-hand combat, in which a smaller and weaker man learns to use his opponent's strength to defeat him.

> Mother was wise enough to know that American children could not be reared like Japanese children, that we were products of the new world and we required freedom.

> Judo was as much fun as football.

The first and last sentences show how the Japanese sport of judo is similar both to wrestling and to football. The second sentence, though, implies that there is a difference between parental attitudes in Japan and in the United States.

Using What You Have Learned

You can often use comparisons to help you understand a larger point, or theme, that an author is trying to express. In "The Way It Was *And Is*" for example, Bill Cosby writes about the "generation gap" that existed first between him and his father, and then between him and his children. Skim "The Way It Was *And Is*" in order to refresh your memory. Then answer the questions below.

1. What *similarities* does Bill Cosby see between himself and his father? Between himself and his daughter?
2. What *differences* does Bill Cosby see between himself and his father? Between himself and his daughter?

As You Read

The next story you will read, "Leaving Home," is about a girl who is going away to a new school in a city that is very different from her small village. As you read the story, try to compare her new life with the life she has left behind.

Decisions can be very hard—especially when they mean leaving the familiar and going off to face the unknown. Dawan has already made her decision, but now she's having second thoughts.

LEAVING HOME

by Minfong Ho

Dawan and her brother, Kwai, have lived in a small Thai farming village all their lives. They both worked hard to earn a scholarship to attend school in the city; but there could be only one recipient. When Dawan finished first in the competition, a disappointed Kwai helped convince their father that Dawan deserved the chance to continue her education. Now, on the morning Dawan is to leave for school, both she and Kwai must face the consequences of their decisions.

Dawan could not believe that she was leaving in an hour, and yet she sensed that everything, the river, the fields, the bridge, even her brother, Kwai, were all bidding her goodbye.

She walked over to the bridge, her feet knowing their own way. Kwai took no notice of her approach, but was completely absorbed in throwing pebbles into the river, sullenly watching each one as it hit the water and sank from sight.

When she reached the foot of the bridge, she called up to him, but he gave no sign of acknowledgment.

"Kwai," she called again, "can I come up too?" Still he ignored her, and continued to throw his pebbles in, each one with more force and anger.

Finally he muttered to himself, "Stupid stones! All they can do is sink, sink, sink, to the bottom. No matter how hard you throw them, no matter how big a splash they make, all they do is sink." He threw another one in and watched in disgust as it sank from sight. "And even their ripples fade away, and the water flows on, as if nothing ever happened. Stupid, stupid, stupid." He stopped abruptly and glared down at his sister. "I didn't get in your way after all, did I? Now are you satisfied?"

Dawan felt a sharp pain and pity shoot though her, and she wanted to run up to him and hold him, rock him clumsily like she did when they were both very little. Instead, she climbed up on the bridge and sat down next to him, with the little pile of pebbles between them.

They maintained an uneasy silence, each staring directly ahead into the tendrils of the rising sun. Finally Dawan said gently, "Kwai, thank you. Thank you very much."

For answer, Kwai threw another pebble into the water. "Why do you have to go anyway?" he challenged. And although his voice was hostile, Dawan knew that, in his way, this was a plea too. Quietly, without looking up, she said to the ripples in the water, "You know why. We've just begun studying, and there's still so much more I need to learn, Kwai."

"Why go and study more when all you're going to end up doing sooner or later is cook and raise babies anyway, like Mama?" he demanded, punctuating every few words by hurling a pebble onto the smooth river surface.

"Well, why do *you* want to go study then?" she retorted angrily. She reached over for a pebble and flung one into the water herself. "All father's ever done with *his* life is plant some rice and raise chickens, and a buffalo or two. He's never gone to school, so why should you, when all you're going to be is just another peasant anyway?"

She grabbed another pebble from the pile, but her fingers touched something warm and bony: it was Kwai's hand reaching for his own pebble. They glared at each other for a split second, and then Dawan snatched her hand away.

"Kwai," Dawan continued in a softer tone, "I'm not even sure I really want to go to the City to study. You know how scared I am of crowded places. You're not helping me any with your angry questions, Kwai. Can't you see that I'm confused and scared too?"

She could feel the tears welling up from her lower eyelids as she spoke. All the things that had been pent up inside her for the past few days streamed forth as she continued, "Why can't you be happy for me, Kwai? I know it's hard, but if you had won the scholarship and were going instead of me, I would have been so happy for you, really, really, I would have! Remember all the ideas you used to talk about? You dreamed of learning enough to help Father improve his crops, or to take the land away from the land-lord and divide it among all the villagers, or to . . ."

"Well, I can't do any of that now, can I?" Kwai broke in bitterly, and although he still sounded angry, his voice was choked.

"But Kwai, don't you see? I can do all those things," Dawan continued eagerly. "All those mornings that we watched the sun rising, I listened to you talk of building a new world. I never said anything much because I never thought I'd have a chance to fulfill our ideals. You should be glad for me. Oh Kwai, everything will be better, I promise! I'll make things better!"

Kwai stared at his sister, whose face was shining with a new hope and strength. Then he lowered his gaze to his small pile of pebbles, and felt all the more lonely and deserted.

"Sure, things will be better," he blurted out. "Better for you! What am I supposed to do while you tromp off to a big fancy school in the City? Go sit with the dirty old buffalo all day and be glad for you? And in the early mornings, am I supposed to come out to this stupid old bridge and watch the stupid old sunrise and talk to myself?"

His voice broke, but he took a deep breath and went on more calmly, and yet with more urgency. "Nothing will ever be the same, Sister. I don't care if things will be better or worse, it's just that when . . . if you come back, we couldn't ever sit on the bridge and just watch the dawn like we used to anymore. You've changed that, you've gone and changed all that already." Almost automatically, Kwai's hand stretched out for a pebble, then stopped half-way in midair. "Oh, what's the use?" he said softly to himself.

In the silence that followed, he picked up a lotus bud lying on the other side of him, and began restlessly plucking off its petals.

Dawan noticed this, and because she hated to see fresh flowers destroyed, said sharply, "Stop that! Why are you tearing that lotus apart?" She was about to snatch it away from him when he shrugged, and tossed the bud aside.

"I liked watching the dawn with you too," she continued in a gentler, sad tone. "Can't you imagine how much I will miss that when I'm alone in the City? I won't have a chance to watch a quiet sunrise over river water anymore. Kwai, you know I'll keep wishing I could be back here on the bridge with you. I'll miss everything so much."

There was a pause, and then she said softly, "Hey, Kwai, when you're out here in the early mornings, will you watch the dawn for me too? And maybe you can sing my morning song for me, because it belongs here, and I'll never sing it anywhere else. Please, Kwai? Do you understand? Watch the dawn for me, and sing."

Her brother's face was now streaked with tears, cool, lonely tears which he didn't want his sister to see. Abruptly, without looking at her, he ran down the bridge and across to the fields, until he disappeared between the tall ricestalks. Dawan watched him run away, but this time made no move to follow him.

She picked up a pebble and dropped it into the water, and as the ripples slowly quivered their way outwards, she started singing her morning song one last time:

Misty morning,
mist is rising,
melody of trees,
slowly sifting . . .

and as she sang, she let the hope of the morning light filter through her pores, until the delicate wonder of being home and leaving home blended together like sunlight through rainclouds in her heart. "How can I leave this?" she thought to herself, her song left unfinished. "How can I bear the loneliness in the big City, without friends, without Kwai, without the quiet dawns? I don't want to go off all alone and yet I have to. I don't, don't, want to but I have to, have to leave." It was as if these confused thoughts swirling inside her blurred over the morning scene itself with a misted film. Funny, she thought to herself, how the world looks like after-rain when I'm crying inside.

Then she noticed the half-torn lotus bud lying forlornly by her side, where Kwai had tossed it just now. Out of some feeling of kinship for it, Dawan reached over and picked it up, holding it with both hands, much the way she used to hold onto her grand-

110

mother's thumb when she was just learning to walk. Then she knelt up and carefully gathered the petals Kwai had stripped off and sprinkled them gently over the surface of the klong-water.

Like a fleet of tiny pink boats, the petals floated lazily down the water, rising and falling with each ripple of the river. Dawan watched them silently, then whispered, "See, see, Kwai, these don't sink. See, don't be sad, don't be sad, these don't sink." Then wiping away a stray tear, she got up and walked slowly down the bridge.

She knew that at home the bus would soon be arriving, and people would be waiting for her to leave.

Peering out from the leafy shelter of the path, Dawan watched the crowd of villagers gathered around her home. Naked babies scurried between people's legs chasing chickens; a cluster of solemn young monks talked in low whispers among themselves; little girls peeped out from behind the curtain of their mother's sarongs.

Dawan caught glimpses of a few people who were special to her. Her teacher was standing rather awkwardly by himself, Bao was carelessly holding onto her baby brother while arguing with her older one. Noi was chattering and giggling with a knot of young wives while Ghan stood behind her sullenly.

Dawan stared at all this bustle for a moment, then hastily retreated into the shadows of the tree. But her mother, tying the last rope around her daughter's luggage, caught sight of the movement. She straightened up and hurried over to her daughter, shouting, "There you are! I was getting worried, child. Your father has already gone out to look for you. We thought you had suddenly decided not to go. It's a good thing you didn't run off for the day, child. Why, look at all the people here to see you off . . ."

By this time the villagers were swarming around, fussing and cooing over her. Dawan cringed back, muttered something about having to change her clothes, and wiggled her way through them. She clambered up the ladder to the hut, which she knew would be empty except for her old grandmother.

In the dim light of the house, Dawan saw a pair of steady eyes gleaming in the corner. "Don't be afraid child. Calm down," her grandmother said gently. "I have put your new clothes and shoes on the matting there. Are they all waiting for you outside?" She clucked softly, "Never *mind*, child, take your time."

Dawan smiled gratefully at her grandmother, and walked over to the piece of matting where her new things lay waiting. As she bent down to put her shoes on, she realized that she was still clutching Kwai's discarded lotus bud in her hand. Tossing the bud aside, she dressed hurriedly, her nervousness increasing as she heard the sound of the heavy old bus rumbling in. Outside, the noise of the crowd grew, like palm fronds rustling in the wind before a monsoon storm.

"Child, you come here."

Dawan obediently crawled to the corner where her grand-mother sat, and knelt down in front of the old woman, hands neatly folded and head bowed. This was the leavetaking that pained her most.

In a voice slow and heavy with age, the old woman said, "You have a long life ahead of you yet, child, and this is just the first step. If you're this timid now, how on earth are you going to face the world out there with clear bold eyes? You hear me?"

Dawan nodded, but did not budge. It was the rhythm more than the meaning of the aged voice that calmed the young girl.

Her grandmother gave her a gentle shove, "Well, child, you must go now. You've packed everything you want to take with you, haven't you?"

Dawan stared at her blankly, then shook her head. "No, no, I can't go yet!" she blurted out. Swallowing hard, she continued desperately, "Please Grandmama, I'm not ready. I haven't packed everything yet. There's the sunrise I want to take, and the bridge over the river-bend. And, oh Grandma, how can I pack Kwai, and home here, and the chickens, even the bullfrogs in the forest, and . . ." She could feel a sob rising from her throat, but could not stop it.

Already it seemed as if these precious drops of childhood were slipping through her fingers, like sun-sparkles when she washed her hands in the river. Dawan glanced down at her one outstretched hand, and it looked so small, so helplessly empty. She wept then, shoulders hunched over as sob after sob was wrenched from her thin frame.

The old woman reached out and cupped her granddaughter's ears with feeble hands, but Dawan only shook them off.

"Let me cry, Grandmama," she sobbed brokenly. "Let me cry now and I promise, I won't ever cry anymore. Oh, let me cry now!"

So the grandmother withdrew her hands, and waited patiently until Dawan's sobs began to subside.

After a while the gentle old woman got up and hobbled, back-bent, to the rain barrel. There, she picked up a small glass jar and scooped some fresh rainwater into it. Walking back to where the lotus bud lay on the matting, she bent over and put it carefully in the jar.

Dawan wiped away her tears with the back of her hand, and watched curiously. There was a solemnity about her grandmother's movements that suggested a sacred ritual, like the sprinkling of holy water over a newly-wed couple.

It was not until the old woman had unhurriedly reseated herself beside Dawan, that she handed the glass jar to her granddaughter.

"Hold on to this lotus carefully, child," the grandmother said. "Watch it unfold during your long bus-ride to the City. It's like yourself, this lotus bud, all shut up tight, small and afraid of the outside. But with good water and strong sunlight, it'll unfold, petal by petal by petal. And you will too, Dawan, you will unfold too."

"But, but I don't want to," the school girl mumbled. "I don't want to change."

"I'm sure that bud you have there is pretty contented the way it is," the old woman smiled, nodding towards the lotus. "But if it refuses to change, it'll never become a lotus in full bloom, will it?"

Dawan shook her head reluctantly.

"And remember, the lotus shrinks back into a bud when night falls, only to unfold again in the dawn. Just because you're leaving now doesn't mean you'll never come back. And when you come back, of course some things will change. Anybody can see there's always change. What people seem to forget is that there is a beautiful pattern to all this change."

"But I'm not afraid I won't ever come back, Grandma," Dawan protested weakly. "Right now I don't know if I even want to leave in the first place."

"Don't think of this as leaving, then," the old woman answered firmly. "Think of it as just another of your petals unfolding. For me, child, life has always been an endless unfolding: night unfolding into day, girls unfolding into women, women unfolding babies from themselves. Why, life itself unfolds to death, and death unfolds to life again. There is no cause for sorrow or for fear in this."

Then, as Dawan still hesitated, her grandmother gave her another light push and said, "Go now, child."

Dawan looked at the lotus bud uncertainly. The glass jar was smooth and cool in her hands; somehow it seemed able to absorb the anxiety within her. She swept her eyes over the familiar walls of her home. Sunlight and laughter stole in through the windows and hopped about on the wooden floorboards. Dawan took a deep breath, and nodded. She was ready now.

Setting the jar aside, Dawan pressed her palms together and bent her head over them to her grandmother in the traditional gesture of leave-taking. Then she stood up and, lotus-jar in hand, went outside to the veranda. Her mother and some other women were busy loading her luggage onto the already crowded bus, trying to wedge the bags between a big basket full of bananas and a coop full of squawking chickens. Everybody was fluttering about excitedly trying to help.

As she climbed down the stairs, her father rushed out from the jungle path, panting and scowling fiercely. He caught sight of Dawan at once, and strode up to her.

"Why did you disappear like that just before you're supposed to leave?" he yelled at her angrily. "Do you know that I've been chasing around the countryside the whole morning looking for you and Kwai? I thought the two of you had taken off together, until I saw Kwai alone. Where have you been anyway?"

Ignoring his last question, Dawan said eagerly, "Where is Kwai, Father? Where did you see him? Is he coming?"

Her father snorted loudly. "Huh! That brother of yours! And I thought the two of you were such good friends!"

"But where is he, Father? Is he coming?" Dawan craned her neck to peer behind her father, but no one was in sight.

"Where is he? He's sitting out on the old bridge, calm as a water-buffalo, that's where he is. I asked him where you were, and he said he didn't know and didn't care. Then I asked if he was coming back to see you off. He . . ." The strong peasant paused and eyed his daughter shrewdly, "You two had a fight, didn't you?"

Dawan did not seem to have heard the question. "Is he coming or not, Father? What did he say?" she asked tersely.

"You really want to know what he said? He looked down at me from his bridge and said, 'She's got the whole village seeing her off. Isn't that enough? What does she need me there for?' And I thought you two were . . ."

Dawan turned away so that her father could not see her face. She felt more lonely on the fringe of that chattering crowd than she had ever felt before. Looking at all the faces around her, she realized that there was not a single one she really cared to say goodbye to.

So her brother was still bitter and angry at her. She wondered again if fighting with him to go to the City had been worth it after all. She was leaving, but there was nothing left to say goodbye to.

The bus honked sharply, and Dawan saw the bus driver wave impatiently for her to board. Immediately the crowd surged over to her, and she was shoved, patted, hugged and somehow pushed to the steps of the bus. She caught a glimpse of her mother crying, but she herself felt no more sadness, only a throbbing disappointment.

As soon as she got on, the big bus ground to a start and roared off. She groped her way clumsily to a seat and leaned out the window to watch the crowd. Her grandmother was standing on the veranda above them all, smiling slightly. Then the faces all receded into the distance. When they had disappeared from view, green stretches of paddy-fields slid past her window, going by as quickly as slippery fish. Ahead of them now was the river, and Dawan stuck her head way out of the window to catch a last glimpse of the bridge on which she had so often greeted the sun.

Suddenly, carried by the breeze, she heard a very familiar voice singing a very familiar song—

Misty morning,
mist is lifting,
melody of trees
slowly sifting . . .

He was there. Etched sharply against the cloudless sky, Kwai was standing on the old arched bridge, both arms thrown back in a gesture meant both to embrace her and send her off.

Dawan burst out laughing and the laughter was so strong and round that it seemed to jam in her throat. Flinging her arms out too, to hug him and the land, she joined him in song.

Dappled morning,
sun is flying
breaths of breezes
rising, dying,
brushing over the earth's brown skin . . .

The bus was fast approaching the slim figure now. A grin, a streak of wetness gleaming on one cheek, an outstretched palm, and Kwai had already flashed past her.

Leaning out as far as she could, Dawan watched her brother wave until he was only a speck on the bridge, until the bridge was only a speck on the river, and until finally even the ribbon of water faded into the distance.

Dawan watched for a moment longer, and then, gently picking up the glass jar from her seat, she leaned back. The morning song was still in her. So, brushing the lotus bud with her fingertips, she sang the last verse.

> Happy morning
> my heart is singing
> arms spread wide,
> the dawn is bringing
> its sunglow to this land, my home.

And as she sang, a shaft of sunlight pierced through the grimy bus windows and cradled the lotus. Dawan noticed that the first few petals of the flower had already begun to unfold.

♦ LIBRARY LINK ♦

Would you like to find out more about Dawan and her brother? Read the book from which this excerpt was taken, Sing to the Dawn, *by Minfong Ho.*

Reader's Response

If you were Dawan's friend, what advice would you have given her about leaving the village?

LEAVING HOME

Checking Your Comprehension

1. Why did Kwai feel so upset about his sister's departure?
2. How did Dawan plan to use her education?
3. In what way were Dawan's lotus petals an answer to Kwai's pebbles?
4. What kind of person was Dawan's grandmother?
5. Why did the entire village turn out to see Dawan off?
6. At the end of the story, what was Kwai trying to communicate to Dawan? How do you know?
7. Do you think Dawan will do well in school and come back to help Kwai achieve their dreams? Explain your answer.

Writing to Learn

THINK AND PLAN "Reader's Theater" is a story rewritten as play dialogue. Read this scene from "Leaving Home" and compare it with the original scene in the story.

> **Narrator:** Her grandmother gave her a gentle shove.
> **Dawan:** No, no, I can't go yet!
> **Narrator:** Swallowing hard, she continued desperately.
> **Dawan:** Please Grandmama, I'm not ready. I haven't packed everything yet. There's the sunrise I want to take, and the bridge over the river-bend. And, oh Grandma, how can I pack Kwai . . .

WRITE Find another scene from "Leaving Home." Write a Reader's Theater version of the scene you choose. Under the scene, tell why the lines you chose were important in this story.

DAYDREAMERS

by Eloise Greenfield

Daydreamers . . .
holding their bodies still
for a time
letting the world turn around them
while their dreams hopscotch,
doubledutch, dance,
thoughts rollerskate,
crisscross,
bump into hopes and wishes.
Dreamers
thinking up new ways,
looking toward new days,
planning new tries,
asking new whys.

Before long,
hands will start to move again,
eyes turn outward,
bodies shift for action,
but for this moment they are still,
they are
the daydreamers,
letting the world dizzy itself
without them.
Scenes passing through their minds
make no sound
glide from hiding places
promenade and return
silently
the children watch their memories
with spirit-eyes
seeing more than they saw before
feeling more
or maybe less
than they felt the time before
reaching with spirit-hands
to touch the dreams
drawn from their yesterdays.
They will not be the same
after this growing time,
this dreaming.
In their stillness they have moved forward
toward womanhood
toward manhood.
This dreaming has made them
new.

Dawan had a chance to start down a path that was very different from any her parents had ever taken. But some teenagers want to follow the path that their parents took. Joel Holland certainly feels that way.

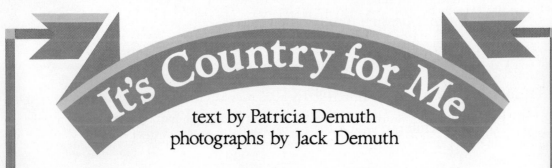

It's Country for Me

text by Patricia Demuth
photographs by Jack Demuth

It was 11:15 at night when Joel, reading in bed, heard his mother call up, "Joel, come and feed Lamby, will you?" She usually fed the orphaned lamb, but tonight she had come home late from a meeting and did not want to go to the barn wearing good clothes.

The family dog, Jessica, jumped up from the doorstep as Joel came outside, a pair of overalls pulled over his pajamas, the laces of his boots dangling loose. "Hey, Jess," he greeted her, ruffling the dog's thick fur with one hand as they loped together to the barn. In his other hand he carried Lamby's meal—milk replacement in a soda-pop bottle capped by a black nipple.

The March air was cold and the yard light caught the mist of Joel and Jessica's breaths. A dim crescent moon hung low over the east hayfield. Otherwise, the night was black.

"Here, Lamby," called Joel, opening the door to the barn where the sheep are kept in the winter. The lamb sprang up from her warm straw bedding and sucked down the bottle in thirty seconds. Her mother had died giving birth to her a week before.

This may have been Joel's thirty-three-thousandth trip to the barn, since he goes in and out of barns at least ten times a day. Joel knows these farm buildings better than he knows his own bedroom. He surely spends more waking hours in them. He knows how to care for the animals they shelter as well as he knows how to care for himself. Farming is Joel's world.

Joel Holland has lived on this 245-acre farm since he was born, thirteen years ago. It is the farm of his ancestors. He lives in the house that his great-grandfather built. The land he helps his father and brothers farm is land that his great-great-grandfather James Holland bought in 1860. James was an Irish immigrant. He drove a team of horses to plow the land and make it ready for corn. Now, five generations later, Joel plows the same land atop a tractor that has the power of 120 horses. The rich, black soil has been pampered by Hollands for over 120 years. Farming it is Joel's heritage.

The Holland farm is near Scales Mound, a tiny town of 400 people snuggled in the northwestern corner of Illinois. The land there is hilly, rolling in great waves. In fact, just a few miles away is the highest point in the state.

Joel attends public school in Scales Mound in a split-level brick building with 235 other grade school and high school pupils. About half the students are farmers. This year Joel will graduate from eighth grade and begin ninth, but his class will not get larger. Except for three foster children who came and left, Joel has been with the same nineteen kids since first grade.

"I know every kid in practically the whole school," he says. "Some of those guys in schools on TV don't even know the people in their own class."

Joel is a good student, though reluctant to discuss it. "Yeah, I guess I pull mostly A's, some B's." In national testing Joel scored an overall 99 percent, meaning that only 1 percent of students scored higher. His studies are typical of any eighth grader's in the United States. "We're doing percents in math. English, forget it. In history we're up to F.D.R. In science we do experiments like taking this chemical HCl and blowing up pieces of chalk."

But when the school bus drops Joel off and he runs up the quarter-mile lane to his farmhouse, slips out of his sneakers, and pulls on his boots—then his life is no longer typical of an average teenager. His footgear is the clue. Joel wears boots every day, no matter what the season. That's because he does chores every night after school and for several hours on weekends. The chores are boot work—hard, heavy, and sometimes dirty.

The daily chores that Joel does help run the farm and help support the family. Joel is a teenager, but he does the work of an adult. Unlike most families, where the parents alone make the money, farm families work together. Each child's labor is not only important to the family's well-being, it is essential.

The Hollands operate a self-sufficient farm, typical of many in the Corn Belt. They raise livestock—pigs, cattle, a few sheep. In each herd, they keep some females to replenish the stock. The rest of the animals are sold for slaughter, to become the pork, beef, and lamb on America's tables. The Hollands grow virtually all the food their animals need—corn, oats, and hay. They sell the surplus, though most of their money comes from selling the animals themselves.

To run a farm like this, farmers have to have many skills. They have to be machine operators, driving immense and powerful vehicles; they have to be mechanics, repairing them; husbandmen, raising livestock; veterinarians, tending them when sick; agriculturists, growing food on a large scale; and businesspeople, managing (like Joel's father) a farm operation worth nearly one million dollars. As Joel works on the farm, he is all these workers.

Yet he is a boy still and, like an apprentice, continues to learn new skills. Joel takes his learning seriously because his goal is to become a farmer. He is extremely alert and watchful, like a cat. Even when not actively involved in a chore, Joel can readily answer any question about what is going on. He listens as his dad counsels a seed customer in the kitchen, as his brother Terry consults a vet about recent deaths in his hog herd, as his older brothers discuss soil planning while they mend a fence. Knowledge seems to be constantly seeping, sometimes flowing, into Joel's mind.

Even before he could spell his name, Joel began learning about the farm, bumping along on a tractor seat between his dad's legs. He was doing hog chores by age seven, inoculating baby pigs by eleven, buying and feeding his own calves when he was twelve. Now, at thirteen, Joel is virtually head of a hog operation that grosses over forty-thousand dollars a year.

Joel is the youngest of Ed and Betty Holland's six children. Only he and his brother Marty, sixteen, still live at home. Two other brothers, Bill and Terry, come home each day to eat meals with the family. Bill and Terry rent neighboring farms. Each has his own livestock herd, but they farm their land collectively with their father.

Two other children, Kevin and Kathy, do not live at home. This year Kevin, twenty-two, will graduate from college in Chicago. He will be the fourth college graduate among the Holland children. "We insist they all go to college and get a taste of what it's like off the farm," says Betty. "Then if they want to come back to farming, that's fine."

Kathy, twenty-four, is the oldest child and the only daughter. She is now a Roman Catholic nun doing graduate study in Dubuque, Iowa. But, like her brothers, she grew up farming, and she still misses it. Kathy called this May during her final exams and said, "I'd give anything to be plowing instead!"

As the youngest, Joel has at times had more farming "teachers" than he's wanted. One night he sat at the kitchen table listening to his dad and brothers talk about the rewards of farming.

"It's a good, independent life," said Bill. "You're your own boss."

"I wouldn't know," said Joel, grinning. "I've got a boss."

"Who?" asked his dad.

Joel pointed to each one around the table.

Joel used to be largely at somebody's side, watching and listening, lending a hand, or going on the run for a tractor or forgotten tool. He took the occasional bossing he got in stride. Now, he is so busy with his own work that he is no longer available to be everybody's "go-fer."[1]

"If I had just one word to describe Joel, it would be *enthusiasm*," says Betty. He uses his youthful energy indiscriminately. On one summer day, he jumped 15 fences, drove farm machinery 25 miles, fed 320 animals, opened and closed 8 gates, walked and ran about 8 miles, jumped on and off the tractor 26 times, lifted 900 pounds of grain, shoveled 4,000 pounds, ate about 2600 calories!

On weekends and during the summer, Joel works outdoors anywhere from eight to fifteen hours a day. The only time he

[1]go-fer (gō′ fər): slang term for a person who performs a variety of errands

129

minds it is during early spring. Then the snow melts and rain often pours down daily, turning the farmyard into a swamp. Mud sucks at his boots, making walking itself a tedious chore. More than the bother, though, Joel hates the ugliness. "When it rains, everything seems so awful."

Regardless of how much energy his work consumes, Joel has plenty left over for sports. He hunts deer and traps wildlife in the fall, and snowmobiles in the winter. Spring brings softball and basketball games, and summer provides weather for water-skiing and fishing. Nearly all his favorite sports are played outdoors.

If he had to live in the city for a year, Joel says he would mostly miss "the land. I'd miss seeing things grow. The change of seasons." In fact, if Joel could choose any place in the world to live, he guesses he'd live "right here. It'd have to be country. After living out here, I don't think I'd ever want to be in the city. You just don't have the freedom. Or the responsibilities. I'm not saying a city kid doesn't have responsibilities. But you don't work as a family the way you do on a farm. It'd just have to be country for me."

◆ LIBRARY LINK ◆

Get to know Joel better by reading the book Joel: Growing Up a Farm Man, *by Patricia Demuth.*

Reader's Response

Joel says that of all the places on earth, he would choose to live "right here"—on the farm. Do you think his choice is a good one?

It's Country for Me

Checking Your Comprehension

1. How does Joel feel about getting out of bed at 11:15 P.M. to feed the lamb? How can you tell?
2. Describe the Holland farm.
3. In what ways does Joel play the role of an adult?
4. Does Joel agree with his brother Bill about the rewards of a farming life?
5. What skills must a farmer have to run a farm like the Hollands'?
6. In a sentence, state the main idea of this article.

Writing to Learn

THINK AND RECALL Joel is a busy teenager. How does your schedule compare with his? A schedule of Joel's activities might look like this:

5:00 A.M.	feed farm animals
6:00 A.M.	breakfast
7:00 A.M.	milking chores
9:00 A.M.	field work
11:00 A.M.	dinner
12:00 noon	repair machinery
2:00 P.M.	repair fences
4:00 P.M.	Future Farmers meeting
5:00 P.M.	supper
11:15 P.M.	feed baby lamb

WRITE Make a list of the important activities in your own typical day. Use the information to make a chart like Joel's for yourself.

Lee Bennett Hopkins
INTERVIEWS

Scott O'Dell

"Los Angeles, California, was a frontier town when I was born there. It had more horses than automobiles, and more jack rabbits than people. The very first sound I remember was a wildcat scratching on the roof as I lay in bed," stated Scott O'Dell. Mr. O'Dell is the author of *The Black Pearl,* from which the next selection, "A Dream So Wild," is taken.

"My father was a railroad man so we moved a lot, but never far. Wherever we went, it was into frontier country like Los Angeles. There was San Pedro, which is a part of Los Angeles, and Rattlesnake Island, across the bay from San Pedro, where we lived in a house on stilts, where the waves came up and washed under us every day. That is why, I suppose, the feel of the frontier and the sound of the sea are in my books. This also explains why many of the people I have written about are Indians, Spaniards, and Chicanos."

After high school, Mr. O'Dell attended several colleges. Discouraged with academic courses, he abandoned the idea of graduating and instead concentrated on subjects that appealed to him. Eventually he went into filmwork as a cameraman. One feature film he worked on was the original version of *Ben Hur.*

After one year with the Air Force in Texas during World War II, he became a book editor for a Los Angeles newspaper. Soon after taking this job, he became a full-time writer of books for adults.

In 1960, his first book for young adults, *Island of the Blue Dolphins,* appeared, and it quickly established him as an important

writer of historical fiction. *Island of the Blue Dolphins* won the prestigious Newbery Award, a host of other national and international awards, and was made into a film. *Island of the Blue Dolphins* was based upon the true story of a girl who was stranded on an island off the coast of southern California. She lived there for eighteen years, building shelter, making weapons, finding food, and fighting her enemies, the wild dogs.

Mr. O'Dell said, "I didn't know what young people were reading and I didn't consider it a children's book, necessarily. *Island of the Blue Dolphins* was a protest against the hunters who came into our mountains and killed everything that crept or walked or flew.

"I sent the story to my agents. They sent it back to me by return mail, saying that if I was serious about the story I should change the girl to a boy, because girls were only interested in romance and such. This seemed silly to me. So I picked up the story, went to New York City, and gave it to my editor, who accepted it the next day. When it won the Newbery Medal, I was launched into writing for children and young adults."

Six years later, *The King's Fifth* was published, followed by *The Black Pearl.* Both novels brought him Newbery Honor Book Awards.

In 1972, Mr. O'Dell was awarded the Hans Christian Anderson International Medal by the International Board on Books for Young People, an award presented to a living author and a living artist who has made an outstanding contribution to children's literature.

"Writing for young people is more fun than writing for adults and more rewarding," he said. "If young people like your books, they respond with thousands of letters, asking a lot of questions. One of the frequent questions is, 'What is the most important thing a writer should have?' Anthony Trollope, the great English story-teller said that it was a piece of sealing wax with which to fasten your pants to a chair. I agree. Writing is hard, harder than digging a ditch, and it requires patience.

"The hardest part is to sit down at an empty desk, pick up a pen, face a blank page, and write the first sentence. The best part is the research, which takes several months. The story itself, as a rule, takes about six months.

"For *The Black Pearl,* I went to La Paz twice. For the Maya/Aztec trilogy [*The Captive, The Feathered Serpent,* and *The Amethyst Ring*] I traveled through Mexico and Central America and to the Amazon River. For *Streams to the River, River to the Sea,* I followed—by car, foot, and boat—Sacagawea's long trail through the Rocky Mountains."

I asked Mr. O'Dell what advice he could offer to young adults who might be interested in pursuing a writing career. He told me, "I suggest they read a lot. We learn to write by imitation. I think young people interested in writing should select a favorite author and read his or her books for pure pleasure. Ask such questions as why the author used the title, why the author opens the story at a particular point, how characters are introduced and developed, how they are described, how the author builds suspense, pace. Analyze the whole from beginning to end.

"Then, using your own material, try to write a book of your own. You will find that you will develop your own style, your own voice, as you learn how to build a story."

Mr. O'Dell's personal models were works by authors such as Joseph Conrad, Herman Melville, and Ernest Hemingway.

Mr. O'Dell and his wife, Elizabeth Hall, a writer of college textbooks, live in upstate New York.

"I love to travel. Travel to me is more important than anything. When I am at home I enjoy gardening and repairing the miles of stone fences around the house which were first built by farmers in the area. The winters are severe here and hard on the fences. It seems they are always in need of repair."

His recent novel, *Black Star, Bright Dawn,* is based on the famous Iditarod, the 1100-mile dogsled race from Anchorage to Nome, Alaska.

"To do the novel," he said, "I attended the races at Saranac Lake, New York. And I own a blue-eyed Siberian husky, named 'Black Star.' I bought her with the thought of acquainting myself with this extraordinary breed. She is a medium-sized dog, but she can pull me off my feet. I take her in the car so if we break down she can pull us into a garage!"

In 1981, Mr. O'Dell established the Scott O'Dell Award for Historical Fiction, an annual award of $5,000 for a book of historical fiction set in the the Americas and written in English by a United States citizen. Several authors who have received the award include Avi, Jean Fritz, Patricia MacLachlan, and Elizabeth George Speare.

After reading the next selection, you will probably want to go to the library for other books by Mr. O'Dell.

Reader's Response

Based on the interview, do you think you would like to read a book by Scott O'Dell? Explain why or why not.

LEE BENNETT HOPKINS INTERVIEWS
Scott O'Dell

Checking Your Comprehension

1. Describe Los Angeles, California, as it was when Scott O'Dell lived there as a boy.
2. How did growing up in the Los Angeles area influence Scott O'Dell's writing?
3. Why does Mr. O'Dell enjoy writing for young people?
4. What do you think Scott O'Dell meant when he said that doing research is "the best part" of writing his books?
5. How does Mr. O'Dell think that reading can help someone become a writer?
6. What are some things you can tell about Scott O'Dell's personality from reading the interview? How did you arrive at your conclusions?
7. Write one question you would like to ask Mr. O'Dell if you could interview him.

Writing to Learn

THINK AND SYNTHESIZE Before you read the interview, Scott O'Dell may have been just a name to you. Now you should know quite a lot about him. Look at the chart below and add at least one item to each category.

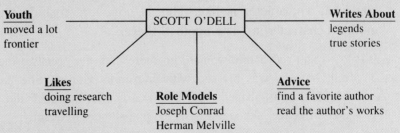

Youth
moved a lot
frontier

SCOTT O'DELL

Writes About
legends
true stories

Likes
doing research
travelling

Role Models
Joseph Conrad
Herman Melville

Advice
find a favorite author
read the author's works

WRITE Scott O'Dell's stories are usually based on legends, true stories, or historical events. What do you think would be a good topic for his next book? Use what you know about Mr. O'Dell and write a persuasive paragraph to convince him to use the topic that you suggest.

READING FICTION

Literature:

Characterization

Have you ever read a story in which the characters actually seemed to be real people? Sometimes an author succeeds in creating characters that are so believable you almost suspect they lead their own lives outside the pages of the book.

An author often helps you get to know a character by revealing his or her *character traits,* or qualities of personality. The particular mix of traits a character has will make that character seem unique.

A well-defined character, like a real person, will usually possess many different traits, but one or two may especially stand out. For example, when you think of Miguel in "The Obsidian Ring," you may remember him as friendly and outgoing; you may remember Jim Yoshida's father in "The Football Player" as strict and gruff.

Developing Characters

One way an author can reveal a character's traits is simply to *tell* you what a character is like. This is how Jim Yoshida reveals his mother's character in "The Football Player":

> She was a tiny woman, no more than five feet two inches tall, but she was blessed with enormous vitality. She had a beautiful heart-shaped face. She was gentle; not once did she ever strike me, although I deserved punishment frequently.

This description tells you what Jim's mother looked like, and it also tells you about her character traits: she was a gentle person who had enormous vitality.

Very often an author will reveal a character's traits by describing how that person behaves. Even though the author does not tell you directly, you can infer the character's traits by observing what that person says, does, thinks, and feels. When you put these observations together, you may be able to draw some conclusions about the character's personality. In "Blues Busters," for instance, the author never writes, "Reese is resourceful." Instead, the author *shows* that Reese is resourceful when she describes how he uses old mattresses to soundproof the garage.

Using Character Traits

When you learn about the traits of the characters in the stories you read, you get to know them as people. You begin to think of them in the same way you think about people you know—and the same way you think about yourself. You begin to understand their *motivations*, or why they do certain things. You may even be able to predict what they will do in new situations. For example, in "Leaving Home" you learn that Dawan is a caring, sensitive person. You can understand, therefore, why she reaches out to her brother even though they had argued. You can also predict that she will continue to show her concern for others in the future.

Everything that characters say or do helps to define them as people; their traits and motives grow directly out of their personalities. If a character has a very happy personality, for example, then he or she should not suddenly begin to act sad unless the author shows that there is a good reason for it. If you can try to understand the traits and motives of the characters you meet in books, you'll get more out of what you read, and you may even make some new "friends" along the way!

Read and Enjoy

In the next story you will read, "A Dream So Wild," you will meet Ramón. As you read, think about how Ramón's qualities and character traits might help him or hinder him in his chosen occupation.

When Ramón's ambitions conflict with his father's plans for the future, Ramón makes a bold decision.

A DREAM SO WILD

~~~

by Scott O'Dell
from <u>The Black Pearl</u>

Ramón Salazar[1] is a sixteen-year-old boy living in the small town of La Paz, Mexico, where his family makes their living pearling the waters of Baja California. He has grown up hearing the legends of the area—about the great Black Pearl waiting to be found and the monster called the Manta Diablo[2] lurking in the deep. Ramón's father has made him a full partner in the family pearl business, but Ramón's ambition is to sail with the fleet and to learn to dive for pearls. One day he overcomes his father's objections by agreeing to stay on deck and hold the ropes while others dive. The best diver in the fleet is Gaspar Ruiz,[3] known as the Sevillano.[4] He's a braggart who always seems to be taunting Ramón, but Ramón is determined that nothing will diminish this experience.

[1]Ramón Salazar (rä mōn′ sal ä sar′)
[2]Manta Diablo (män′ tä dē ä′ blō)
[3]Gaspar Ruiz (gas par′ rōō ēs′)
[4]Sevillano (se vē yä′no)

We reached the pearling beds at dawn and anchored the five boats in a cluster over a reef where the shells grew.

Everything was new to me. I had heard many stories of the pearling beds since the time I was old enough to listen, from my father and grandfather and from my friends who were the sons of pearlers. But to be really there on the sea with the sun coming up in a coppery haze and watch the men slip out of the boats into water clear as air, was to me a part of a long dream come true.

My father showed me how to pull up the basket when it was full and how to stack the shells in the boat. Then he took the sink stone in one hand, carefully coiled the rope that was attached to it and tied to the boat, picked up the basket and its rope, and went over the side. Down he went with the heavy stone until he reached the bottom.

Through the clear water I watched him drop the stone, take the big knife from his belt, and start to pry the oyster shells from the rocks. When the basket was full he gave a tug at the rope and I pulled it up. A moment later he rose, trailing a stream of bubbles from his mouth, and I stacked the shells as I had been told and drew up the sink stone for the next dive.

The Sevillano had gone down before my father and was still down as he dived again. When the Sevillano came to the surface he held onto the side of the boat and glanced up at me.

"How does the work go?" he said.

"I learn."

"There is not much to learn, mate. You pull the shells up and then the sink stone and you stack the shells and then you wait a while and do it all over again. It is work for children."

He spoke softly and smiled, but I knew what he meant. "It would be fun to dive," I answered him.

"More fun, mate, but more danger too."

He pointed to the arm he was resting on the gunwale. From his elbow to wrist ran a long, jagged scar, as if the arm had been pulled through the jaws of a steel trap.

"This one," he said, "I got from a burro clam. I put my hand down deep into a crevice and snap, it was not a crevice but the

142

mouth of a burro, the father of all burros. Señor Clam had me tight, but I did not leave my arm with him, as you can see. That was in the Gulf, yet there are many burros here in the Vermilion." He looked up at me again and smiled. "It is better, mate, that you stay in the boat."

The Indian who was working with the Sevillano handed him the sink stone and the Sevillano went down, saying nothing more to me. Nor did he speak to me again that morning. At midday the *Santa Teresa* was loaded with shells and low in the water, because the Sevillano did the work of three divers, so my father sent him out to help in the other boats.

From time to time during the afternoon, when he came up for air, he would call over to me, "Be careful, mate, and do not get your foot caught in the rope," or "There are sharks around, Señor Salazar, mind that you do not fall in the water."

Such things as that I heard during the whole of the afternoon. My father also heard them, though the Sevillano usually spoke to me when he thought my father was not listening.

"He is a troublemaker," my father said, "but let him talk. What do you care what he says? Remember that he is the best gatherer of pearls we have. And it is for pearls that we are here on the sea, not for other reasons."

By dark the boats were piled high with cargo and we set sail for La Paz. The moon came up and a brisk wind that filled the sails. The Sevillano was in good spirits, as if he had not made dozens of deep dives that day. He perched himself on the mound of shells and once more told how he had found the great pearl in the Gulf of Persia, the same tale he had told before but longer. Again I had the feeling that his story was meant for me more than the others.

And as I listened to him a dream began to take shape in my mind. It was a fanciful dream that made me forget the insults that I had suffered silently. I saw myself in a boat anchored in a secret lagoon somewhere on the Vermilion Sea. I put a knife in my belt and grasped the basket and the heavy sink stone and plunged to the bottom. There were sharks swimming around me in slow circles, but I gave no heed to them. I pried clump after clump of shells from the rocks, filling my basket. After I had been down for three or four minutes, I floated to the surface through the circling sharks, and climbed into the boat and pulled up the basket. Then I pried open the shells, one after the other. Nothing. At last there was only one shell left. Discouraged, I opened it and was about to toss it away when I saw before me a pearl larger than my fist that shone as if a fire burned inside . . .

Right at that moment, just as I was about to clutch the pearl in my hand, the Sevillano stopped talking. Suddenly he stood up on the mound and pointed astern, along the path the moon was making on the sea.

"Manta," he shouted, "Manta Diablo."

I jumped to my feet. I could see nothing at first. Then the boat rose on a wave and I made out a silvery shape swimming half out of the water not more than a furlong away.

Truthfully, I must say that for all its beauty the manta is a fearsome sight to those who sail our Vermilion Sea. There are small mantas, no larger when they are full grown than ten feet from one wing tip to the other. But there are some that measure twice that length and weigh most of three tons.

Both kinds are shaped very much like a giant bat and they swim through the water with a regular upward and downward beat of their flippers. And both have a mouth so enormous that a man may easily put his head into it and on either side of this maw are large lobes like arms, which the manta pushes out and then draws in to capture its prey.

Their prey surprisingly is not the shoals of fish that abound in our sea, but shrimp and crabs and such small things. Most of the mantas have a pilot fish that swims along beneath them. These fish swim in and out of their mouths, it is said, to clean up the pieces of food that catch in their plate-like teeth.

And yet for all of his friendly ways, the manta is a fearsome beast. When aroused by some careless insult, it can break a man's neck with a flick of its long tail or lift one flipper and wreck the strongest boat.

"Manta," the Sevillano shouted again. "El Manta Diablo!" His Indian helper quickly scrambled away and crouched down in the bow of the boat and began to mutter to himself.

"No," said my father, "It is not the Diablo. Him I have seen and he is bigger by twice than this one."

"Come where you can see better," said the Sevillano. "It is the Manta Diablo. I know him well."

I was certain that he was trying to scare the Indian and my father was certain of it, too, for he lashed the tiller and climbed to where the Sevillano stood. He glanced astern for a moment and then went back to the tiller.

"No," he said, loud enough for the Indian to hear, "It is not even the small sister of the Diablo."

The Indian fell silent, but he was still frightened. And as I watched the manta swimming along behind us, its outstretched fins like vast silvery wings, I remembered that once I had also been frightened at the very sound of the name.

At last the manta disappeared and near dawn we rounded El Magote, the lizard tongue of land that guards the harbor, and anchored our boats. As my father and I walked home in the moonlight, he said,

"About the Sevillano, let me repeat to you. Treat him with courtesy. Listen to his boasts as if you believed them. For he is a very dangerous young man. Only last week I learned from a friend who lives over in Culiacán that the Sevillano was born there. And that he has never been in Seville nor any part of Spain nor in the Gulf of Persia nor anywhere except here on the Vermilion."

I promised my father that I would obey him, but as we walked toward home I again thought of my dream and the big pearl I had found and how surprised the Sevillano would be when he saw it.

Four days passed and I was standing at the desk, with a pen over my ear and the leather-bound ledger open in front of me. I was watching a canoe that moved around the tip of the lizard tongue. It was a red canoe and came swiftly, so I knew it belonged to the Indian Soto Luzon.

I was glad to see old Luzon. He had sold pearls to my father for many years. He came about every three months and never brought more than one, but it always was a pearl of good quality. Soon after I began to work with my father he had brought in a beautiful pearl of more than two carats.

As I watched Luzon beach the canoe and come up the path, I hoped he was bringing another like it, for the yield from our last trip had been poor. Five boatloads of shells had yielded no round or pear-shaped pearls and only a handful of buttons and baroques,[5] all of them dull.

I opened the door at his timid knock and invited him to come in and sit down.

"I have traveled all night," Luzon said. "If it pleases you, I would like to stand."

Luzon never sat. He had an Indian's thin legs but a powerful chest and thick arms that could wield a paddle for hours and not grow tired.

"I passed your boats this morning," he said. "They were near Maldonado."

"They are going to Isla Cerralvo."[6]

The old man gave me a shrewd look. "The fishing is not good around here?"

"Good," I said. It was not wise to say that it was poor, when he had come to sell a pearl. "Very good."

"Then why, señor, do the boats go to Cerralvo?"

"Because my father wants to search there for the black ones."

The old man fumbled in his shirt and pulled out a knotted rag and untied it. "Here is a black one," he said.

I could see at a glance that it was round and of a good quality, like the pearl I had bought from him three months before.

[5]baroques (bä rō′kes): irregularly shaped pearls
[6]Isla Cerralvo (ēs′ lä se räl′ vō)

I placed it on the scales and balanced it against the small copper weights.

"Two and a half carats," I said.

My father never haggled with Luzon and always gave him a fair price and had told me to do the same. For that reason old Luzon always brought his pearls to Salazar and Son, although there were four other dealers in our town.

"Two hundred pesos," I said.

This sum was about fifty pesos more than my father would have offered, but a plan was taking shape in my mind and I needed the old man's help. I counted out the money and he put it in his shirt, probably thinking to himself that I was not so smart as my father.

"You always bring in good pearls. Black ones," I said. "There must be many in your lagoon. If you permit me I will come and dive there. All the pearls I find I will pay you for."

The old man looked puzzled. "But you are not a diver," he said.

"You can teach me, señor."

"I have heard your father say many times, since the time you were a child, that he did not raise you to drown in the sea or to give an arm or a leg to a burro shell."

"My father," I said, "has gone to Cerralvo and he will not return for a week or more."

"And your mother and your sister, what will they say?"

"They will say nothing because today they go to Loreto." I paused. "You will teach me to dive and I will look for the big one and when I find it I will pay you what it is worth."

"The big one I have searched for many years," Luzon said. "How is it found in a week?"

"You can find the big one in a single dive."

The old man pulled at his stubbly chin. He was thinking, I knew, about his wife and his two unmarried daughters and his three young sons, and all these mouths he had to feed every day.

"When do you wish to go?" he said.

"I wish to go now."

Luzon hitched up his frayed trousers. "After I buy a sack of frijoles and a sack of flour, then we go."

The old man left and I put the pearls away and locked the safe. I took the bundle from under the desk, my pants, a shirt, and the knife. I closed the door and locked it. As I walked down to the beach, I thought about the great pearl I had dreamed of while the Sevillano was bragging. I thought of how surprised he would be when he came back from Cerralvo and found the whole town of La Paz talking about the monster pearl Ramón Salazar had found.

It was a dream so wild that only a very young man and a stupid one could dream it. And yet, as happens sometimes, the dream came true.

The lagoon where the old man lived was about seven leagues from La Paz and we should have reached it by midnight. But the currents and the wind were against us, so it was near dawn before we sighted the two headlands that marked the lagoon's hidden entrance.

You could pass this entrance many times and think that it was only an opening in the rocks that led nowhere. As soon as you passed the rocks, however, you came to a narrow channel that wound like a snake between the two headlands for a half mile or farther.

The sun was just rising when the channel opened out and suddenly we were in a quiet oval-shaped lagoon. On both sides of the lagoon steep hills came down to the water and at the far end lay a shallow beach of black sand. Beyond were two scraggly trees and beneath them a cluster of huts where breakfast fires were burning.

It was a peaceful scene that lay before me, much like many other lagoons that dot our coast. But there was something about the place that made me feel uneasy. At first I thought it must be the barren hills that closed in upon the lagoon and the coppery haze that lay over it, and the beach of black sand and the quiet. I

was soon to hear that it was something else, something far different from what I thought.

The old man paddled slowly across the lagoon, carefully raising and lowering the paddle, as if he did not want to disturb the water. And though he had talked most of the time before we reached the lagoon he now fell silent. A gray shark circled the canoe and disappeared. He pointed to it, but said nothing.

Nor did he speak again until we beached the canoe and were walking up the path to the huts. Then he said, "It is well to hold the tongue and not to talk needlessly when you are on the lagoon. Remember this when we go out to dive, for there is one who listens and is quickly angered."

Indians are superstitious about the moon and the sun and some animals and birds, especially the coyote and the owl. For this reason I was not surprised that he wished to warn me.

"Who is it that listens and grows angry?" I asked him.

Twice he glanced over his shoulder before he answered. "The Manta Diablo," he said.

"El Diablo?" I asked, holding back a smile. "He lives here in your lagoon?"

"In a cave," he answered, "a big one which you can see just as you leave the channel."

"The channel is very narrow," I said, "barely wide enough for a canoe. How does a giant like El Diablo swim through it? But perhaps he does not need to. Perhaps he stays here in your lagoon."

"No," the old man said. "He travels widely and is gone for many weeks at a time."

"Then he must swim through the channel somehow."

"Oh, no, that would be impossible, even for him. There is another opening, a secret one, near the place where you enter the channel. When he swims out to sea, it is this one he uses."

We were nearing the huts clustered beneath the two scraggly trees. A band of children came running out to meet us and the old man said nothing more about El Diablo until we had eaten breakfast, slept the morning away, eaten again, and gone back to the lagoon.

As we floated the canoe and set off for the pearling reefs, the old man said, "When the mist goes, that means El Diablo has gone, too."

It was true that the red mist was gone and the water now shone green and clear. I still smiled to myself at the old man's belief in El Diablo, yet I felt a little of the excitement that I had felt long ago when my mother threatened me with the monster.

"Now that he is gone," I said, "we can talk."

"A little and with much care," Luzon replied, "for he has many friends in the lagoon."

"Friends?"

"Yes, the shark you saw this morning and many small fish. They are all friends and they listen and when he comes back they tell him everything, everything."

"When he leaves the lagoon, where does he go?"

"That I do not know. Some say that he takes the shape of an octopus and seeks out those pearlers who have done him a wrong or spoken ill of him. It is also said that he takes the shape of a human and goes into La Paz and seeks his enemies there in the streets and sometimes even in the church."

"I should think that you would fear for your life and leave the lagoon."

"No, I do not fear El Diablo. Nor did my father before me. Nor his father before him. For many years they had a pact with the Manta Diablo and now I keep this pact. I show him proper respect and tip my hat when I come into the lagoon and when I leave it. For this he allows me to dive for the black pearls which belong to him and which we now go to search for."

Silently the old man guided the canoe toward the south shore of the lagoon, and I asked no more questions for I felt that he had said all he wished to say about the Manta Diablo. In two fathoms

152

of water, over a reef of black rocks, he dropped anchor and told me to do the same.

"Now I teach you to dive," he said. "First we start with the breathing."

The old man lifted his shoulders and began to take in great gulps of air, gulp after gulp, until his chest seemed twice its size. Then he let out the air with a long whoosh.

"This is called 'taking the wind'," he said. "And because it is very important you must try it."

I obeyed his command, but filled my lungs in one breath.

"More," the old man said.

I took in another gulp of air.

"More," the old man said.

I tried again and then began to cough.

"For the first time it is good," the old man said. "But you must practice this much so you stretch the lungs. Now we go down together."

We both filled our lungs with air and slipped over the side of the canoe feet first, each of us holding a sink stone. The water was as warm as milk but clear so that I could see the wrinkled sand and the black rocks and fish swimming about.

When we reached the bottom the old man put a foot in the loop of the rope that held his sink stone and I did likewise with my stone. He placed his hand on my shoulder and took two steps to a crevice in a rock that was covered with trailing weeds. Then he took the knife from his belt and thrust it into the crevice. Instantly the crevice closed, not slowly but with a snap. The old man wrenched the knife free and took his foot out of the loop and motioned for me to do the same and we floated up to the canoe.

The old man held out the knife. "Note the scratches which the burro shell leaves," he said. "With a hand or a foot it is different. Once the burro has you he does not let go and thus you drown. Take care, therefore, where you step and where you place the hand."

We dived until night came, and the old man showed me how to walk carefully on the bottom, so as not to muddy the water,

and how to use the knife to pry loose the oysters that grew in clumps and how to get the shells open and how to search them for pearls.

We gathered many baskets that afternoon but found nothing except a few baroques of little worth. And it was the same the next day and the next, and then on the fourth day, because the old man had cut his hand on a shell, I went out on the lagoon alone.

It was on this day that I found the great Pearl of Heaven.

EPILOGUE

Ramón does find the great black pearl of his dream, but Luzon insists that it belongs to Manta Diablo. He warns Ramón that he'd better give it back, but Ramón refuses. Then something happens that makes him wonder if he made the right decision.

♦ LIBRARY LINK ♦

Read about Ramón's exciting encounters with Manta Diablo in the book from which this excerpt was taken, The Black Pearl, *by Scott O'Dell.*

Reader's Response

What do you think of Mr. Salazar's attitude toward Ramón's wish to dive for pearls?

WRITING —ABOUT— READING

Writing a "Turning Point" Story

The stories you have just read introduced you to characters who were at turning points in their lives and had to make decisions. From reading the stories, you know that a turning point occurs when a character confronts a problem, reviews all aspects of the problem, and makes a decision that might have lifelong implications.

Write a two-page story for your classmates that tells about a character who is at a turning point.

Prewriting

Think about an important decision that you have made, and reflect on your feelings about it. Then review the conflicts that the characters faced in this unit. Prepare for writing a story by doing two things.

1. Create a character. You may wish to base your character on one that you have read about or on your own life. Think about your character's personality traits and goals.

2. Find a problem. Focus on a turning point that requires your character to make a decision.

Read the decision chart on the next page. Then organize your thoughts by developing a decision chart for your character. State the decision the character may have to make. List the good and bad points of each choice. Tell what your character does and why.

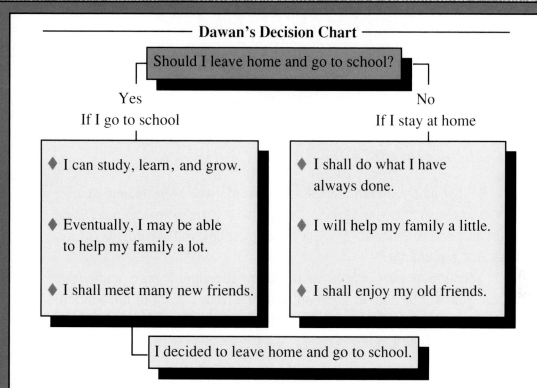

Dawan's Decision Chart

Should I leave home and go to school?

Yes
If I go to school

♦ I can study, learn, and grow.

♦ Eventually, I may be able to help my family a lot.

♦ I shall meet many new friends.

No
If I stay at home

♦ I shall do what I have always done.

♦ I will help my family a little.

♦ I shall enjoy my old friends.

I decided to leave home and go to school.

Writing

As you write your character's story, include the good points and bad points of the choices the character must make. Try to include some of the character's own ideas about the problem.

Revising

Read your story aloud and listen to your story. Does your character seem real? What is the turning point? How is the problem resolved? Does the resolution fit with the character's personality and goals?

Proofreading

If you have used dialogue in your story, make sure you have used quotation marks correctly.

Publishing

Prepare a class collection of short stories entitled *Turning Points*.

WORKING TOGETHER

Preparing Questions for a Press Conference

In this unit you read stories about people who were facing change. For example, in "Leaving Home," Dawan's wise grandmother helped Dawan face an uncertain future. Do you have questions you would like to ask Dawan's grandmother?

Your group will imagine that you are attending a press conference where you will be able to question someone from a story in this unit. To help your group work together, make sure you do one or more of these tasks:

♦ Encourage everyone in the group to share ideas

♦ Record people's questions on a list

♦ Summarize the group's discussion about each question

♦ Make sure your group finishes on time

Together, recall the characters you read about in this unit. Discuss why each one might be interesting to interview and select one character. Next, everyone should contribute questions to ask that person. Make a list of the group's questions. Then, agree on four questions your group would like to ask that character at a press conference.

Choose one person in your group to take the part of the story character you selected. Others in the group will take turns asking the questions you have agreed upon. The person taking the part of the story character should try to answer the questions in the same way that the character might respond. People asking questions may want to follow up with additional questions.

Questions for
Dawan's grandmother
1. Did change ever frighten you?
2. How do you know there is a pattern to change?
3. How did you know what to say to Dawan?
4. Did anyone ever help you face another change?

Romeo and Juliet: Together (and Alive!) At Last by Avi *(Orchard, 1987)* Pete has fallen for Anabell, but each is too shy to look at the other. Their classmates try to get them together by having them star in a play. The result is a hilarious production of *Romeo and Juliet*!

A Gathering of Days: A New England Girl's Journal by Joan Blos *(Scribner, 1979)* Catherine Hall tries to deal with her mother's death, a new stepmother, and the hardships and joys of the year 1830.

Dicey's Song by Cynthia Voight *(Atheneum, 1982)* Dicey learns about reaching out and building new ties as the Tillerman children start a new life with their feisty grandmother.

M.V. Sexton Speaking by Suzanne Newton *(Viking, 1981)* Sixteen-year-old M.V. had hoped for a relaxed summer, but her guardian, Aunt Gert, had a different idea—a summer job. M.V. tackles her first job—in a small town bakery—with humor, energy, and imagination.

Bill Cosby: Family Funny Man by Larry Kettelkamp *(Simon and Schuster, 1987)* This biography tells the story of how Bill Cosby came to be the person we know so well today. It tells of his difficult childhood, his devotion to his hard-working mother, and how he faced the turning points along the way with characteristic humor and insight.

MAKING
CONNECTIONS

We are beginning to understand how animals communicate.

What do they have to say to each other and to us?

detail of THE SLEEPING GYPSY,
oil on canvas by Henri Rousseau, French, 1897

TO BUILD A FIRE

BY JACK LONDON

A lone man and a dog trudged across a frozen wilderness of ice and snow. Each knew certain things about the bitter, deadly cold that they were challenging—but perhaps they did not know enough.

Day had broken cold and gray, exceedingly cold and gray, when the man turned aside from the main Yukon trail and climbed the high earth-bank, where a dim and little-traveled trail led eastward through the fat spruce timberland. It was a steep bank, and he paused for breath at the top, excusing the act to himself by looking at his watch. It was nine o'clock. There was no sun nor hint of sun, though there was not a cloud in the sky. It was a clear day, and yet there seemed an intangible pall over the face of things, a subtle gloom that made the day dark, and that was due to the absence of sun. This fact did not worry the man. He was used to the lack of sun. It had been days since he had seen the sun, and he knew that a few more days must pass before that cheerful orb, due south, would just peep over the skyline and dip immediately from view.

The man flung a look back along the way he had come. The Yukon lay a mile wide and hidden under three feet of ice. On top of this ice were as many feet of snow. It was all pure white, rolling in gentle undulations where the ice jams of the freeze-up had formed. North and south, as far as his eye could see, it was unbroken white, save for a dark hairline that curved and twisted from around the spruce-covered island to the south, and that curved and twisted away into the north, where it disappeared behind another spruce-covered island. This dark hairline was the trail—the main trail—that led south five hundred miles to the Chilcoot Pass, Dyea, and salt water; and that led north seventy miles to Dawson, and still on to the north a thousand miles to Nulato, and finally to St. Michael, on Bering Sea, a thousand miles and half a thousand more.

But all this—the mysterious, far-reaching hairline trail, the absence of sun from the sky, the tremendous cold, and the strangeness and weirdness of it all—made no impression on the man. It was not because he was long used to it. He was a newcomer in the land, a *chechaquo*,[1] and this was his first winter. The trouble with him was that he was without imagination. He was quick and alert in the things of life, but only in the things, and not in the significances. Fifty degrees below zero meant eighty-odd degrees of frost. Such a fact impressed him as being cold and uncomfortable, and that was all. It did not lead him to meditate upon his frailty as a creature of temperature, and upon man's frailty in general, able only to live within certain narrow limits of heat and cold; and from there on it did not lead him to the conjectural field of immortality and man's place in the universe. Fifty degrees below zero stood for a bit of frost that hurt and that must be guarded against by the use of mittens, ear flaps, warm moccasins, and thick socks. Fifty degrees below zero was to him just precisely fifty degrees below zero. That there should be anything more to it than that was a thought that never entered his head.

As he turned to go on, he spat speculatively. There was a sharp, explosive crackle that startled him. He spat again. And again, in the air, before it could fall to the snow, the spittle crackled. He knew that at fifty below spittle crackled on the snow, but this spittle had crackled in the air. Undoubtedly it was colder than fifty below—how much colder he did not know. But the temperature did not matter. He was bound for the old claim on the left fork of

[1]chechaquo (chā chä′ kwō)

Henderson Creek, where the boys were already. They had come over across the divide from the Indian Creek country, while he had come the roundabout way to take a look at the possibilities of getting out logs in the spring from the islands in the Yukon. He would be in to camp by six o'clock; a bit after dark, it was true, but the boys would be there, a fire would be going, and a hot supper would be ready. As for lunch, he pressed his hand against the protruding bundle under his jacket. It was under his shirt, wrapped up in a handkerchief and lying against the naked skin. It was the only way to keep the biscuits from freezing. He smiled agreeably to himself as he thought of those biscuits, each cut open and sopped in bacon grease, and each enclosing a generous slice of fried bacon.

He plunged in among the big spruce trees. The trail was faint. A foot of snow had fallen since the last sled had passed over, and he was glad he was without a sled, traveling light. In fact, he carried nothing but the lunch wrapped in the handkerchief. He was surprised, however, at the cold. It certainly was cold, he concluded, as he rubbed his numb nose and cheekbones with his mittened hand. He was a warm-whiskered man, but the hair on his face did not protect the high cheekbones and the eager nose that thrust itself aggressively into the frosty air.

At the man's heels trotted a dog, a big native husky, the proper wolf dog, gray-coated and without any visible or temperamental difference from its brother, the wild wolf. The animal was depressed by the tremendous cold. It knew that it was no time for traveling. Its instinct told it a truer tale than was told to the man by the man's judgment. In reality, it was not merely colder than fifty below zero; it was colder than sixty below, than seventy below. It was seventy-five below zero. Since the freezing point is thirty-two above zero, it meant that one hundred and seven degrees of frost obtained. The dog did not know anything about thermometers. Possibly in its brain there was no sharp consciousness of a condition of very cold such as was in the man's brain. But the brute had its instinct. It experienced a vague but menacing apprehension that subdued it and made it slink along at the man's heels, and that made it question eagerly every unwonted movement of the man as if expecting him to go into camp or to seek shelter somewhere and build a fire. The dog had learned fire, and it wanted fire, or else to burrow under the snow and cuddle its warmth away from the air.

The frozen moisture of its breathing had settled on its fur in a fine powder of frost, and especially were its jowls, muzzle, and eyelashes whitened by its crystalled breath. The man's red beard and mustache were likewise frosted, but more solidly, the deposit taking the form of ice and increasing with every warm, moist breath he exhaled.

The man held on through the level stretch of woods for several miles, crossed a wide flat, and dropped down a bank to the frozen bed of a small stream. This was Henderson Creek, and he knew he was ten miles from the forks. He looked at his watch. It was ten o'clock. He was making four miles an hour, and he calculated that he would arrive at the forks at half-past twelve. He decided to celebrate that event by eating his lunch there.

The dog dropped in again at his heels, with a tail drooping discouragement, as the man swung along the creek bed. The furrow of the old sled trail was plainly visible, but a dozen inches of snow covered the marks of the last runners. In a month no man had come up or down that silent creek. The man held steadily on. He was not much given to thinking, and just then particularly he had nothing to think about save that he would eat lunch at the forks and that at six o'clock he would be in camp with the boys. There was nobody to talk to; and, had there been, speech would have been impossible because of the ice muzzle on his mouth.

Once in a while the thought reiterated itself that it was very cold and that he had never experienced such cold. As he walked along he rubbed his cheekbones and nose with the back of his mittened hand. He did this automatically, now and again changing hands. But, rub as he would, the instant he stopped his cheekbones went numb, and the following instant the end of his nose went numb. He was sure to frost his cheeks; he knew that, and experienced a pang of regret that he had not devised a nose strap of the sort Bud wore in cold snaps. Such a strap passed across the cheeks, as well, and saved them. But it didn't matter much, after all. What were frosted cheeks? A bit painful, that was all; they were never serious.

Empty as the man's mind was of thoughts, he was keenly observant, and he noticed the changes in the creek, the curves and bends and timber jams, and always he sharply noted where he placed his feet. Once, coming around a bend, he shied abruptly, like a startled horse, curved away from the place where he had been walking, and retreated several paces back along the trail. The creek he knew was frozen clear to the bottom—no creek could contain water in that arctic winter—but he knew also that there were springs that bubbled out from the hillsides and ran along under the snow and on top the ice of the creek. He knew that the coldest snaps never froze these springs, and he knew likewise their danger. They were traps. They hid pools of water under the snow that might be three inches deep, or three feet. Sometimes a skin of ice half an inch thick covered them, and in turn was covered by the snow. Sometimes there were alternate layers of water and ice skin, so that when one broke through he kept on breaking through for a while, sometimes wetting himself to the waist.

That was why he had shied in such panic. He had felt the give under his feet and heard the crackle of a snow-hidden ice skin. And to get his feet wet in such temperature meant trouble and danger. At the very least it meant delay, for he would be forced to stop and build a fire, and under its protection to bare his feet while he dried his socks and moccasins. He stood and studied the creek bed and its banks, and decided that the flow of water came from the right. He reflected awhile, rubbing his nose and cheeks, then skirted to the left, stepping gingerly and testing the footing for each step. Once clear of the danger, he swung along at his four-mile gait.

In the course of the next two hours he came upon several similar traps. Usually the snow above the hidden pools had a sunken, candied appearance that advertised the danger. Once again, however, he had a close call; and once, suspecting danger, he compelled the dog to go on in front. The dog did not want to go. It hung back until the man shoved it forward, and then it went quickly across the white, unbroken surface. Suddenly it broke through, floundered to one side, and got away to firmer footing. It had wet its forefeet and legs, and almost immediately the water that clung to it turned to ice. It made quick efforts to lick the ice off its legs, then dropped down in the snow and began to bite out the ice that had formed between the toes. This was a matter of instinct. To permit the ice to remain would mean sore feet. It did not know this. It merely obeyed the mysterious prompting that arose from the deep crypts of its being. But the man knew, having achieved a judgment on the subject, and he removed the mitten from his right hand and helped tear out the ice particles. He did not expose his fingers more than a minute, and was astonished at the swift numbness that smote them. It certainly was cold. He pulled on the mitten hastily, and beat the hand savagely across his chest.

At twelve o'clock the day was at its brightest. Yet the sun was too far south on its winter journey to clear the horizon. The bulge of the earth intervened between it and Henderson Creek, where the man walked under a clear sky at noon and cast no shadow. At half-past twelve, to the minute, he arrived at the forks of the creek. He was pleased at the speed he had made. If he kept it up, he would certainly be with

the boys by six. He unbuttoned his jacket and shirt and drew forth his lunch. The action consumed no more than a quarter of a minute, yet in that brief moment the numbness laid hold of the exposed fingers. He did not put the mitten on, but, instead, struck the fingers a dozen sharp smashes against his leg. Then he sat down on a snow-covered log to eat. The sting that followed upon the striking of his fingers against his leg ceased so quickly that he was startled. He had had no chance to take a bite of biscuit. He struck the fingers repeatedly and returned them to the mitten, baring the other hand for the purpose of eating. He tried to take a mouthful, but the ice muzzle prevented. He had forgotten to build a fire and thaw out. He chuckled at his foolishness, and as he chuckled he noted the numbness creeping into the exposed fingers. Also, he noted that the stinging which had first come to his toes when he sat down was already passing away. He wondered whether the toes were warm or numb. He moved them inside the moccasins and decided that they were numb.

He pulled the mitten on hurriedly and stood up. He was a bit frightened. He stamped up and down until the stinging returned into the feet. It certainly was cold, was his thought. That man from Sulphur Creek had spoken the truth when telling how cold it sometimes got in the country. And he had laughed at him at the time! That showed one must not be too sure of things. There was no mistake about it, it *was* cold. He strode up and down, stamping his feet and threshing his arms, until reassured by the returning warmth. Then he got out matches and proceeded to make a fire. From the undergrowth, where high water of the previous spring had lodged a supply of seasoned twigs, he got his firewood. Working carefully from a small beginning, he soon had a roaring fire, over which he thawed the ice from his face and in the protection of which he ate his biscuits. For the moment the cold of space was outwitted. The dog took satisfaction in the fire, stretching out close enough for warmth and far enough away to escape being singed.

When the man had finished, he pulled on his mittens, settled the ear flaps of his cap firmly about his ears, and took the creek trail up the left fork. The dog was disappointed and yearned back toward the fire. This man did not know cold. Possibly all the generations of his ancestry had been ignorant of cold, of real cold, of cold one hundred and seven degrees below freezing point. But the dog knew; all its ancestry knew, and it had inherited the knowledge. And it knew that it was not good to walk abroad in such fearful cold. It was the time to lie snug in a hole in the snow and wait for a curtain of cloud to be drawn across the face of outer space whence this cold came. On the other hand, there was no keen intimacy between the dog and the man. The one was the toil slave of the other, and the only caresses it had ever received were the caresses of the whip lash and of harsh and menacing throat sounds that threatened the whip lash. So the dog made no effort to communicate its apprehension to the man. It was not concerned in the welfare of the man; it was for its own sake that it yearned back toward the fire. But the man whistled, and spoke to it with the sound of whip lashes, and the dog swung in at the man's heels and followed after.

There did not seem to be so many springs on the left fork of the Henderson, and for half an hour the man saw no signs of any. And then it happened. At a place where there were no signs, where the soft, unbroken snow seemed to advertise solidity beneath, the man broke through. It was not deep. He wet himself halfway to the knees before he foundered out to the firm crust.

He was angry, and cursed his luck aloud. He had hoped to get into camp with the boys at six o'clock, and this would delay him an hour, for he would have to build a fire and dry out his footgear. This was imperative at that low temperature—he knew that much; and he turned aside to the bank, which he climbed. On top, tangled in the underbrush about the trunks of several small spruce trees, was a high-water deposit of dry firewood—sticks and twigs, principally, but also larger portions of seasoned branches and fine, dry, last year's grasses. He threw down several large pieces on top of the snow. This served for a foundation and prevented the young flame from drowning itself in the snow it otherwise would melt. The flame he got by touching a match to a small shred of birch bark that he took from his pocket. This burned even more readily than paper. Placing it on the foundation, he fed the young flame with wisps of dry grass and with the tiniest dry twigs.

He worked slowly and carefully, keenly aware of his danger. Gradually, as the flame grew stronger, he increased the size of the twigs with which he fed it. He squatted in the snow, pulling the twigs out from their entanglement in the brush and feeding directly to the flame. He knew there must be no failure. When it is seventy-five below zero, a man must not fail in his first attempt to build a fire—that is, if his feet are wet. If his feet are dry, and he fails, he can run along the trail for half a mile and restore his circulation. But the circulation of wet freezing feet cannot be restored by running when it is seventy-five below. No matter how fast he runs, the wet feet will freeze the harder.

All this the man knew. The old-timer on Sulphur Creek had told him about it the previous fall, and now he was appreciating the advice. Already all sensation had gone out of his feet. To build the fire he had been forced to remove his mittens, and the fingers had quickly gone numb. His pace of four miles an hour had kept his heart pumping blood to the surface of his body and to all the extremities. But the instant he stopped, the action of the pump eased down. The cold of space smote the unprotected tip of the planet, and he, being on that unprotected tip, received the full force of the blow. The blood of his body recoiled before it. The blood was alive, like the dog, and like the dog it wanted to hide away and cover itself up from the fearful cold. So long as he walked four miles an hour, he pumped the blood, willy-nilly, to the surface; but now it ebbed away and sank down into the recesses of his body. The extremities were the first to feel its absence. His wet feet froze the faster, and his exposed fingers numbed the faster, though they had not begun to freeze. Nose and cheeks were already freezing, while the skin of all his body chilled as it lost its blood.

But he was safe. Toes and nose and cheeks would be only touched by the frost, for the fire was beginning to burn with strength. He was feeding it with twigs the size of his fingers. In another minute he would be able to feed it with branches the size of his wrist, and then he could remove his wet footgear, and, while it dried, he could keep his naked feet warm by the fire, rubbing them at first, of course, with snow. The fire was a success. He was a success. He was safe. He remembered the advice of the old-timer on Sulphur Creek, and smiled. The old-timer had been very serious laying down the law that no man must travel alone in the Klondike after fifty below. Well, here he was; he had had the accident; he was alone, and he had saved himself. But it was surprising, the rapidity with which his cheeks and nose were freezing. And he had not thought his fingers could go lifeless in so short a time. Lifeless they were, for he could scarcely make them move together to grip a twig, and they seemed remote from his body and from him. When he touched a twig, he had to look and see whether or not he had hold of it. The wires were pretty well down between him and his finger ends.

All of which counted for little. There was the fire, snapping and crackling and promising life with every dancing flame. He started to untie his moccasins. They were coated with ice; the thick German socks were like sheaths of iron halfway to the knees; and the moccasin strings were like rods of steel all twisted and knotted as by some conflagration. For a moment he tugged with his numb fingers, then, realizing the folly of it, he drew his sheath knife.

But before he could cut the strings, it happened. It was his own fault or, rather, his mistake. He should not have built the fire under the spruce tree. He should have built it in the open. But it had been easier to pull the twigs from the brush and drop them directly on the fire. Now the tree under which he had done this carried a weight of snow on its boughs. No wind had blown for weeks, and each bough was fully freighted. Each time he had pulled a twig he had communicated a slight agitation to the tree—an imperceptible agitation, so far as he was concerned, but an agitation sufficient to bring about the disaster. High up in the tree one bough capsized its load of snow. This fell on the boughs beneath, capsizing them. This process continued, spreading out and involving the whole tree. It grew like an avalanche, and it descended without warning upon the man and the fire, and the fire was blotted out! Where it had burned was a mantle of fresh and disordered snow.

The man was shocked. It was as though he had just heard his own sentence of death. For a moment he sat and stared at the spot where the fire had begun. Then he grew very calm. Perhaps the old-timer on Sulphur Creek was right. If he had only had a trail mate he would have been in no danger now. The trail mate could have built the fire. Well, it was up to him to build the fire over again, and this second time there must be no failure. Even if he succeeded, he would most likely lose some toes. His feet must be badly frozen by now, and there would be some time before the second fire was ready.

Such were his thoughts, but he did not sit and think them. He was busy all the time they were passing through his mind. He made a new foundation for a fire, this time in the open, where no treacherous tree could blot it out. Next he gathered dry grasses and tiny twigs from the high-water flotsam. He could not bring his fingers together to pull them out, but he was able to gather them by the handful. In this way he got many rotten twigs and bits of green moss that were undesirable, but it was the best he could do. He worked methodically, even collecting an armful of the larger branches to be used later when the fire gathered strength. And all the while the dog sat and watched him, a certain yearning wistfulness in its eyes, for it looked upon him as the fire provider, and the fire was slow in coming.

When all was ready, the man reached in his pocket for a second piece of birch bark. He knew the bark was there, and, though he could not feel it with his fingers, he could hear its crisp

173

rustling as he fumbled for it. Try as he would, he could not clutch hold of it. And all the time, in his consciousness, was the knowledge that each instant his feet were freezing. This thought tended to put him in a panic, but he fought against it and kept calm. He pulled on his mittens with his teeth, and threshed his arms back and forth, beating his hands with all his might against his sides. He did this sitting down, and he stood up to do it; and all the while the dog sat in the snow, its wolf brush of a tail curled around warmly over its forefeet, its sharp wolf ears pricked forward intently as it watched the man. And the man, as he beat and threshed with his arms and hands, felt a great surge of envy as he regarded the creature that was warm and secure in its natural covering.

After a time he was aware of the first faraway signals of sensations in his beaten fingers. The faint tingling grew stronger till it evolved into a stinging ache that was excruciating, but which the man hailed with satisfaction. He stripped the mitten from his right hand and fetched forth the birch bark. The exposed fingers were quickly going numb again. Next he brought out his bunch of sulphur matches. But the tremendous cold had already driven the life out of his fingers. In his effort to separate one match from the others, the whole bunch fell in the snow. He tried to pick it out of the snow, but failed. The dead fingers could neither touch nor clutch. He was very careful. He drove the thought of his freezing feet, and nose, and cheeks, out of his mind, devoting his whole soul to the matches. He watched, using the sense of vision in place of that of touch, and when he saw his fingers on each side of the bunch, he closed them—that is, he willed to close them, for the wires were down, and the fingers did not obey. He pulled the mitten on the right hand, and beat it fiercely against his knee. Then, with both mittened hands, he scooped the bunch of matches, along with much snow, into his lap. Yet he was no better off.

After some manipulation he managed to get the bunch between the heels of his mittened hands. In this fashion he carried it to his mouth. The ice crackled and snapped when by a violent effort he opened his mouth. He drew the lower jaw in, curled the upper lip out of the way and scraped the bunch with his upper teeth in order to separate a match. He succeeded in getting one, which he dropped on his lap. He was no better off. He could not pick it up. Then he devised a way. He picked it up in his teeth and scratched it on his leg. Twenty times he scratched before he succeeded in lighting it. As it flamed he held it with his teeth to the birch bark. But the burning brimstone went up his nostrils and into his lungs, causing him to cough spasmodically. The match fell into the snow and went out.

The old-timer on Sulphur Creek was right, he thought in the moment of controlled despair that ensued: after fifty below, a man should travel with a partner. He beat his hands, but failed in exciting any sensation. Suddenly he bared both hands, removing the mittens with his teeth. He caught the whole bunch between the heels of his hands. His arm muscles not being frozen enabled him to press the hand heels tightly against the matches. Then he scratched the bunch along his leg. It flared into flame, seventy sulphur matches at once! There was no wind to blow them out. He kept his head to one side to escape the strangling fumes, and held the blazing bunch to the birch bark. As he so held it, he became aware of sensation in his hand. His flesh was burning. He could smell it. Deep down below the surface he could feel it. The sensation developed into pain that grew acute and still he endured it, holding the flame of the matches clumsily to the bark that would not light readily because his own burning hands were in the way, absorbing most of the flame.

At last, when he could endure no more, he jerked his hands apart. The blazing matches fell sizzling into the snow, but the birch bark was alight. He began laying dry grasses and the tiniest twigs on the flame. He could not pick and choose, for he had to lift the fuel between the heels of his hands. Small pieces of rotten wood and green moss clung to the twigs, and he bit them off as well as he could with his teeth. He cherished the flame carefully and awkwardly. It meant life, and it must not perish. The withdrawal of blood from the surface of his body now made him begin to shiver, and he grew more awkward. A large piece of green moss fell squarely on the little fire. He tried to poke it out with his fingers, but his shivering frame made him poke too far, and he disrupted the nucleus of the little fire, the burning grasses and the tiny twigs separating and scattering. He tried to poke them together again, but in spite of the tenseness of the effort, his shivering got away with him, and the twigs were hopelessly scattered. Each twig gushed a puff of smoke and went out. The fire provider had failed. As he looked apathetically about him, his eyes chanced on the dog, sitting across the ruins of the fire from him, in the snow, making restless, hunching movements, slightly lifting one forefoot and then the other, shifting its weight back and forth on them with wistful eagerness.

The sight of the dog put a wild idea into his head. He remembered the tale of the man, caught in a blizzard, who killed a steer and crawled inside the carcass, and so was saved. He would kill the dog and bury his hands in the warm body until the numbness went out of them. Then he could build another fire. He spoke to the dog, calling it to him; but in his voice was a strange note of fear that frightened the animal, who had never known the man to speak in such a way before. Something was the matter, and its suspicious nature sensed danger—it knew not what danger, but somewhere, somehow, in its brain arose an apprehension of the man. It flattened its ears down at the sound of the man's voice, and its restless, hunching movements and the liftings and shiftings of its forefeet became more pronounced; but it would not come to the man. He got on his hands and knees and crawled toward the dog. This unusual posture again excited suspicion, and the animal sidled mincingly away.

The man sat up in the snow for a moment and struggled for calmness. Then he pulled on his mittens, by means of his teeth, and got upon his feet. He glanced down at first in order to assure himself that he was really standing up, for the absence of sensation in his feet left him unrelated to the earth. His erect position in itself started to drive the webs of suspicion from the dog's mind; and when he spoke peremptorily, with the sound of whip lashes in his voice, the dog rendered its customary allegiance and came to him. As it came within reaching distance, the man lost his control. His arms flashed out to the dog, and he experienced genuine surprise when he discovered that his hands could not clutch, that there was neither bend nor feeling in the fingers. He had forgotten for the moment that they were frozen and that they were freezing more and more. All this happened quickly, and before the animal could get away, he encircled its body with his arms. He sat down in the snow, and in this fashion held the dog, while it snarled and whined and struggled.

But it was all he could do, hold its body encircled in his arms and sit there. He realized that he could not kill the dog. There was no way to do it. With his helpless hands he could neither draw nor hold his sheath knife nor throttle the animal. He released it, and it plunged wildly away, with tail between its legs, and still snarling. It halted forty feet away and surveyed him curiously, with ears sharply pricked forward.

The man looked down at his hands in order to locate them, and found them hanging on the ends of his arms. It struck him as curious that one should have to use his eyes in order to find out where his hands were. He began threshing his arms back and forth, beating the mittened hands against his sides. He did this for five minutes, violently, and his heart pumped enough blood up to the surface to put a stop to his shivering. But no sensation was aroused in the hands. He had an impression that they hung like weights on the ends of his arms, but when he tried to run the impression down, he could not find it.

A certain fear of death, dull and oppressive, came to him. This fear quickly became poignant as he realized that it was no longer a mere matter of freezing his fingers and toes, or of losing his hands and feet, but that it was a matter of life and death with the chances against him. This threw him into a panic, and he turned and ran up the creek bed along the old dim trail. The dog joined in behind and kept up with him. He ran blindly, without intention, in fear such as he had never known in his life. Slowly, as he plowed and floundered through the snow, he began to see things again—the banks of the creek, the old timber jams, the leafless aspens, and the sky. The running made him feel better. He did not shiver. Maybe, if he ran on, his feet would thaw out; and anyway, if he ran far enough, he would reach camp and the boys. Without doubt he would lose some fingers and toes and some of his face; but the boys would take care of him, and save the rest of him when he got there. And at the same time there was another thought in his mind that said he would never get to the camp and the boys; that he would soon be stiff and dead. This thought he kept in the background and refused to consider. Sometimes it pushed itself forward and demanded to be heard, but he thrust it back and strove to think of other things.

It struck him as curious that he could run at all on feet so frozen that he could not feel them when they struck the earth and took the weight of his body. He seemed to himself to skim above the surface, and to have no connection with the earth. Somewhere he had once seen a winged Mercury, and he wondered if Mercury felt as he felt when skimming over the earth.

His theory of running until he reached camp and the boys had one flaw in it: he lacked the endurance. Several times he stumbled, and finally he tottered, crumpled up, and fell. When he tried to rise, he failed. He must sit and rest, he decided, and next time he would merely walk and keep on going. As he sat and regained his breath, he noted that he was feeling quite warm and comfortable. He was not shivering, and it even seemed that a warm glow had come to his chest and trunk. And yet, when he touched his nose or cheeks, there was no sensation. Running would not thaw them out. Nor would it thaw out his hands and feet. Then the thought came to him that the frozen portions of his body must be extending. He tried to keep the thought down, to forget it, to think of something else; he was aware of the panicky feeling it caused, and he was afraid of the panic. But the thought asserted itself, and persisted, until it produced a vision of his body totally frozen. This was too much, and he made another wild run along the trail. Once he slowed down to a walk, but the thought of the freezing extending itself made him run again.

And all the time the dog ran with him, at his heels. When he fell down a second time, it curled its tail over its forefeet and sat in front of him, facing him, curiously eager and intent. The warmth and security of the animal angered him, and he cursed it till it flattened down its ears appeasingly. This time the shivering came more quickly upon the man. He was losing in his battle with the frost. It was creeping into his body from all sides. The thought of it drove him on, but he ran no more than a hundred feet, when he staggered

and pitched headlong. It was his last panic. When he recovered his breath and control, he sat up and entertained in his mind the conception of meeting death with dignity. However, the conception did not come to him in such terms. His idea of it was that he had been making a fool of himself, running around like a chicken with its head cut off—such was the simile that occurred to him. Well, he was bound to freeze anyway, and he might as well take it decently. With this new-found peace of mind came the first glimmerings of drowsiness. A good idea, he thought, to sleep off to death. It was like taking an anesthetic. Freezing was not so bad as people thought. There were lots worse ways to die.

He pictured the boys finding his body the next day. Suddenly he found himself with them, coming along the trail and looking for himself. And, still with them, he came around a turn in the trail and found himself lying in the snow. He did not belong with himself

any more, for even then he was out of himself, standing with the boys and looking at himself in the snow. It certainly was cold, was his thought. When he got back to the States he could tell the folks what real cold was. He drifted on from this to a vision of the old-timer at Sulphur Creek. He could see him quite clearly, warm and comfortable.

"You were right, old hoss; you were right," the man mumbled to the old-timer of Sulphur Creek.

Then the man drowsed off into what seemed to him the most comfortable and satisfying sleep he had ever known. The dog sat facing him and waiting. The brief day drew to a close in a long, slow twilight. There were no signs of a fire to be made, and, besides, never in the dog's experience had it known a man to sit like that in the snow and make no fire. As the twilight drew on, its eager yearning for the fire mastered it, and with a great lifting and shifting of forefeet, it whined softly, then flattened its ears down in anticipation of being chidden by the man. But the man remained silent. Later the dog whined loudly. And still later it crept close to the man and caught the scent of death. This made the animal bristle and back away. A little longer it delayed, howling under the stars that leaped and danced and shone brightly in the cold sky. Then it turned and trotted up the trail in the direction of the camp it knew, where were the other food providers and fire providers.

Reader's Response

Do you think that the man's feelings and actions were true to life? Tell why or why not.

TO BUILD A
FIRE

Checking Your Comprehension

1. Where was the man going?
2. How did the man's judgment about the cold differ from the dog's instinct about it?
3. The man disregarded the old timer's advice about not traveling alone when the temperature was more than fifty below zero. What does this tell you about the man?
4. What happened to the man as a result of his building a fire under a tree?
5. If the dog could have spoken or communicated his instincts clearly to the man, do you think this story might have ended differently? Why?
6. What point do you think the author is trying to make in this story? What makes you think so?

Writing to Learn

THINK AND ANALYZE Jack London was an author with a unique writing style. Read the phrases below, and copy the ones that describe London's style.

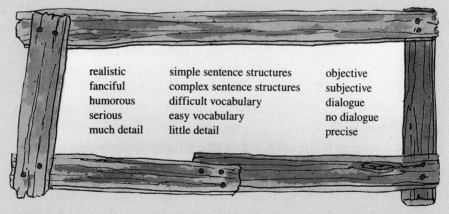

realistic	simple sentence structures	objective
fanciful	complex sentence structures	subjective
humorous	difficult vocabulary	dialogue
serious	easy vocabulary	no dialogue
much detail	little detail	precise

WRITE Review the story and find examples of London's sentences that illustrate the descriptive phrases you chose. Use your information and write a description of Jack London's unique writing style.

A Strategy for Thinking:

Making a Before-and-After Chart

You know much more now than you did two or three years ago, and every day you learn a bit more. Each bit of new knowledge is added to your existing storehouse of knowledge. You can use the knowledge you have to help you predict what may happen in a story. Then you can take note of new information in the story and see if it changes your prediction. By looking at new information in light of your existing knowledge, you will gain better understanding from and retain more of what you read in the future.

Learning the Strategy

One way to help compare old and new information and to check your predictions about what you read is to make a before-and-after chart. To make a before-and-after chart, first write down what you know about the subject of a story based on the title and clues in the first page. Make a prediction about what might happen in the story. Then, add to your knowledge, or revise your old knowledge, and check your prediction as you read. For example, read the following introduction to the story "To Build a Fire."

> A lone man and a dog trudged across a frozen wilderness of ice and snow. Each knew certain things about the bitter, deadly cold that they were challenging—but perhaps they did not know enough.

Now, look at the before-and-after chart for "To Build a Fire."

WHAT YOU KNOW...

Before reading:	After reading:
Everything is frozen when it is very cold.	When it is 70 below zero, spittle freezes in mid-air. Even at 70 below, you can go through the ice.
The cold can nip your fingers and toes when it is cold.	Your feet can freeze solid if they get wet.
You can always get warm if you have matches to start a fire.	If your hands are numb, you can't even hold matches.
Prediction: The man will survive.	Prediction check: The man died.

Do you see how using a before-and-after chart can help you add to your storehouse of knowledge and revise your predictions?

Using the Strategy

Make a before-and-after chart. On the left, write what you know about having cold hands. Then read the following passage from "To Build a Fire" and add any new information on the right. How did the story change what you knew?

> After a time he was aware of the first faraway signals of sensations in his beaten fingers. The faint tingling grew stronger till it evolved into a stinging ache that was excruciating, but which the man hailed with satisfaction.

Applying the Strategy to the Next Selection

The next selection, "Animal Language," is filled with interesting information that may be new to you. As you read, you will be asked to make a before-and-after chart.

◆◆◆ The writing connection can be found on page 239.

ANIMAL LANGUAGE

by Bil Gilbert

It may be that all animals, not just humans, use language, but the mysteries of animal language are only beginning to be solved.

Two neighbors, Rich and Jo Zimmerman, live the kind of life that most animal lovers would envy. They own and manage a Game Park. The stock of this unusual farm ranges from penguins to bison. However, to me, the Zimmermans' most interesting and spectacular animals are three cheetahs— a full-grown pair, Top Cat and Petter, and Chief, a young male. ◀◆▶

◀◆▶

Make a before-and-after chart. Fill in the left-hand side of the chart with what you already know about animal communication. Then write your prediction about what the article will say.

The cheetah is a big, lithe, spotted cat that looks much like a long-legged leopard. These cats are the fastest of all mammals, able to run seventy miles per hour for short distances. Natives of Africa and Asia, cheetahs for centuries have been trained to hunt with and for people. Leashed, and with their eyes hooded, the big cats are led until antelope or deer are sighted. Then the cheetah is freed and simply runs down the quarry. Those who have been fortunate enough to watch such chases say that no other form of hunting is quite so thrilling.

The Zimmermans obtained the three cheetahs principally in the hope of mating Top Cat with one of the males. However, they also wished

to exhibit the animals and wanted them to be sufficiently tame to walk politely on a lead in public. Since the work of caring for several hundred exotic animals is hard and constant, the Zimmermans asked me to help with this project of developing good manners in the cheetahs. Long an admirer of these clean-limbed, graceful cats, I needed no second invitation.

Top Cat and Petter, both full-grown, presented no problems.

A cheetah's fear automatically triggers unmistakable alarm signals: layed back ears, raised hair, and warning snarl.

Though both had been captured wild, they had been raised from kittens by humans. Both were exceedingly friendly. Though occasionally their play, sort of catch-as-catch-can wrestling, became a bit rough, their intentions were as peaceable as those of a pair of house cats. Chief, the half-grown male, was a different matter. When he arrived at the Zimmermans' he was about half the size of an Airedale dog, and while not vicious in the sense of making unprovoked attacks, he was aloof and obviously frightened.

When I first met Chief he had grown to half his adult size and weighed about seventy pounds. We certainly did not become friends at first sight. As I entered Chief's big cage, he backed slowly and warily away from the door, watching every move I made, his muscles tense. As I approached, he retreated to a corner and there crouched, hissing and snarling. His ears were flattened against his skull, his lips were drawn back exposing his already formidable fangs, his hair stood up on the nape of his neck, and his long tail was stiff as a bottle brush. Perhaps somewhere there is an animal which could have misinterpreted Chief's message, but as far as I was concerned he was expressing himself as clearly as if he had said in English, "Keep away."

Is this information new to you? If so, use it to fill in your chart.

It was not that Chief had any desire to attack me (a hunting, stalking cat has a remarkably pleasant, relaxed look about it). Quite the contrary—Chief was terrified that I might attack him. Every instinct of the cheetah warned him that an animal of my size which would advance toward him was up to no good. Had he been free, he would have fled, but caged, he could only retreat until cornered and then make it clear that as a last resort he would fight.

Again, one must avoid attributing human motives and thought processes to animals. Chief did not reason, "If I lay back my ears, snarl, and raise my hair, this man will keep away." Rather, the cheetah was afraid and fear triggered a muscular reaction that resulted in these unmistakable alarm signals. Cornered in a similar situation, a human could argue, scream, threaten, plead, make any number of defiant gestures which might protect him or her and avoid a showdown. Still it is doubtful if any person could express the basic information, "Keep away," any more emphatically than Chief did by his reflexive, involuntary gestures.

These warning symbols are about the same in cat language the world over. A house cat cornered by a dog will respond much as Chief did to me and there is a good chance the dog will keep its distance as I did. Few if any animals are fearless, though we often hear the expression. Meeting another creature which is simply strange or large enough to be formidable, most animals will try to escape. If they cannot, their usual reaction is to do what they can to avoid hostilities. A great many animals have evolved sounds, signs, or gestures which they use to warn off other creatures and avoid violence.

Beyond my reluctance to be mauled by a seventy-pound cheetah, it would have destroyed any chance I might have had for making friends with Chief, if, after being warned, I had tried to come closer at our first meeting. I did the only thing that could be done. I stood for a few minutes motionless, and then left, hoping I had made a start at the first lesson which any wild animal must learn—that its trainer is not hostile.

During the following days our relations improved. By feeding Chief bits of meat, by avoiding sudden moves, by sitting on the floor rather than standing over him, and finally by playing football with him, I won his trust. The football was invaluable. Chief loved to pounce on the ball, and kittenlike, bat the eccentric sphere around his cage. Occasionally he jumped directly over my head in pursuit of the ball.

In time when I

entered, Chief would come to me, rub against my leg, purr, lick my hand with his rough tongue. He began to play, slapping at my boots, hugging me about the legs, jumping up to put his forepaws on my shoulders. In the course of this play he would sometimes take my pants leg in his mouth and give an exploratory nip. Not wishing to encourage this kind of fun, I would give him a brisk slap on the nose and follow the slap with a sharp command, "No." At first Chief responded with his old fear signals, backing off, snarling. Gradually he learned that the slap and "no" were not overtures to an attack but only my sign that I did not want to be nipped. Soon the command alone was enough to halt this kind of biting.

Slowly, Chief and I came to trust one another, principally because we were able to establish a rudimentary sort of communication, able to read certain signs and sounds well enough to understand the feelings and wishes of the other. I learned enough cheetah to know how Chief indicated that he was afraid, contented, playful, or bored. He learned enough human to know that I was friendly, that a whistle meant food, "ball" meant a game, and "no" was a command to stop biting. Certainly this was not much of a vocabulary, but it was enough to let us meet in peace, a condition all animals need at times, and a condition which could not be established if animals could not communicate their intentions and desires.

The questions, Do animals communicate? Are there animal languages? have fascinated and puzzled people for many centuries. Wizards, magicians, philosophers of old long sought the key that would enable them to converse with animals. Not infrequently individuals have claimed to have discovered this secret. In every land, in every age, there are stories, myths, folk tales about talking beasts who brought power, wealth, or sometimes disaster to people who could understand them. Not all the stories are told as myths; some are reported as fact, of children who, raised with wolves, bears, monkeys, learned the language of their foster parents. Stories of talking animals persist even in this so-called age of science. For example, naturalists studying the habits of orangutans in the East Indies were told by native hunters that these great apes could talk as sensibly and eloquently as people. When asked why it was that orangutans never displayed this talent, the hunters explained that the captured orangutans remained silent for fear that if they talked they would be forced to pay taxes and serve as soldiers. ◆◈◆

◆◈◆

Is this information new to you? If so, use it to fill in your chart.

188

The intelligent orangutan is a good subject for studying animal language.

Ultimately the answer to the question, Do animals communicate? depends upon what is meant by communication. The system of communication used by *most* animals, *most* of the time, might be called the language of reaction, while that used by people, *most* of the time, might be designated as the language of reason. These labels are not entirely satisfactory, but they do emphasize the principal characteristics of the two languages.

Many of the communicative signs animals use appear to be made in reaction to some immediate event or situation. Thus Chief, the cheetah, snarls at my approach, which creates an inner feeling of fear or anxiety and his snarl is the outward expression of this inner mood. The snarl is not made because he "intends" (as we use the word) to communicate with me. The snarl is a reaction over which he has very little control, to something that has happened and affected his inner mood.

Humans also react to immediate events and express their reactions with what we might call involuntary signals. A scream of fright is a human signal, very similar to the snarl of a cat. However, the distinctive characteristic of our language is not the relatively few reactive signals we use, but the great many which reflect our ability to reason. Our language not only expresses our reaction to the present but also expresses our ideas about what has been, might have been, might be, what is probable and improbable. We can, for example, discuss something frightening long after or before we have been frightened. We can even illustrate what our mood was or might be by giving a scream of fright. For the cheetah this appears to be impossible. He snarls when he is frightened, but cannot modify the signal to inform another creature about the abstract idea of fright when he is no longer frightened. The cheetah must encounter the actual frightening situation before he can display the fright sign. ◆◆◆

◆◆◆

Is this information new to you? If so, use it to fill in your chart.

Another characteristic of our language is that it is almost entirely learned. Animals also learn some of their signals but a proportionately larger share of an animal's vocabulary is inherited. The snarl of a cheetah is an innate signal. He is born with the ability to make this sign. Chief, for example, was taken from the company of other cheetahs as a very small kitten, yet he snarled in about the same fashion as any other of his kind.

Individual animals can learn to make and respond to signs that are entirely foreign to their species. A dog, for example, learns to obey the command "sit," and learns to "speak" to express its desire to be let in a house. But these learned signals are neither as important nor as numerous in the language of reaction as they are in the language of reason. A great many of the innate signals an animal makes it can no more alter than it can change the color of its coat or the length of its tail.

The language behavior of chicks and children illustrates this difference between these two systems of communication. Recent studies indicate that all chickens have a vocabulary of about twenty-five signals. If a chick is raised by a duck, it will continue to use the chicken vocabulary it has inherited. Also a chick hatched in Germany will make and respond to approximately the same signs as one raised in the United States. The language of chickens is more or less universal. Every chicken can use it, and individual experiences only slightly modify a chicken's communicative methods.

A child, however, born to English-speaking parents will, if adopted into a French family, learn

The signals that these chicks will use automatically throughout their lives are an example of the language of reaction inherited by animals.

French as easily as he or she would have his or her native language. Also, a child, because our language is learned, not inherited, can learn a number of other sign vocabularies—Spanish, German, Chinese, etc.

Until relatively recent times, the division between the language of reaction and the language of reason was considered to be hard and fast. All animal behavior and communication was thought to be "instinctive." Now both the idea and the term "instinctive" are being challenged and are used much more cautiously than they once were. In every animal, individual experience (what it learns) modifies inherited (instinctive) characteristics. Thus a dog has the innate ability to bark, but it learns to bark in different ways to express its reaction to different situations. ◀◆▶

◀◆▶

Is this information new to you? If so, use it to fill in your chart.

There is still much to be learned about how intelligence, experience, and learning influence the language of animals (as well as how instinct influences our language). Therefore it is impossible to make an absolute division between what we have called the language of reaction and the language of reason. It is quite possible that we may find the language of a cheetah is somewhat closer to our own than we have supposed and that the language of certain other animals may be very much closer to ours than is now thought. It is a matter of degree. Chickens appear

to learn very little of their language, dogs a bit more, and humans far more.

Another of the distinctive characteristics of humans is the arrogance of our species. Automatically, one might almost say instinctively, we judge the abilities of other animals in terms of our own accomplishments and needs. An animal, lacking human skills or possessing ones we do not have, is considered "lower," inferior. We seldom speculate on the question, Inferior to what? It is true that a bird cannot draw or read a blueprint. However, it has little need for this skill since it has the innate ability to build its own home. For many years this basic arrogance blocked serious consideration of animal communication. Except for herdsmen, hunters, animal breeders, and trainers, who had to learn something practical about animal communication, the whole subject was left to fairy-tale tellers. The "intelligent" opinion was

191

that since animals apparently could not use or understand language as humans did, they obviously had nothing of importance to say. This view has proved to be as much at odds with easily observable facts as the other extreme opinion—that in private, orangutans argue about taxes.

Modern students of animal behavior are not patronizing about how little and how poorly animals communicate. Rather, they are constantly discovering how much and how well animals use their own languages. For centuries the study of animal communication has been dominated by the wizard attitude, the belief that there must be some way to lure, trick, or teach animals to communicate as humans do. The current approach is somewhat more practical.

Since our behavior is more flexible than that of animals, it is more reasonable for us to learn animal languages and try to communicate in animal than it is for animals to learn to use human. Working on this assumption, recent observers have compiled "dictionaries," lists of standard communication symbols, for fish, bees, ants, crows, chickens, gulls, ducks, dogs, monkeys, and many other species.

The study of animal communication, now being carried on both in the laboratory and in the field, is one of the most challenging in modern biology. It seeks answers to riddles that have teased people in every age: What are animals saying? What can we say to animals?

❖❖❖

❖❖❖

Review your before-and-after chart. What new information did you add to your storehouse of knowledge by reading this article? How accurate was your prediction about what the article would say?

♦ LIBRARY LINK ♦

If you want to know even more about how animals communicate, look for the book from which this excerpt was taken, How Animals Communicate, *by Bil Gilbert.*

Reader's Response

Do you agree with the author that it is important for people to try to learn animal languages?

ANIMAL LANGUAGE

Checking Your Comprehension

1. What was Chief trying to tell the author at the beginning of their first meeting?
2. What did the author try to communicate to Chief in response?
3. How might a person's response to fear be similar to that of an animal? How might a person's response be different?
4. How do animals know how to communicate? How is this different from the ways in which humans know how to communicate?
5. Why does the author think that it is important to communicate with animals?
6. How might animals help us if we were better able to communicate with them? What led you to think of these ways?

Writing to Learn

THINK AND DISCOVER Make a list of three new ideas you discovered by reading "Animal Language."

> a large share of an animal's vocabulary is inherited.

WRITE Use one of your new ideas to design a poster for a veterinarian's reception room. Select information that will be of special interest to people who are fond of animals.

193

READING NON-FICTION

Vocabulary:

Word Play

If you went to a zoo and asked to see a herd of fish and a school of elephants, you'd probably get some pretty strange looks. Have you ever wondered why we always use certain words to describe particular groups of animals? It's because back in the Middle Ages it was considered very important for knights and ladies to be able to describe groups of animals properly. People compiled lists of the "correct" terms to use, and many of those terms are still in use today.

The terms often describe some characteristic of the animal. For example, groups of fish were originally called "shoals," which is a good name because fish tend to live in shoals, or shallow water. At some point, however, people began to mistake the word *shoals* for the word *schools,* and that is why we now talk about "schools" of fish.

You have probably heard of other imaginative names for groups of animals, such as a *gaggle of geese* or a *swarm of bees*. (Can you hear the geese gaggling and see the bees swarming?) Other names for groups of animals are not as well known. Have you ever heard of a *leap of leopards,* or a *crash of rhinoceroses*? These names really exist—and they make sense. A "leap of leopards" stresses what leopards do. A "crash of rhinoceroses" picks up on the sound of a group of stampeding rhinos.

Animal Idioms

An *idiom* is an expression that means something very different from the individual words in it. If you "get my goat," for example, you do not literally take an animal away from me. You annoy me. Idioms can be fun because of the contrast between the meanings of

194

the individual words and the meaning of the whole expression. Idioms are often used in conversation. In writing, idioms are appropriate if they are used in dialogue or in very informal writing. In most of your writing, though, you should avoid using idioms.

The following paragraph contains five idioms that refer to animals. Do you know what they mean?

> Justin can be so pig-headed at times. He heard Maria tell Jim about the surprise party, and he went ape. He said she could wait till the cows come home before he'd tell her another secret. But Justin had to eat crow in the end. He found out that Maria's little brother was the one who let the cat out of the bag.

Of course, Justin does not really have a head like a pig's. *Pig-headed* is an idiom that means "stubborn." Nor did he turn into an ape. The idiom *went ape* means "became wild." *Till the cows come home* is also an idiom, referring to something that will never happen. And Justin did not really have crow for supper—*eat crow* means "admit a mistake." *Let the cat out of the bag* means "reveal the information," not "set free a cat."

Using What You Have Learned

1. Choose the best group name for each animal. Explain why the names are appropriate.
   Animals: gnats, lions, chickens, ducks
   Group names: pride, paddling, cloud, peep
2. Use each of the idioms below in a sentence. If you are not sure what the idioms mean, check your dictionary.
   a. raining cats and dogs   c. sounds fishy
   b. a wild-goose chase   d. horsing around

As You Read

When you read "Helping Hands," think about whether the characteristics of the monkeys would inspire an interesting group name.

Going upstairs, switching on a light, drinking a glass of water—these "simple" activities are not so simple for those who don't have the use of their arms and legs.

Helping Hands

by J. Tevere MacFadyen

Try this: take the most comfortable chair you own into the pleasantest room in your house. Arrange it in a convenient location and sit down. Don't move. Wait fifteen or twenty minutes for your muscles to loosen up. Relax. Look around; take stock of your surroundings. If any visitors walk in, you can turn your head to greet them but you can't stand or shake hands. You can admire the view out your window, but you can't crack it open for a breath of fresh air. Wait another hour. Are you bored yet? Hungry? Thirsty? Sorry, but you'll just have to wait until somebody happens by. Don't worry,

it shouldn't be too long—probably no more than a couple of hours.

Welcome to the world of the quadriplegic, Gary Finkle's world. Gary has been paralyzed ever since he was injured in a swimming-pool accident seven years ago. He is one of an estimated 90,000 Americans who have lost almost all of the feeling and movement below their shoulders due to severe spinal-cord injuries. Gary lives in a new home on a hilltop outside the village of Andes, New York, about three hours north of New York City. Living with him are his wife, Micki, and a female capuchin monkey

Gary Finkle with Jo.

named Jo. When I visited him there recently, Jo was perched protectively on the back of his wheelchair.

Gary Finkle was one of the first quadriplegics to be helped by a group called Helping Hands: Simian Aides for the Disabled. The nonprofit organization was started by a psychologist, Dr. Mary Joan Willard. It gives disabled people trained capuchin monkeys to help them become more independent. Shortly after it started up, Helping Hands received publicity in newspapers, magazines, and on television. Now it is no longer a novelty but a proven success that makes a real difference in the lives of the people it serves.

Just look at Gary and Jo. Gary uses his mouth to control a small laser pointer attached to his wheelchair. With it, he directs

Jo to open and shut doors, turn lights on or off, change books or magazines in a reading stand or tapes in a cassette player. She brings him prepared snacks and drinks from the refrigerator and clears away empties. She will even feed him. On command, Jo fetches the remote control for Gary's TV, placing it on the chair where he can work it with his mouthstick. The mouthstick is a quadriplegic's main tool. It is used for practically everything: turning the pages of a book, dialing the telephone, changing channels on the TV, working at a typewriter or computer. If Gary's mouthstick drops to the floor, Jo will pick it up and gently place it back into his mouth. "I definitely cannot imagine living without her," he says.

Jo has been with the Finkles for more than three years. She has become so much a part of their lives that, in describing her, they tend to talk more about her personality and style than about what she does. "She's smarter than we give her credit for," Gary says fondly. "Sometimes she's too smart," adds Micki, who once spotted a missing tube of lipstick in Jo's cage: she'd apparently found the stuff quite tasty.

"The main thing is independence," Gary reflects. He knows that he will always need human help for such things as getting in and out of bed, bathing, or changing his clothes. But having Jo means that he needs Micki's help less. She can work afternoons in town without worrying about how her husband is doing. Besides being useful, Jo is a good companion. "She's a constant source of entertainment," Gary marvels, "and she just keeps getting smarter. The more she's exposed to, the more she learns. I want to teach her to play backgammon."

Gary came to Helping Hands by way of New York's Rusk Institute, a renowned rehabilitation center. "It seemed like a great challenge," he recalls. "I've been around animals all my life and I guess I just thought this would be fun." Nowadays Jo goes almost everywhere with him, indoors and out, on social calls or errands. Wherever they go, they draw attention. "I've certainly met people I wouldn't have met without her," Gary says. When I ask if a robot might not one day be able to do many of the jobs Jo does for him now, Gary answers, "Robots won't play with you. They won't jump around your living room or wrestle with the dogs.

They won't comb your hair and beard with their hands or sit on the laser, chewing at your face. A robot would be pretty dull."

A VISIT TO HELPING HANDS

On the sixth floor of Abraham Mazer Hall at the Albert Einstein College of Medicine in New York, the corridor is alive with shrieking chirrups and trills. Ringing bells sound amid a hubbub of hollers and howls, weird catcalls and cries, crashes, claps, and bangs. The cinder-block walls are dull institutional yellow; the floor is faded linoleum. What little furniture there is appears to have taken quite a beating. Windows are missing from the doors to several offices and have been replaced with wire mesh. If the place looks a bit of a mess, there is good reason. Here, in cubicles where medical students once crammed for exams, "organ-grinder monkeys" are learning to help the disabled. "We're very lucky to be here," Dr. Mary Joan Willard tells me as we step from the elevator to be greeted by a chattering capuchin chorus. As well as being the founder and director of Helping Hands, Dr. Willard is an assistant professor of rehabilitation medicine at Einstein. "People kill for space at this institution," she explains. "If we weren't here, we'd probably be down in the basement or someplace awful."

In 1977, Willard was a postdoctoral fellow in psychology at Tufts New England Medical Center in Boston. There she became friends with a twenty-three-year-old quadriplegic. Visiting him, she became aware of how dependent a paralyzed person is on others. There was almost nothing he could do without help. "As a psychologist," she says, "I was obsessed with the notion that there had to be some way to increase his independence."

Dr. Willard with a new trainee.

Willard had spent three years as a research assistant to B. F. Skinner, the famous psychologist at Harvard University. Skinner had developed techniques of changing behavior by using reward and punishment. It occurred to Dr. Willard that Skinner's reward-and-punishment techniques might be used to train monkeys to help the disabled. "I was literally lying in bed one night when it hit me," she remembers. "Why not use chimps?" Chimpanzees, it turned out, had some practical drawbacks: they grow to be nearly as big as people and a good deal stronger, and adult chimps tend to be moody at times.

But Skinner thought the idea was a good one and suggested capuchins instead. Adult capuchins weigh roughly five pounds and stand less than eighteen inches tall. They respond well to training and form loyal bonds with humans. After some investigation, Willard decided to go ahead. Armed with a small grant from Tufts Medical School, she bought four laboratory-bred capuchins, and Helping Hands was on its way.

Dr. Willard's manner is direct and informal. When she calls a lunchtime meeting in her office, everyone sits on the floor. Present are Alison Pascoe, Lauren Westbrook and Alice Levee, the three young women who form the core of the training staff at Einstein. Other key staffers are not based in New York. David Taylor, a high school science teacher from Byfield, Massachusetts, coordinates the "foster family" network. His group places infant capuchins in human homes before they're ready for training. Judi Zazula, a biomedical engineer in Boston, oversees the actual placement of monkeys. She screens disabled applicants to see if they are suitable for the program. Her partner, Doug Ely, a physicist with Arthur D. Little Inc., designs and builds much of the specialized equipment the project requires.

A SCHOOL FOR MONKEYS

On the agenda this noon are a review of current training and an evaluation of the volunteer trainers. There are fourteen

199

volunteers in all, most of them undergraduates at nearby Fordham University. Alison's pet capuchin, Amelia, nestles in my lap. "You'd never know how mean she was, would you?" Alison chuckles as Amelia attempts to relieve me of my pen. Amelia is a *Cebus apella*, a kind of capuchin that is considered more obedient and relaxed than the constantly playful *albifrons*. The first monkey permanently placed with a quadriplegic was an *albifrons*, but the seven

An aide practices turning the pages of a magazine.

placed since have been calmer *apella/albifrons* mixtures. All but one of the monkeys used as helpers thus far have been females, who are less aggressive, have fewer bad habits and seem to form stronger bonds than males.

Until recently, most of the animals obtained by the program have been adults with checkered pasts. Some are cast-off pets or zoo monkeys, others veterans of laboratory experimentation. A capuchin named Freeway was found wandering alongside an interstate. As Helping Hands has become more widely known, the word

has gotten around that it is a safe place for homeless monkeys. Alison notes some problems in working with animals from unknown backgrounds. "We never have any idea how they've been treated," she says. Cleo, for instance, who will soon be placed with a young cerebral-palsy victim, arrived at Einstein shy and malnourished.

While older animals will still be accepted, young monkeys will be the majority in the future. Many of them will be born at the Mannheimer Primatological Foundation in Florida where Helping Hands now has a breeding colony. Four of the six animals now at Einstein were raised especially for Helping Hands, and another twenty-five or so are currently living with foster families. Foster care begins immediately after weaning, at six to eight weeks. Three years later, when the monkeys are grown, their teeth are pulled to guard against the chance that they might wound someone with a bite. Then they are ready for six months or so of training. The animals are trained as early as possible so that they will be able to help someone for a long time. They live for about thirty years.

Down the hall in a battered training room a monkey named Marylin is burning off some excess energy. She jumps from table to chair to wardrobe to windowsill to chair, flicking the lights on and off, repeatedly testing the knob of the firmly locked door, yowling and cheeping and making faces. "She'll settle down," Alison promises, and soon enough she does. I sit very still in a wheelchair, playing the role of a quadriplegic, as Alison puts the capuchin through her paces. After spending several months with a fifty-four-year-old quadriplegic man in New Jersey, Marylin has returned to Einstein for a refresher course. "Change, Marylin," Alison instructs. "Change."

The trainer directs a laser pointer toward a magazine in a plastic binder on a shelf. Marylin, after a brief hesitation, crosses the room and picks up the magazine. She carries it to a nearby reading stand, removes the binder already on the stand and puts the new one in its place. Then she claps a steel washer attached to the binder onto a bell, signaling success. She scoots over to my chair for her reward—a sip of a sticky, strawberry-flavored drink. I'm able to give this to her by blowing into a plastic tube mounted beside my headrest. The tube descends into a bottle fixed to the chair's frame. Blowing into it forces a thimbleful of liquid into a cup in the bottle's cap, which Marylin greedily licks clean.

Whenever a monkey properly completes an assignment it receives a reward. If the task is not completed, or is done incorrectly, the reward is denied. Many different behaviors can be taught using this system. The monkeys learn to respond to verbal commands like "Fetch" or "Change," as well as visual signals from the laser pointer. Complex activities, such as bringing food and feeding, are divided into smaller tasks. Once the animal has

The laser pointer is used to show the aide which block to pick up.

mastered a small task, it is taught the next small task and so on until finally it has mastered the whole activity.

Trainers often give rewards in the form of a bit of peanut butter dabbed onto a finger, but quadriplegics use mouth-activated dispensers. These may be either the liquid type or a container loaded with food pellets. Punishment, or negative reinforcement, is given by means of a tiny battery-powered backpack which can deliver a slight electric shock. Alison compares the shock to the static charge sometimes received by touching a metal doorknob.

Willard remembers one early placement that had a tendency to "tear up the house" when she wasn't working. The solution to that was the shock-pack, used along with little white circular stickers called coding dots. The animal quickly learned to associate the dots with a shock and henceforth avoided touching anything with a sticker attached to it. In practice, quadriplegics seldom shock their monkeys and some abandon the shock-pack altogether.

Capuchins sleep in large wire-mesh cages that are prominent features of their owners' households. Unlike most children, the monkeys will go to their "rooms" on command and obediently close the door behind them. Capuchins tend to be fastidious. "In general, they're very clean," Alison reports. "Some of them don't even like to eat bananas because they don't want to get their hands dirty. You have to wrap the fruit in napkins."

THE EARLY DAYS

More than once in its early years, Helping Hands came close to shutting down. Even after the first experiments proved promising, thirty-eight possible sponsors refused Willard's requests for financial help. When she turned to the Veterans Administration, an official there told her, "Look, this is a fantastic idea and if it works, great. But if it doesn't work you're going to get the Golden Fleece award, and we don't want to be funding you when you get it." The agency eventually went on to become the project's principal backer, but it was the Paralyzed Veterans of America that really got things going by awarding Willard her first major grant, late in 1979.

Though she admits to some frustration over the constant grind of fund raising, Willard finds some comfort in history. After all, she points out, training guide dogs to lead the blind did not begin in earnest until a century after the idea was first proposed in 1819. Even today, only five percent of all blind persons use Seeing Eye dogs. "We expect to be placing ten to twenty animals a year soon, and expanding from there," she predicts.

THE DEMAND GROWS

On the sixth floor of Mazer Hall, using mostly begged and borrowed equipment, the Helping Hands staff has just finished videotaping the entire training process.

Along with a 108-page instructional manual, these tapes should go a long way toward helping other groups be as successful as Helping Hands. Already, rehabilitation centers in Canada, Argentina, and Israel have begun simian-aide programs of their own. In this country, requests for capuchin aides far outstrip the available supply. Willard has received more than 600 inquiries from quadriplegics or their families.

Some rehabilitation specialists argue that simian aides will work for only a fraction of the nation's disabled, and that research money might be better directed to other areas, such as developing better robots. Willard disagrees. "We're training the animals to do some things that will be very difficult for robots to accomplish," she says. "Monkeys aren't for everyone, but dollar for dollar I can't think of anything that will have a greater positive impact on a quadriplegic's life." Monkeys are "all over their owners," says Alison Pascoe, "kissing and touching and exploring, and I think that's terribly meaningful."

Judi Zazula, who's been part of Helping Hands from the early days, carefully evaluates every applicant to the program. "Not all quadriplegics are super people," she says. "A lazy person before an accident will likely be a lazy paralyzed person." Zazula looks for people who are interested and energetic, and who have the kinds of particular needs that monkeys can help meet.

Quadriplegics need special equipment in order to work well with their monkeys.

The feeding tray, for instance, is fitted with attachments and containers exactly matched to the drink bottles and food holders a quadriplegic will use. Now made of a very strong molded plastic, earlier models were fashioned from plastic, cardboard, and duct tape. "We use off-the-shelf components whenever we can," Doug Ely tells me, "but some things have to be specially made." The socket into which a sandwich holder fits looks vaguely familiar. As well it might, Ely confirms. It's a modified vacuum-cleaner crevice tool.

A TRUE COMPANION

Given her special training, Judi Zazula might be expected to focus on Helping Hands' more practical aspects: the ways in which capuchins can help disabled people accomplish basic tasks. But like everyone else I spoke with, she seems most deeply affected by the monkeys' impact on the quality of the quadriplegics' lives. As part of the research for her master's thesis she watched people react to a quadriplegic in a shopping center. When he was alone, only two strangers approached the young man to talk in the course of an hour. When he was accompanied by his capuchin, seventy-one passersby paused to chat. Says Zazula, "Giving a quadriplegic a monkey makes him an 'expert' on something that fascinates able-bodied people." Sue Strong puts it this way: "When I go outdoors in my wheelchair, all that people see is the wheelchair. But when

I go out with my monkey, the only thing they see is the monkey. Nobody notices the chair at all."

When she was twenty, Sue Strong was on her way West for a summer of fun when the steering wheel of the van in which she was riding separated from the steering column. The vehicle crashed and rolled, and Sue awoke to the world of quadriplegia. She now lives in a rent-controlled apartment on Manhattan's East Side. Part-time attendants see to most of her daily needs. Her only full-time companion is a female capuchin named Henri, which is short for Henrietta. "Having her has completely changed my life," Sue says. "Before, I had to depend on people coming to work, and worry about whether or not they'd show up on time. Now, if I'm up in my chair and feeling OK, Henri and I can get along fine on our own."

When Strong drops her mouthstick, she quietly says "Mouth, Henri. Mouth!" The capuchin searches until she locates the lost tool, then hops lightly up and returns it to Sue's mouth. "We've had to learn how each other thinks," says Sue. "I have to be careful not to expect too much. I forget that she can't read my mind."

Henri is dispatched to the kitchen for a sandwich. She returns with the food and positions it in the holder on the feeding tray so that Sue can eat, but she can't quite resist trying a small bite for herself. Instantly, she realizes she's made a mistake, and almost before her owner gives the command she rushes yowling into her cage. "Door, Henri!" Sue intones with mock sternness. Henri yanks the door closed, then peers anxiously out, awaiting a reprieve. It is not long in coming.

"Oh, all right," Sue concedes, laughing as she guides her chair over to free the sad-looking capuchin. Once out, Henri curls up on her mistress' ankles, craning her neck to gaze up at Sue, the very picture of remorse. Sue laughs out loud. "Look at that, will you!" she says. "A face only a mother could love."

Reader's Response

In what ways do you think owning a capuchin might be preferable to having a full-time nurse?

Helping Hands

Checking Your Comprehension

1. In your opinion, why did the author begin the selection in the way he did?
2. What is a mouthstick and why is it so important to a quadriplegic?
3. How does Gary Finkle's capuchin, Jo, help him?
4. How did Dr. Willard develop the Helping Hands organization?
5. In what ways are capuchin monkeys superior to robots and chimps as aides for the disabled? How did you identify these ways?
6. For what reasons do you think the monkeys are returned to Helping Hands for refresher courses?

Writing to Learn

THINK AND IMAGINE This article suggests that a capuchin could be trained to help with chores in a number of situations. The chart below shows what the capuchin could do to assist a librarian. Copy and complete the other chart by filling in the tasks a capuchin could do to help a gas station attendant.

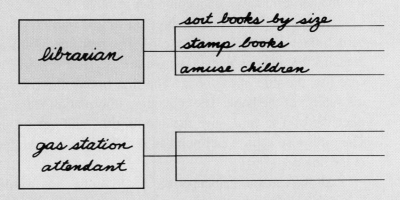

librarian — sort books by size / stamp books / amuse children

gas station attendant —

WRITE Imagine that you have been given a capuchin. Write a list of all the household tasks that you would train your pet to do.

READING AND STUDYING

Study Skill:

Using the Library

If reading "Helping Hands" made you wonder what other ways animals can be trained to help disabled people, you can satisfy your curiosity with a trip to the library. The library provides valuable tools for finding information. Two of these tools are the card catalogue and the *Readers' Guide to Periodical Literature*.

The Card Catalogue

The card catalogue lists all the books in the library. In most libraries, the catalogue is compiled on index cards found in a bank of file drawers. However, many libraries now use a computer to catalogue their books. In such libraries, you find the same information at a computer terminal or on a computer printout.

The catalogue contains three cards for each book: an author card, a title card, and a subject card. The first line on the author card contains the author's name, last name first. The first line on the title card lists the title of the book. The first line of the subject card lists the subject of the book. The remaining information is the same on all three cards. The cards give the author, title, and date of publication. The cards also show a call number, which will help you find the book in the library.

All the cards are alphabetized based on the first word on the top line. If you know exactly what book you want, look for the title card. If you want to find additional books by an author you like, look for the author card. If you want to find books on a certain subject, look for the subject card.

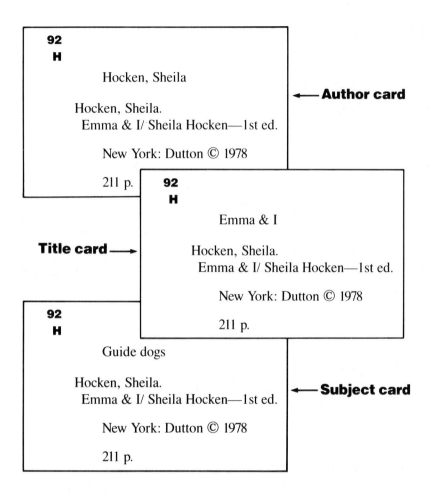

**92
H**

Hocken, Sheila

Hocken, Sheila.
Emma & I/ Sheila Hocken—1st ed.

New York: Dutton © 1978

211 p.

←— **Author card**

Title card —→

**92
H**

Emma & I

Hocken, Sheila.
Emma & I/ Sheila Hocken—1st ed.

New York: Dutton © 1978

211 p.

**92
H**

Guide dogs

Hocken, Sheila.
Emma & I/ Sheila Hocken—1st ed.

New York: Dutton © 1978

211 p.

←— **Subject card**

To find more information about animals trained to help the handicapped, you would look for subject cards. You might have to try a number of subjects before finding the one that includes the books you want. You might, or example, look under these headings: disabled; handicapped—home care; working animals; animals—training of guide dogs.

The catalogue includes some cross-references to aid you in your search. For example, the first card headed "Animals—training of" might say "*See also* Working animals, Working dogs, Guide dogs."

Once you locate the book in the card catalogue, use the call number in the upper left-hand corner of the card to find the book itself.

Readers' Guide

With the exception of guide dogs, the training of animals to help the handicapped is a new field, so you may not find many books about it. You may find more information in magazines. You can use the *Readers' Guide to Periodical Literature* to locate magazine articles that might interest you. The *Readers' Guide* has a large volume for each year and some smaller supplements for recent months. It contains listings of all the articles in most major periodicals, or magazines, published in the United States.

The *Readers' Guide* includes listings by author and subject. Most often, you will be looking for information on a certain subject. You may have to check a number of subject headings. The *Readers' Guide* contains cross-references that make this task easier. Under "disabled," you will find the following:

Disabled *See* Handicapped

In this case, therefore, you would look for your topic under *handicapped.* A heading under *handicapped* has just what you want.

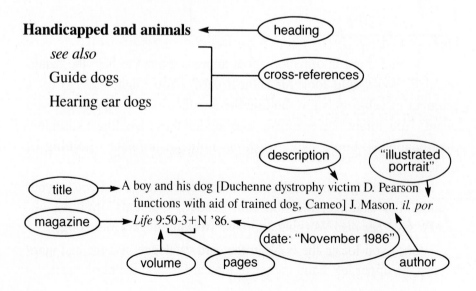

208

Some of the information at the end of the listing may be unclear because of the abbreviations. If so, check the key to abbreviations at the front of the book. The article in the entry above appeared in the November 1986 issue of *Life* magazine, beginning on page 50.

Guidelines for Finding Books and Magazines in the Library

1. Use the card catalogue to find books.

2. Look up the author, title, or subject of the book.

3. Use the call number to find the book on the shelves.

4. Use the *Readers' Guide* to find magazine articles.

5. Look up the author or subject of the article.

6. When you want a book or article on a particular subject, try different likely headings until you find what you need.

Using What You Have Learned

Suppose you were writing a report about wild animals that have learned to live with people. Answer the following questions about finding information in the library.

1. Would you use the card catalogue or the *Readers' Guide* or both? Why?

2. You have heard of a book called *Born Free* about a lion who lives with a family. How would you find the book?

3. What subject headings would you check in order to find other books or articles?

It's more than the fresh spring breeze that draws Grandpa outside after the long, cold, shut-in days of winter; he's going to see an old friend—a mysterious old friend in the garden.

Another April

by Jesse Stuart

"Now, Pap, you won't get cold," Mom said as she put a heavy wool cap over his head.

"Huh, what did ye say?" Grandpa asked, holding his big hand cupped over his ear to catch the sound.

"Wait until I get your gloves," Mom said, hollering real loud in Grandpa's ear. Mom had forgotten about his gloves until he raised his big bare hand above his ear to catch the sound of Mom's voice.

"Don't get 'em," Grandpa said, "I won't ketch cold."

Mom didn't pay any attention to what Grandpa said. She went on to get the gloves anyway. Grandpa turned toward me. He saw that I was looking at him.

"Yer Ma's a-puttin' enough clothes on me to kill a man," Grandpa said, then he laughed a coarse laugh like March wind among the pine tops at his own words. I started laughing but not at Grandpa's words. He thought I was laughing at them and we both laughed together. It pleased Grandpa to think that I had laughed with him over something funny that he had said. But I was laughing at the way he was dressed. He looked like a picture of Santa Claus. But Grandpa's cheeks were not cherry-red like Santa Claus's cheeks. They were covered with white thin beard—and above his eyes were long white eyebrows almost as white as percoon petals and very much longer.

Grandpa was wearing a heavy wool suit that hung loosely about his big body but fitted him tightly 'round the waist where he was as big and as round as a flour barrel. His pant legs were as big 'round his pipestem legs as emptied meal sacks. And his big shoes, with heavy wool socks dropping down over their tops, looked like sled runners. Grandpa wore a heavy wool shirt and over his wool shirt he wore a heavy wool sweater and then his coat over the top of all this. Over his coat he wore a heavy overcoat and about his neck he wore a wool scarf.

The way Mom had dressed Grandpa you'd think there was a heavy snow on the ground but there wasn't. April was here instead and the sun was shining on the green hills where the wild plums and the wild crab apples were in bloom enough to make you think there were big snowdrifts sprinkled over the green hills. When I looked at Grandpa and then looked out the window at the sunshine and the green grass I laughed more. Grandpa laughed with me.

"I'm a-goin' to see my old friend," Grandpa said just as Mom came down the stairs with his gloves.

"Who is he, Grandpa?" I asked, but Grandpa just looked at my mouth working. He didn't know what I was saying. And he hated to ask me the second time.

Mom put the big wool gloves on Grandpa's hands. He stood there just like I had to do years ago, and let Mom put his gloves on. If Mom didn't get his fingers back in the glovefingers exactly right Grandpa quarreled at Mom. And when Mom fixed his fingers exactly right in his gloves the way he wanted them Grandpa was pleased.

"I'll be a-goin' to see 'im," Grandpa said to Mom. "I know he'll still be there."

Mom opened our front door for Grandpa and he stepped out slowly, supporting himself with his big cane in one hand. With the other hand he held to the door facing. Mom let him out of the house just like she used to let me out in the spring. And when Grandpa left the house I wanted to go with him, but Mom wouldn't let me go. I wondered if he would get away from the house—get out of Mom's sight—and pull off his shoes and go barefooted and wade the creeks like I used to do when Mom let me out. Since Mom wouldn't let me go with Grandpa, I watched him as he walked slowly down the path in front of our house. Mom stood there watching Grandpa too. I think she was afraid that he would fall. But Mom was fooled; Grandpa toddled along the path better than my baby brother could.

"He used to be a powerful man," Mom said more to herself than she did to me. "He was a timber cutter. No man could cut more timber than my father; no man in the timber wood could sink an ax deeper into a log than my father. And no man could lift the end of a bigger saw log than Pop could."

"Who is Grandpa goin' to see, Mom?" I asked.

"He's not goin' to see anybody," Mom said.

"I heard 'im say that he was goin' to see an old friend," I told her.

"Oh, he was just a-talkin'," Mom said.

I watched Grandpa stop under the pine tree in our front yard. He set his cane against the pine tree trunk, pulled off his gloves and put them in his pocket. Then Grandpa stooped over slowly, as slowly as the wind bends down a sapling, and picked up a pine cone in his big soft fingers. Grandpa stood fondling the pine cone

in his hand. Then, one by one, he pulled the little chips from the pine cone—tearing it to pieces like he was hunting for something in it—and after he had torn it to pieces he threw the pine-cone stem on the ground. Then he pulled pine needles from a low-hanging pine bough and he felt each pine needle between his fingers. He played with them a long time before he started down the path.

"What's Grandpa doin'?" I asked Mom.

But Mom didn't answer me.

"How long has Grandpa been with us?" I asked Mom.

"Before you's born," she said. "Pap has been with us eleven years. He was eighty when he quit cuttin' timber and farmin'; now he's ninety-one."

I had heard her say that when she was a girl he'd walk out on the snow and ice barefooted and carry wood in the house and put it on the fire. He had shoes but he wouldn't bother to put them on. And I heard her say that he would cut timber on the coldest days without socks on his feet but with his feet stuck down in cold brogan shoes, and he worked stripped above the waist so his arms

would have freedom when he swung his double-bitted ax. I had heard her tell how he'd sweat and how the sweat in his beard would be icicles by the time he got home from work on the cold winter days. Now Mom wouldn't let him get out of the house for she wanted him to live a long time.

As I watched Grandpa go down the path toward the hog pen he stopped to examine every little thing along his path. Once he waved his cane at a butterfly as it zigzagged over his head, its polka-dot wings fanning the blue April air. Grandpa would stand when a puff of wind came along, and hold his face against the wind and let the wind play with his white whiskers. I thought maybe his face was hot under his beard and he was letting the wind cool his face. When he reached the hog pen he called the hogs down to the fence. They came running and grunting to Grandpa just like they were talking to him. I knew that Grandpa couldn't hear them trying to talk to him but he could see their mouths working and knew they were trying to say something. He leaned his cane against the hog pen, reached over the fence, and patted the hogs' heads. Grandpa didn't miss patting one of our seven hogs.

As he toddled up the little path alongside the hog pen he
stopped under a blooming dogwood. He pulled a white blossom
from a bough that swayed over the path above his head, and he
leaned his big bundled body against the dogwood while he tore
each petal from the blossom and examined it carefully. There
wasn't anything his dim blue eyes missed. He stopped under a redbud tree before he reached the garden to break a tiny spray of
redbud blossoms. He took each blossom from the spray and examined it carefully.

"Gee, it's funny to watch Grandpa," I said to Mom, then I
laughed.

"Poor Pap," Mom said. "He's seen a lot of Aprils come and go.
He's seen more Aprils than he will ever see again."

I don't think Grandpa missed a thing on the little circle he
took before he reached the house. He played with a bumblebee
that was bending a wildflower blossom that grew near our corncrib
beside a big bluff. But Grandpa didn't try to catch the bumblebee
in his big bare hand. I wondered if he would and if the bumblebee
would sting him, and if he would holler. Grandpa even pulled a
butterfly cocoon from a blackberry briar that grew beside his path.

215

I saw him try to tear it into shreds but he couldn't. There wasn't any butterfly in it, for I'd seen it before. I wondered if the butterfly with the polka-dot wings, that Grandpa waved his cane at when he first left the house, had come from this cocoon. I laughed when Grandpa couldn't tear the cocoon apart.

"I'll bet I can tear that cocoon apart for Grandpa if you'd let me go help him," I said to Mom.

"You leave your Grandpa alone," Mom said. "Let 'im enjoy April."

Then I knew that this was the first time Mom had let Grandpa out of the house all winter. I knew that Grandpa loved the sunshine and the fresh April air that blew from the redbud and dogwood blossoms. He loved the bumblebees, the hogs, the pine cones, and pine needles. Grandpa didn't miss a thing along his walk. And every day from now on until just before frost Grandpa would take this little walk. He'd stop along and look at everything as he had done summers before. But each year he didn't take as long a walk as he had taken the year before. Now this spring he didn't go down to the lower end of the hog pen as he had done last year. And when I could first remember Grandpa going on his walks he used to go out of sight. He'd go all over the farm. And he'd come to the house and take me on his knee and tell me about all that he had seen. Now Grandpa wasn't getting out of sight. I could see him from the window along all of his walk.

Grandpa didn't come back into the house at the front door. He toddled around back of the house toward the smokehouse and I ran through the living room to the dining room so I could look out the window and watch him.

"Where's Grandpa goin'?" I asked Mom.

"Now never mind," Mom said. "Leave Grandpa alone. Don't go out there and disturb him."

"I won't bother 'im, Mom," I said. "I just want to watch 'im."

"All right," Mom said.

But Mom wanted to be sure that I didn't bother him so she followed me into the dining room. Maybe she wanted to see what Grandpa was going to do. She stood by the window and we watched Grandpa as he walked down beside our smokehouse where a tall sassafras tree's thin leaves fluttered in the blue April wind. Above the smokehouse and the tall sassafras was a blue April sky—so high you couldn't see the sky-roof. It was just blue space and little white clouds floated upon this blue.

When Grandpa reached the smokehouse he leaned his cane against the sassafras tree. He let himself down slowly to his knees as he looked carefully at the ground. Grandpa was looking at something and I wondered what it was. I just didn't think or I would have known.

"There you are, my good old friend," Grandpa said.

"Who is his friend, Mom?" I asked.

Mom didn't say anything. Then I saw.

"He's playin' with that old terrapin, Mom," I said.

"I know he is," Mom said.

"The terrapin doesn't mind if Grandpa strokes his head with his hand," I said.

"I know it," Mom said.

"But the old terrapin won't let me do it," I said. "Why does he let Grandpa?"

"The terrapin knows your Grandpa."

"He ought to know me," I said, "but when I try to stroke his head with my hand, he closes up in his shell."

Mom didn't say anything. She stood by the window watching Grandpa and listening to Grandpa talk to the terrapin.

"My old friend, how do you like the sunshine?" Grandpa asked the terrapin.

The terrapin turned his fleshless face to one side like a hen does when she looks at you in the sunlight. He was trying to talk to Grandpa; maybe the terrapin could understand what Grandpa was saying.

"Old fellow, it's been a hard winter," Grandpa said. "How have you fared under the smokehouse floor?"

"Does the terrapin know what Grandpa is sayin'?" I asked Mom.

"I don't know," she said.

"I'm awfully glad to see you, old fellow," Grandpa said.

He didn't offer to bite Grandpa's big soft hand as he stroked his head.

"Looks like the terrapin would bite Grandpa," I said.

"That terrapin has spent the winters under that smokehouse for fifteen years," Mom said. "Pap has been acquainted with him for eleven years. He's been talkin' to that terrapin every spring."

"How does Grandpa know the terrapin is old?" I asked Mom.

"It's got 1847 cut on its shell," Mom said. "It was wrong to do that, but we know he's ninety-five years old. He's older than that. We don't know how old he was when that date was cut on his back."

"Who cut 1847 on his back, Mom?"

"I don't know, child," she said, "but I'd say whoever cut that date on his back has long been under the ground."

Then I wondered how a terrapin could get that old and what kind of a looking person he was who cut the date on the terrapin's back. I wondered where it happened—if it happened near where our house stood. I wondered who lived here on this land then, what kind of a house they lived in, and if they had a sassafras with tiny thin April leaves on its top growing in their yard, and if the person that cut the date on the terrapin's back was buried at Plum Grove, if he had farmed these hills where we lived today and cut timber like Grandpa had—and if he had seen the Aprils pass like Grandpa had seen them and if he enjoyed them like Grandpa was enjoying this April. I wondered if he had looked at the dogwood blossoms, the redbud blossoms, and talked to this same terrapin.

"Are you well, old fellow?" Grandpa asked the terrapin.

The terrapin just looked at Grandpa.

"I'm well as common for a man of my age," Grandpa said.

"Did the terrapin ask Grandpa if he was well?" I asked Mom.

"I don't know," Mom said. "I can't talk to a terrapin."

"But Grandpa can."

"Yes."

"Wait until tomatoes get ripe and we'll go to the garden together," Grandpa said.

"Does the terrapin eat tomatoes?" I asked Mom.

"Yes, that terrapin has been eatin' tomatoes from our garden for fifteen years," Mom said. "When Mick was tossin' the terrapins out of the tomato patch, he picked up this one and found the date cut on his back. He put him back in the patch and told him to help himself. He lives from our garden every year. We don't bother him and don't allow anybody else to bother him. He spends his winters under our smokehouse floor buried in the dry ground."

"Gee, Grandpa looks like the terrapin," I said.

Mom didn't say anything; tears came to her eyes. She wiped them from her eyes with the corner of her apron.

"I'll be back to see you," Grandpa said. "I'm a-gettin' a little chilly; I'll be gettin' back to the house."

The terrapin twisted his wrinkled neck without moving his big body, poking his head deeper into the April wind as Grandpa pulled his bundled body up by holding to the sassafras tree trunk.

"Good-by, old friend!"

The terrapin poked his head deeper into the wind, holding one eye on Grandpa, for I could see his eye shining in the sinking sunlight.

Grandpa got his cane that was leaned against the sassafras tree trunk and hobbled slowly toward the house. The terrapin looked at him with first one eye and then the other.

Reader's Response

What did you find special about Grandpa's walk?

Another April

Checking Your Comprehension

1. Why did the narrator laugh at the way Grandpa was dressed?
2. Why do you think Grandpa hated to ask the narrator to repeat what he had said to him?
3. What reason do you think the mother had for forbidding the boy to follow his grandfather? How did you reach this conclusion?
4. Describe how Grandpa greeted the spring.
5. Why do you think the terrapin allowed Grandpa to stroke him?
6. Explain how the terrapin's life paralleled, or was similar to, Grandpa's.
7. What do you think would happen if Grandpa did not find the terrapin in the spring?

Writing to Learn

THINK AND COMPARE Grandpa today is very different from the man he used to be. Note three of these differences from the story. Copy and complete the chart below.

Category	Grandpa Today	Grandpa When Young
1. Way of moving	*slow, tottering, feeble*	*fast, active, powerful*
2. Style of clothing		
3. Length of walks		

WRITE Make a similar chart about yourself. Compare the "you" of today with the "you" of years ago, perhaps in the first grade. Write a short autobiographical sketch, using details to show the differences between the younger and the older you.

The Peace of Wild Things

When despair for the world grows in me
and I wake in the night at the least sound
in fear of what my life and my children's lives may be,
I go and lie down where the wood drake
rests in his beauty on the water, and the great heron feeds.
I come into the peace of wild things
who do not tax their lives with forethought
of grief. I come into the presence of still water.
And I feel above me the day-blind stars
waiting with their light. For a time
I rest in the grace of the world, and am free.

Wendell Berry

A Blessing

Just off the highway to Rochester, Minnesota,
Twilight bounds softly forth on the grass.
And the eyes of those two Indian ponies
Darken with kindness.
They have come gladly out of the willows
To welcome my friend and me.
We step over the barbed wire into the pasture
Where they have been grazing all day, alone.
They ripple tensely, they can hardly contain their happiness
That we have come.
They bow shyly as wet swans. They love each other.
There is no loneliness like theirs.
At home once more,
They begin munching the young tufts of spring in the darkness.
I would like to hold the slenderer one in my arms.
For she has walked over to me
And nuzzled my left hand.
She is black and white,
Her mane falls wild on her forehead,
And the light breeze moves me to caress her long ear
That is delicate as the skin over a girl's wrist.
Suddenly I realize
That if I stepped out of my body I would break
Into blossom.

James Wright

If you were lost or injured in the woods, you could call out or build a signal fire or try some other way of attracting the attention of rescuers. A wolf, however, calls for help in other ways.

THE WOUNDED WOLF

by Jean Craighead George

A wounded wolf climbs Toklat Ridge, a massive spine of rock and ice. As he limps, dawn strikes the ridge and lights it up with sparks and stars. Roko, the wounded wolf, blinks in the ice fire, then stops to rest and watch his pack run the thawing Arctic valley.

They plunge and turn. They fight the mighty caribou that struck young Roko with his hoof and wounded him. He jumped between the beast and Kiglo, leader of the Toklat pack. Young Roko spun and fell. Hooves, paws, and teeth roared over him. And then his pack and the beast were gone.

Gravely injured, Roko pulls himself toward the shelter rock. Weakness overcomes him. He stops. He and his pack are thin and hungry. This is the season of starvation. The winter's harvest has been taken. The produce of spring has not begun.

Young Roko glances down the valley. He droops his head and stiffens his tail to signal to his pack that he is badly hurt. Winds wail. A frigid blast picks up the long shawls of snow and drapes them between young Roko and his pack. And so his message is not read.

225

A raven scouting Toklat Ridge sees Roko's signal. "Kong, kong, kong," he bells—death is coming to the ridge; there will be flesh and bone for all. His voice rolls out across the valley. It penetrates the rocky cracks where the Toklat ravens rest. One by one they hear and spread their wings. They beat their way to Toklat Ridge. They alight upon the snow and walk behind the wounded wolf.

"Kong," they toll with keen excitement, for the raven clan is hungry, too. "Kong, kong"—there will be flesh and bone for all.

Roko snarls and hurries toward the shelter rock. A cloud of snow envelops him. He limps in blinding whiteness now.

A ghostly presence flits around. "Hahahahahahaha," the white fox states—death is coming to the Ridge. Roko smells the fox tagging at his heels.

The cloud whirls off. Two golden eyes look up at Roko. The snowy owl has heard the ravens and joined the deathwatch.

Roko limps along. The ravens walk. The white fox leaps. The snowy owl flies and hops along the rim of Toklat Ridge.

Roko stops. Below the ledge out on the flats the musk-ox herd is circling. They form a ring and all face out, a fort of heads and horns and fur that sweeps down to their hooves. Their circle means to Roko that an enemy is present. He squints and smells the wind. It carries scents of thawing ice, broken grass—and earth. The grizzly bear is up! He has awakened from his winter's sleep. A craving need for flesh will drive him.

Roko sees the shelter rock. He strains to reach it. He stumbles. The ravens move in closer. The white fox boldly walks beside him. "Hahaha," he yaps. The snowy owl flies ahead, alights, and waits.

The grizzly hears the eager fox and rises on his flat hind feet. He twists his powerful neck and head. His great paws dangle at his chest. He sees the animal procession and hears the ravens' knell of death. Dropping to all fours, he joins the march up Toklat Ridge.

Roko stops; his breath comes hard. A raven alights upon his back and picks the open wound. Roko snaps. The raven flies and circles back. The white fox nips at Roko's toes. The snowy owl inches closer. The grizzly bear, still dulled by sleep, stumbles onto Toklat Ridge.

Only yards from the shelter rock, Roko falls.

Instantly the ravens mob him. They scream and peck and stab at his eyes. The white fox leaps upon his wound. The snowy owl sits and waits.

Young Roko struggles to his feet. He bites the ravens. Snaps at the fox. And lunges at the stoic owl. He turns and warns the

grizzly bear. Then he bursts into a run and falls against the shelter rock. The wounded wolf wedges down between the rock and barren ground. Now protected on three sides, he turns and faces all his foes.

The ravens step a few feet closer. The fox slides toward him on his belly. The snowy owl blinks and waits, and on the ridge rim roars the hungry grizzly bear.

Roko growls.

The sun comes up. Far across the Toklat Valley, Roko hears his pack's "hunt's end" song. The music wails and sobs, wilder than the bleating wind. The hunt song ends. Next comes the roll call. Each member of the Toklat pack barks to say that he is home and well.

"Kiglo here," Roko hears his leader bark. There is a pause. It is young Roko's turn. He cannot lift his head to answer. The pack is silent. The leader starts the count once more. "Kiglo here." —A pause. Roko cannot answer.

The wounded wolf whimpers softly. A mindful raven hears. "Kong, kong, kong," he tolls—this is the end. His booming sounds across the valley. The wolf pack hears the raven's message that something is dying. They know it is Roko, who has not answered roll call.

The hours pass. The wind slams snow on Toklat Ridge. Massive clouds blot out the sun. In their gloom Roko sees the deathwatch move in closer. Suddenly he hears the musk-oxen thundering into their circle. The ice cracks as the grizzly leaves. The ravens burst into the air. The white fox runs. The snowy owl flaps to the top of the shelter rock. And Kiglo rounds the knoll.

In his mouth he carries meat. He drops it close to Roko's head and wags his tail excitedly. Roko licks Kiglo's chin to honor him. Then Kiglo puts his mouth around Roko's nose. This gesture says "I am your leader." And by doing this to Roko, he binds him and all the wolves together.

The wounded wolf wags his tail. Kiglo trots away.

Already Roko's wound feels better. He gulps the food and feels his strength return. He shatters bone, flesh and gristle and shakes the scraps out on the snow. The hungry ravens swoop upon them. The white fox snatches up a bone. The snowy owl gulps down flesh and fur. And Roko wags his tail and watches.

For days Kiglo brings young Roko food. He gnashes, gorges, and shatters bits upon the snow.

A purple sandpiper winging north sees ravens, owl, and fox. And he drops in upon the feast. The long-tailed jaeger gull flies down and joins the crowd on Toklat Ridge. Roko wags his tail.

One dawn he moves his wounded leg. He stretches it and pulls himself into the sunlight. He walks—he romps. He runs in circles. He leaps and plays with chunks of ice. Suddenly he stops. The "hunt's end" song rings out. Next comes the roll call.

"Kiglo here."

"Roko here," he barks out strongly.

The pack is silent.

"Kiglo here," the leader repeats.

"Roko here."

Across the distance comes the sound of whoops and yipes and barks and howls. They fill the dawn with celebration. And Roko prances down the Ridge.

KEEPING
IN TOUCH

by Sylvia A. Johnson and Alice Aamodt

The wolves' ability to communicate with each other saved Roko's life in "The Wounded Wolf." By studying how wolves communicate, scientists have begun to learn not only their language, but also rules that keep the pack safe and strong.

When wolf pups are born into a pack, one of the most important things they must learn is the "language" of the group, the method by which pack members keep in touch with each other, sharing information and communicating their feelings. Scientists have discovered that wolves have a very complicated system of communication, quite different from the language of humans but used in a similar way to convey meaning.

An efficient system of communication is vital to all animals that live in groups. In order for the members of a pack, a family, or a nation to cooperate and to live peacefully together, there must be a way for individuals to let others know what they are planning and feeling. Human societies use words, both spoken and written, as a means of communication among their members. A wolf pack communicates with sounds, but it also employs smells, movements, and body positions to convey information of various kinds.

Because rank and hierarchy are so important to the orderly functioning of a wolf pack, much of the communication among pack members is related to this aspect of their lives. Using movements and body positions, the leaders of the pack continually remind the other wolves of their dominant roles in the group. In return, the subordinate wolves communicate their respect and affection for—and sometimes their fear of—the pack leaders.

One of the clearest symbols of a wolf's rank in a pack is the position of its tail. Unlike the tails of many breeds of dogs, a wolf's long, bushy tail normally hangs down rather than curling up over its back. The alpha wolves in a pack, however, usually hold their tails high in the air instead of letting them droop.

In any pack, the wolf carrying its tail high like a hairy banner will almost always be the alpha male. The alpha female also holds her

tail high, although usually not as high as that of her mate. Wolves occupying positions below the pack leaders keep their tails correspondingly low, especially in any confrontation with the alpha pair. The lowest-ranking members of the pack tuck their tails between their legs to express their inferiority to the wolves above them in the hierarchy.

The positions of other body parts are also used as a means of communicating status in the pack. An alpha wolf usually keeps its ears standing up, while low-ranking pack members lay their ears back. They also keep their fur flat, in contrast to the fluffed-out fur of the pack leaders.

There are some occasions in the life of the pack that call for more specific expressions of the relationships among the pack members. When a low-ranking wolf approaches one of the pack leaders, it keeps its body low to the ground, with its fur and ears flattened. From this position, it reaches up with its muzzle and gently licks or nips the muzzle of the alpha wolf. Sometimes all the pack members gather around the alpha male and greet him in this manner, often when he returns to the pack after being away for a while.

Scientists call this behavior *active submission* and see it as a method whereby the pack members express friendly feelings toward the leaders and respect for their authority. The gesture of licking and nipping a leader's muzzle is similar to the food-begging behavior of wolf pups and may be related to it. By using this gesture, the subordinate wolves seem to be saying to an alpha wolf: We depend on you and look up to you in the same way that pups depend on and look up to the adults that give them food and protection.

Sometimes the interaction between the dominant wolves and the rest of the pack is not so friendly. If an alpha feels that a pack member is resisting its authority, it may take strong measures to bring the rebellious wolf back in line. Often a stern and unwavering stare is enough to convince the rebel that it should submit itself to the pack leader. Like dogs and many other animals, wolves avoid looking each other directly in the eye unless they are trying to exert their authority.

An even stronger message of authority is given when a dominant wolf growls and bares its teeth at an inferior or crouches as if to spring on the offender. When a subordinate wolf is threatened in this way, it usually makes a gesture of *passive submission* by lying on the ground and exposing its side or belly to the threatener. This movement, which is also performed by pups, seems to convey a message of helplessness and dependence—"I'm harmless, please don't hurt me." Satisfied by this admission of inferiority, the dominant wolf accepts the rebel's "apology," and peace is restored in the pack.

The main purpose of all the communications expressing rank and relationships within the pack is to keep peace. Pack members rarely fight with each other because they have so many other ways of settling their differences and establishing their proper positions in the group. Physical conflict, which would be destructive to the well-being of the pack, is avoided by the use of a language of gestures and symbolic actions.

Of course, not all the communications that take place in a pack have to do with such serious subjects. Frequently, the message that one pack member wants to convey to another is, "Let's play!"

Adult wolves, like pups, enjoy chasing, wrestling, and tumbling on the ground. When a wolf is looking for a playmate, it may approach another wolf, bow down low with its front legs flat on the ground, and wag its tail vigorously. If the invitation is not accepted, it will be repeated and sometimes alternated with leaping about in a zig-zag fashion. (Many dogs make almost exactly the same movements when they are in a playful mood.) If the other wolf is willing to play, the two will engage in mock fights or take turns chasing each other until both are worn out and ready to rest.

Invitations to play and messages about social status in the pack are usually conveyed by means of movements and postures, but wolves also use sounds to communicate with each other. The animals are capable of making several kinds of sounds, including the threatening growl or snarl and the whimper used in communications between pups and adults. The most famous wolf sound is, of course, the howl, and it is a very important part of wolf language.

When people think about howling, they usually imagine a mournful, lonely sound made by a wolf sitting all alone on a hilltop in the moonlight. Like most human images of wolves, however, this one is not very accurate. Wolves howl at any time, not just at night, and they often howl together, not alone.

Group or chorus howling is another means by which the members of a wolf pack reaffirm their ties with each other and their closeness as a group. One wolf—often the alpha male—will point its nose at the sky, open its mouth, and start to howl. Immediately the other members of the pack rush to stand beside him, shoulder to shoulder, and join their voices to his. The whole group seems to be excited and happy, tails wagging, and bodies wiggling. Each wolf howls on its own note so that a grand chorus of slightly different sounds is produced.

Chorus howling often takes place before a wolf pack goes out to hunt. This ceremony of togetherness may encourage the pack members to cooperate with each other in the difficult job of finding and bringing down prey. At the end of a successful hunt, the pack may also celebrate with a group howl. While wolves are on the track of prey, they are usually silent.

There are occasions when a wolf will howl by itself. This may happen when an animal is separated from the pack and is trying to locate its companions. Pack members seem to recognize each other's voices and will keep responding to the howl of their wandering relatives until the group is reunited.

Because howling is a sound that carries over a considerable distance, it is very useful in communications among separated members of a pack. Howling is also used when members of different packs have to get in touch with each other to relay information about their location and their intentions.

Wolves usually have other wolves as neighbors, and the way in which neighboring packs live side by side, competing for prey and territory, is another fascinating aspect of the wolf story.

♦ LIBRARY LINK ♦

To find out more about wolves, look for the book from which this excerpt was taken, Wolf Pack: Tracking Wolves in the Wild, *by Sylvia A. Johnson and Alice Aamodt.*

Reader's Response

Did these selections dispel any fears that you may have had about wolves? Why or why not?

THE WOUNDED WOLF

KEEPING IN TOUCH

Checking Your Comprehension

1. Describe the dangers that Roko faced in the story "The Wounded Wolf."
2. How do you think Kiglo was able to find Roko?
3. In your opinion, what would have happened if Kiglo had not brought food to Roko?
4. In "Keeping in Touch," the authors describe various ways wolves can communicate. What are they?
5. Why is the wolves' language of gestures preferable to fighting?
6. Why do you think people study the behavior of wolves?
7. Do you think Jean Craighead George's purpose in writing "The Wounded Wolf" differed from Johnson and Aamondt's purpose in writing "Keeping in Touch"? What examples from the selections led you to your answer?

Writing to Learn

THINK AND GENERALIZE What have you learned about how animals communicate by reading "The Wounded Wolf" and "Keeping in Touch"? Make a before-and-after chart like the one below. Make notes about what you knew before and after you read these selections.

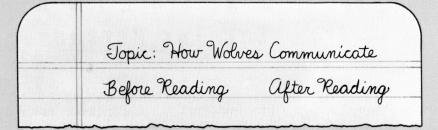

Topic: How Wolves Communicate

| Before Reading | After Reading |

WRITE Review your before-and-after chart. Then write a paragraph summarizing what you have learned from reading "The Wounded Wolf" and "Keeping in Touch" that you didn't know before.

It's not easy to find a good housekeeper. Some people just can't seem to understand what it is that you want . . . especially if you're a very particular Gentleman Cat.

Housekeeper Wanted For

Gentleman Cat

by M·a·y S·a·r·t·o·n
·from The Fur Person·

The Fur Person is a very independent tomcat who has been on his own for two years. Now he has decided it is time to find a suitable housekeeper and settle down. Will he be able to find a happy home?

The Fur Person raised his head and took in a terrible series of smells, the smell of a small stuffy apartment, of overheated radiators, of cheap perfume, of talcum powder, of yesterday's bacon; he stood there,

240

his tail standing out straight behind him in amazement, his nose trembling slightly in dismay. Then he cast a quick glance behind him, but the door was shut tight. No escape. The lady meanwhile had not stopped talking since she set him down. He could hear her while she ran water in the kitchen and rattled the dishes, telling him over and over how much she loved kitties, how much she loved him, and what he would have for breakfast. The Fur Person could not pay attention right away to this. He had first to explore the apartment and any possible avenues of escape. He had first to sniff at every inch of the dirty pink carpet stretched from wall to wall, with moldy crumbs, as he soon discovered, concealed along the edges. He had never been in a human house with so many objects in it, and he was only about a third of the way through, had in fact just reached a stand with three potted ferns on it, had stood up on his hind legs to feel the quality of a green velvet armchair (for claw-sharpening purposes), had taken a quick look at the bed, almost entirely covered with small satin pillows and with, of all things, an imitation cat sitting on it, when the lady suddenly pounced on him from the back and hauled him ignominiously into the kitchen, setting him down in front of a plate of scrambled eggs and bacon. Now, no Gentleman Cat likes to be plunked down in front of his food. The law is that he shall approach it slowly from a distance, without haste, however hungry he

may be, that he shall smell it from afar and decide at least three feet away what his verdict is going to be: Good, Fair, Passable, or Unworthy.

If the verdict is Good, he will approach it very slowly, settle himself down in a crouching position and curl his tail around him before he takes a mouthful. If it is Fair, he will crouch, but leave his tail behind him, stretched out along the floor. If it is merely Passable, he will eat standing up, and if it is Unworthy he will perform the rite of pretending to scratch earth over it and bury it.

The Fur Person backed away, ruffled and indignant, and had to put his clothes in order before he would even look at the food. Then he very carefully extracted the bacon, bit by bit, and ate it with considerable relish. Scrambled eggs were considered "Unworthy" and were left on the plate.

When the lady saw him performing the usual rite demanded by Unworthy food, she clapped her hands with delight and said he was a terribly clever cat (little she knew!), she had never seen anything so sweet in her life, and he should have a can of crabmeat for his lunch.

Then she picked him up and tried to fold him together onto her lap. Foolish woman! Though a little crumbled bacon is not a heavy meal for a Gentleman Cat who has spent the night out, it is enough of a meal to require at least fifteen minutes of solitary meditation after it. The Fur Person jumped down at once and went as far away from her as he could get, as her smell of cheap narcissus or rose (he was not quite sure which) made him feel rather ill. The farthest away he could get was under the bed; there he stayed for some time, licking his chops, for the slightest sensation of oiliness or fat around his whiskers is something a Gentleman Cat cannot endure. Then he sat, crouching, but not in any way "settled," and thought things over. He did not fancy the lady, but she had mentioned crabmeat for lunch. Also there was at present no way of escape that he could see. By now, it should be clear that the Fur Person was of a philosophical nature, capable of considerable reflection. He had waited six months before making up his mind to leave his last home and two years before deciding to settle down, and after all, he had only been here for half an hour. Sometimes first impressions could be misleading. Also he was very susceptible to flattery, and the lady's admiration was unstinted. Although he was completely concealed from her under the bed, she was still talking about him and to him. Things could be worse.

The trouble was, as he soon found out, that as soon as he came into reach, the lady could not resist hugging and kissing him with utter disregard for the dignity of his person. There are times when a Gentleman Cat likes very much to be scratched gently under his chin, and if this is done with *savoir-faire*[1] he may afterwards enjoy a short siesta on a lap and some very refined stroking, but he does not like to be held upside down like a human baby and he does not like to be cooed over, and to be pressed to a body smelling of narcissus or rose. The Fur Person struggled furiously against the ardent ministrations of the lady and took refuge behind the garbage pail in the kitchen when he could. It was crystal clear that he was in jail, and, even at the risk of not having crabmeat for lunch, he must escape. His eyes behind the garbage pail had become slits; he did not tuck his paws in but sat upright, thinking very fast. While he was thinking he nibbled one back foot—he had observed before that there was nothing like thinking to make one itch all over—then he had to bite a place rather difficult to reach on his back, and then his front paw, and soon he was quite absorbed in licking himself all over. It is best to be clean before attempting to escape, and—this thought occurred to him suddenly—it is also best to have sharp claws. From behind the garbage pail he could see the green velvet armchair, and as soon as the lady disappeared for a moment into the bedroom, he emerged from his hiding place and stretched, then walked sedately to the chair, sat up and began to sharpen his claws on the thick plush, a very satisfactory claw-sharpening place indeed.

"Oh," screamed the lady, and swooped down and picked him up, "you naughty cat. Stop it at once!" She even shook him quite violently. This, on top of all he had

[1] savoir-faire (sa′ vwar-fār′): French term indicating the ability to act properly under any conditions

suffered that morning, was suddenly more than the Fur Person could endure. He turned and bit her arm, not very hard, but just enough so she dropped him unceremoniously and gave a penetrating yell.

"You're not a nice cat at all," she said, and she began to whimper. "You don't like me," she whimpered, "do you?"

But this last remark was addressed to his back. He was sitting in front of the door. It is a known fact that if one sits long enough in front of a door, doing the proper yoga exercises, the door will open. It is not necessary to indulge in childish noises. Commandment Four: "A Gentleman Cat does not mew except in extremity. He makes his wishes known and then waits." So he sat with his back to the lady and wished with the whole force of his fur person; his whiskers even trembled slightly with the degree of concentration. Meanwhile the lady grumbled and mumbled to herself and said, "Nobody loves me." But the Fur Person's whiskers only trembled a little more violently, so huge had become his wish to get away. He might even bring himself to eat day-old hamburger if only he could get away from this infernal apartment. He noticed also that it was much too hot and his skin was prickling all over, but he schooled himself not to move, not to lick, not to nibble. He became a single ever-more-powerful WISH TO GET OUT.

"Very well," said the lady, blowing her nose. He gave her one last cold look out of his green eyes, and then she opened the door. She even followed him downstairs, his tail held perfectly straight like a flag to show his thanks, and opened the front door. The Fur Person bounded out and ran all the way up the street, sniffing the fresh air with intense pleasure. He ran halfway up an elm tree and down again before you could say "Gentleman Cat," and then he sauntered down the street, his tail at half-mast, and his heart at peace.

On his roves and rambles, on his rounds and travels, he had never found himself exactly where he now found himself, on the border of a dangerous street—very dangerous, he realized after a short exposure to the roar of cars, the squeaking of brakes, the lurching, weaving, rumbling, interspersed with loud bangs and horns of a really incredible amount of traffic. It was quite bewildering, and the Fur Person looked about for a place where he could withdraw and sit awhile. He was rather tired. It was time, he considered, for a short snooze, after which the question of Lunch might be approached in the proper frame of mind. And there, providentially indeed, he noticed that he was standing in front of a house bounded on one side by a porch with a very suitable railing running along it. He took the porch in one leap, sat for a second measuring the distance to the square platform on top of the railing post, then swung up to it rather casually, and there he was, safe and free as you please, in a little patch of sunlight which seemed to have been laid down there just for him. He tucked in his paws and closed his eyes. The sun was delicious on his back, so much so that he began to sing very softly, accompanying himself this time with one of his lighter purrs, just a tremolo to keep things going.

And there he sat for maybe an hour, or maybe even two, enjoying the peace and quiet, and restoring himself after the rather helter-skelter life he had been leading for two days, since his metamorphosis into a Gentlemen Cat in search of a housekeeper. He was so deep down in the peace and the quiet that when a window went up right beside him on the porch, he did not jump into the air as he might have done had it not been such a very fine May morning or had he been a little less tired. As it was, he merely opened his eyes very wide and looked.

"Come here," a voice said inside the house, "there's a cat on the porch."

The Fur Person waited politely, for he had rather enjoyed the timbre of the voice, quite low and sweet, and he was always prepared to be admired. Pretty soon two faces appeared in the window and looked at him, and he looked back.

"Well," said another voice, "perhaps he would like some lunch."

The Fur Person woke right up then, rose, and stretched on the tips of his toes, his tail making a wide arc to keep his balance.

"He is rather thin," said the first voice. "I wonder where he belongs. We've never seen him before, have we?"

"And what are we having for lunch?" said the second voice.

"There's that haddock left over—I could cream it." The Fur Person pivoted on the fence post and stamped three times with his back feet, to show how dearly he loved the sound of haddock.

"What is he doing now?" said the first voice and chuckled.

"Saying he likes haddock, I expect."

Then, quite unexpectedly, the window was closed. Dear me, he thought, won't I do? For the first time, he began to be really anxious about his appearance. Was the tip of his tail as white as it could be? How about his shirt front? Dear me, he thought, won't I do? And his heart began to beat rather fast, for he was, after all, tired and empty and in a highly emotional state. This made him unusually impulsive. He jumped down to the porch and then to the ground below and trotted round to the back door, for as he expected, there was a garden at the back, with a pear tree at the end of it, and excellent posts for claw-sharpening in a small laundry yard. He could not resist casting a glance at the flower beds, nicely dug up and raked, in just the right condition for making holes, and in fact the thought of a neat little hole was quite irresistible, so he dug one there and then.

When he had finished, he saw that the crocuses were teeming with bees. His whiskers trembled. He crouched down in an ecstasy of impatience and coiled himself tight as a spring, lashed his tail, and before he knew it himself was in the air and down like lightning on an unsuspecting crocus. The bee escaped, though the crocus did not. Well, thought the Fur Person, a little madness in the spring is all very well, but I must remember that this is serious business and I must get down to it. So he sat and looked the house over. It was already evident that there were innumerable entrances and exits like the window opening to the porch, that there were places of safety in case he was locked out, and that (extraordinary bit of luck) he had found not one woman with a garden and a house but *two*. Still, his hopes had been dashed rather often in the last twenty-four hours and he reminded himself this time to be circumspect and hummed a bit of the tune about being a free cat, just to give himself courage.

Then he walked very slowly, stopping to stretch out one back leg and lick it, for he remembered the Fifth Commandment: "Never hurry towards an objective, never look as if you had only one thing in mind, it is not polite." Just as he was nibbling the muscle in his back foot with considerable pleasure, for he was always discovering delightful things about himself, he heard the back door open. Cagey, now, he told himself. So he went on nibbling and even spread his toes and licked his foot quite thoroughly, and all this time, a very sweet voice was saying:

"Are you hungry? Come, kitty . . ."

And so at last he came, his tail tentatively raised in a question mark; he came slowly, picking up his paws with care, and gazing all the while in a quite romantic way (for he couldn't help it) at the saucer held in the woman's hand. At the foot of the back stairs he sat down and waited the necessary interval.

"Well, come on," said the voice, a slightly impatient one, with a little roughness to it, a great relief after the syrupy lady in the hot apartment from which he had escaped.

At this the Fur Person bounded up the stairs, and at the very instant he entered the kitchen, the purrs began to swell inside him and he wound himself round and round two pairs of legs (for he must be impartial), his nose in the air, his tail straight up like a flag, on tiptoe, and roaring with thanks.

"He's awfully thin," said the first voice.

"And not very beautiful, I must say," said the second voice.

But the Fur Person fortunately was not listening. He was delicately and with great deliberation sniffing the plate of haddock; he was settling down; he was even winding his tail around him, because here at last was a meal worthy of a Gentleman Cat.

The most remarkable thing about the two kind ladies was that they left him to eat in peace and did not say one word. They had the tact to withdraw into the next room and to talk about other things, and leave him entirely to himself. It seemed to him that he had been looked up and

down, remarked upon, and hugged and squeezed far too much in the last days, and now he was terribly grateful for the chance to savor this delicious meal with no exclaiming this or that, and without the slightest interruption. When he had finished every single scrap and then licked

over the plate several times (for if a meal is Worthy, the Sixth Commandment says, "The plate must be left clean, so clean that a person might think it had been washed") the Fur Person sat up and licked his chops. He licked them perhaps twenty or twenty-five times, maybe even fifty times, his raspberry-colored tongue devoting itself to each whisker, until his face was quite clean. Then he began on his front paws and rubbed his face gently with a nice wet piece of fur, and rubbed right over his ears, and all this took a considerable time. While he was doing it he could hear a steady gentle murmur of conversation in the next room and pretty soon he stopped with one paw in the air, shook it once, shook his head the way a person does whose hair has just been washed in the bowl, and then took a discreet ramble.

"Just make yourself at home," said the voice he liked best. "Just look around."

His tail went straight up so they would understand that he was out for a rove and did not intend, at the moment, to catch a mouse, that in fact he was looking around, and not committing himself one way or another. The house, he discovered, was quite large enough, quite nice and dark, with a long hall for playing and at least three sleeping places. He preferred a bed, but there was a large comfortable armchair that would do in a pinch. Still, he reminded himself, one must not be hasty. Just then he walked into a rather small room lined with books and with (this was really splendid) a huge flat desk in it. There are times in a Gentleman Cat's life when what he likes best is to stretch out full length (and the Fur Person's length was considerable) on a clean hard place. The floor is apt to be dirty and to smell of old crumbs, but a desk, preferably with papers strewn across

it, is quite the thing. The Fur Person felt a light elegant obligato[2] of purrs rising in his throat.

Neither of the women had, until now, touched him. And this, he felt, was a sign of understanding. They had given him a superior lunch and allowed him to rove and ramble in peace. Now he suddenly felt quite curious to discover what they were like. It is amazing how much a cat learns about life by the way he is stroked. His heart was beating rather fast as he approached the table. One of the two women was still eating her lunch, the brusque one; he did not like to disturb her, so he made a beeline toward the other, gazing out of wide-open eyes, preceded by his purrs.

"Well, old thing, do you want a lap?" the gentle voice inquired very politely. She did not reach down and gather him up. She leaned forward and ran one finger down his head and along his spine. Then she scratched him between the ears in a most delightful way. The purrs began to sound like bass drums very lightly drummed, and the Fur Person felt himself swell with pleasure. It was incredibly enjoyable, after all he had been through, to be handled with such *savoir-faire*, and before he knew it himself he had jumped up on this welcoming lap and begun to knead. The Fur Person, after all, had lost his mother when he was such a small kitten that his ears were still buttoned down and his eyes quite blue, but when he jumped up onto

[2]obligato (ob lə gä′tō): an accompanying part in music

this lady's lap, he seemed dimly to remember kneading his mother like this, with tiny starfish paws that went in and out, in and out.

"I wish he'd settle," the gentle voice said, "his claws are rather sharp."

But the Fur Person did not hear this for he was in a trance of home-coming and while he kneaded he composed a song, and while he composed it, it seemed as if every hair on his body tingled and was burnished, so happy was he at last.

"He actually looks fatter," the brusque voice said, "he must have been awfully hungry."

The Fur Person closed his eyes and sang his song and it went like this:

Thank you, thank you,
You and no other
Dear gentle voice,
Dear human mother,
For your delicate air,
For your savoir-faire
For your kind soft touch
Thank you very much.

He was so terribly sleepy that the last line became inextricably confused in a purr and in his suddenly making himself into a round circle of peace, all kneading spent, and one paw over his nose.

There was an indefinite interval of silence; but it must not be forgotten that the Fur Person had led a hectic and disillusioning life, and while he slept his nose twitched and his paws twitched and he imagined that he was caught and being smothered, and before he even quite woke up or had his eyes open he had leapt off the kind lap, in a great state of nerves.

It is all very well, he told himself severely, but this time you have to be careful. Remember the lady and her suffocating apartment. It was not easy to do, but without giving the women a parting look, he walked in great dignity down the long dark hall to the front door and sat down before it, wishing it to open. Pretty soon he heard footsteps, but he did not turn his head. I must have time to think this over,

he was telling himself. Never be hasty when choosing a housekeeper. The door opened and he was outside. Never be hasty, he was telling himself, as he bounded down the steps and into the sweet May afternoon. But at the same time, quite without intending it, he found that he had composed a short poem, and as he sharpened his claws on the elm by the door and as he ran up it, just to show what a fine Gentleman Cat he was, he hummed it over. It was very short and sweet:

East and West
Home is Best.

And though he spent several days coming and going, it was very queer how, wherever he went, he always found himself somehow coming back to the two women, just to be sure they were still there, and also, it must be confessed, to find out what they were having for supper. And on the fourth day it rained and that settled it: he spent the night. The next morning while he was washing his face after eating a nice little dish of stew beef cut up into small pieces, he made his decision. After all, if a Gentleman Cat spends the night, it is a kind of promise. I will be your cat, he said to himself, sitting on the desk with his paws tucked in and his eyes looking gravely at the two women standing in the doorway, if you will be my housekeepers. And of course they agreed, because of the white tip to his tail, because he hummed such a variety of purrs and songs, because he really was quite a handsome fellow, and because they had very soft hearts.

♦ LIBRARY LINK ♦

Share more of the Fur Person's adventures by reading the book from which this excerpt was taken, The Fur Person, *by May Sarton.*

Reader's **Response**

What do you think of the author's portrayal of cat behavior?

Housekeeper Wanted For Gentleman Cat

Checking Your Comprehension

1. What were some of the sights and smells the Fur Person noticed in the first woman's apartment?
2. What made the Fur Person decide to escape from the apartment?
3. How did the Fur Person meet the two kind women?
4. Compare and contrast the first woman's apartment with the house of the two kind women.
5. The Fur Person seldom used his voice to communicate with his housekeepers. How did he communicate? Give three examples.
6. Do you think the two kind women understood the Fur Person better than the first woman? What led you to this conclusion?

Writing to Learn

THINK AND RECALL The Fur Person has a distinct personality. Read the poem below and observe how it captures the character and appearance of The Fur Person.

Poem	Poem Chart
Gentleman Cat	Subject (1 or 2 words)
sleek, proud	Adjectives (2 words)
strutting, preening, thinking	Participles (3 words)
claws, teeth, fur, bones, tail	Nouns (5 words)
sampling, observing, selecting	Participles (3 words)
happy, content	Adjectives (2 words)
independent!	Adjective (1 word)

WRITE You can write a poem about an animal or person you know well by using the chart on the right. The chart tells you what part of speech to put on each line. Use interesting, descriptive words that capture the character and appearance of the subject of your poem.

251

The Naming

The Naming of Cats is a difficult matter,
    It isn't just one of your holiday games;
You may think at first I'm as mad as a hatter
When I tell you, a cat must have THREE DIFFERENT NAMES.
First of all, there's the name that the family use daily,
    Such as Peter, Augustus, Alonzo, or James,
Such as Victor or Jonathan, George or Bill Bailey—
    All of them sensible everyday names.
There are fancier names if you think they sound sweeter,
    Some for the gentlemen, some for the dames:
Such as Plato, Admetus, Electra, Demeter—
    But all of them sensible everyday names.
But I tell you, a cat needs a name that's particular,
    A name that's peculiar, and more dignified,
Else how can he keep up his tail perpendicular,
    Or spread out his whiskers, or cherish his pride?
Of names of this kind, I can give you a quorum,
    Such as Munkustrap, Quaxo, or Coricopat,

# of Cats

Such as Bombalurina, or else Jellylorum—
    Names that never belong to more than one cat.
But above and beyond there's still one name left over,
    And that is the name that you never will guess;
The name that no human research can discover—
    But THE CAT HIMSELF KNOWS, and will never confess.
When you notice a cat in profound meditation,
    The reason, I tell you, is always the same:
His mind is engaged in a rapt contemplation
    Of the thought, of the thought, of the thought of his name:
        His ineffable effable
        Effanineffable
Deep and inscrutable singular Name.

T. S. Eliot

Writing in the Field of Animal Research

People often have sentimental ideas about animals, and many writers anthropomorphize them; that is, they write about animals as if they had human traits and emotions. Natural scientists, however, try to learn and write about animals in a more objective way. Some of these naturalists have given up the comforts of civilized life to go live with or near the animals they want to study, to observe how animals behave in their own natural surroundings over long periods of time.

Several fascinating books have resulted from these close-up studies of animals in the wild. Among the best known are *In the Shadow of Man* and *The Chimpanzees of Gombe* by Jane Goodall, an English zoologist who began studying chimpanzees in what is now Gombe National Park in Tanzania in 1960. At first, the chimpanzees were frightened of her and would not come close, but as they got used to her she could get nearer to them and study them closely. She got to know the chimps as individuals and could study how they behaved together in a group, which chimps made up families, and how they led their daily lives.

Some of her discoveries surprised other scientists. Previously it had been thought that chimpanzees ate only fruits and vegetables, but Goodall discovered that they often hunt and kill monkeys and pigs. She also observed chimpanzees using tools in ways similar to human beings, and she recorded many years of observations about how they communicate. Many of Jane Goodall's conclusions are controversial, but her books record in fascinating

Joy Adamson recorded her observations of the lion cub Elsa in *Born Free.*
▼

254

detail the longest and most thorough observation of chimpanzees any scientist has yet conducted.

Joy Adamson didn't have to leave civilization to study animals; she already lived among them as the wife of an East African game warden when, in 1956, she and her husband rescued and then reared a lion cub whose mother had been killed. Their plan was that the cub, Elsa, would eventually have to live in a zoo, for no animal reared by humans had ever been known to be able to go back to the wild and survive. How the Adamsons helped Elsa achieve a return to the wild is the engrossing story told in Joy Adamson's famous book *Born Free*.

Two other excellent books by authors who studied animals in the wild are *Never Cry Wolf* by Farley Mowat, who spent half a year living with a family of wolves in subarctic northern Canada, and *Gorillas in the Mist* by Dian Fossey who lived among and studied East African mountain gorillas.

▲
Jane Goodall observed and followed the chimpanzees through the forest.

Not every naturalist who does this kind of close-up study writes a book for the general public, but if you are interested in the topic of animal research in natural environments, you might want to become a reader of magazines such as *National Geographic* and *Natural History*, in which articles about this kind of study often appear.

For those who enjoy reading and learning about animals, there is a great variety of books and magazines, fiction and nonfiction, available at any library.

▶
Jane Goodall has continued to live among the chimpanzees and study them.

A Siamese cat finds comfort and love with the Nurmi family—
and yet the cat is so peculiarly restless.

RIVER
RESCUE

by Sheila Burnford
from The Incredible Journey:
A Tale of Three Animals

Three animals—a Labrador retriever, a bull terrier, and a Siamese
cat—have embarked on a daring 250-mile trek across the Cana-
dian wilderness to return to their home. Together they have battled
hunger, cold, bobcat, and bear—until the moment when the Sia-
mese is unable to cross a large river, and the powerful waters
carry the cat downstream, away from his companions.

Many miles downstream on the side to which the dogs had
crossed, a small cabin stood near the bank of the river, surrounded
by three or four acres of cleared land, its solid, uncompromising
appearance lightened only by the scarlet geraniums at the window
sills and a bright blue door. A log barn stood back from it, and a
steam-bath house at the side nearer the river. The patch of vegetable garden, the young orchard and the neatly fenced fields, each

with their piles of cleared boulders and stumps, were small orderly miracles of victory won from the dark encroaching forest that surrounded them.

Reino Nurmi and his wife lived here, as sturdy and uncompromising as the cabin they had built with their own hand-hewn logs, their lives as frugal and orderly as the fields they had wrested from the wilderness. They had tamed the bush, and in return it yielded them their food and their scant living from trap lines and a wood lot, but the struggle to keep it in subjection was endless. They had retained their Finnish identity complete when they left their homeland, exchanging only one country's set of solitudes and vast lonely forests for another's, and as yet their only real contact with the new world that lay beyond their property line was through their ten-year-old daughter Helvi, who knew no other homeland. Helvi walked the lonely miles to the waiting school bus each day, and through her they strengthened their roots in the security of the New World, and were content meanwhile with horizons limited by their labor.

On the Sunday afternoon that the beaver dam broke, a day of some relaxation, Helvi was down by the river, skipping flat stones across the water, and wishing that she had a companion; for she found it difficult to be entirely fair in a competition always held against herself. The riverbank was steep and high here, so she was quite safe when a rushing torrent of water, heralded by a great curling wave, swept past. She stood watching it, fascinated by the spectacle, thinking that she must go and tell her father, when her eye was caught by a piece of debris that had been whirling around in a back eddy and was now caught on some boulders at the edge of the bank. She could see what looked like a small, limp body on the surface. She ran along by the boiling water to investigate, scrambling down the bank, to stand looking pityingly at the wet, bedraggled body, wondering what it was, for she had never seen anything like it before. She dragged the mass of twigs and branches further up on land, then ran to call her mother.

Mrs. Nurmi was out in the yard by an old wood stove that she still used for boiling the vegetable dyes for her weaving, or peelings and scraps for the hens. She followed Helvi, calling out to her husband to come and see this strange animal washed up by an unfamiliar, swift-surging river.

He came, with his unhurried countryman's walk and quiet thoughtful face, and joined the others to look down in silence at the small limp body, the darkly plastered fur betraying its slightness, the frail skull bones and thin crooked tail mercilessly exposed. Suddenly he bent down and laid his hand lightly on it for a moment, then pulled back the skin above and below one eye and looked more closely. He turned and saw Helvi's anxious, questioning face close to his own, and beyond that her mother's. "Is a drowned *cat* worth trying to save?" he asked them, and when her mother nodded, before Helvi's pleading eyes, he said no more, but scooped the soaking bundle up and walked back to the cabin, telling Helvi to run ahead and bring some dry sacks.

He laid the cat down in a sunny patch by the wood stove and rubbed it vigorously with sacking, turning the body from side to side until the fur stood out in every direction and it looked like some disheveled old scarf. Then, as he wrapped the sacking firmly around and her mother pried the clenched teeth open, Helvi poured a little warm milk and precious brandy down the pale cold throat.

She watched as a spasm ran through the body, followed by a faint cough, then held her breath in sympathy as the cat retched and choked convulsively, a thin dribble of milk appearing at the side of its mouth. Reino laid the straining body over his knee and pressed gently over the rib cage. The cat choked and struggled for breath, until at last a sudden gush of water streamed out, and it lay relaxed. Reino gave a slow smile of satisfaction and handed the bundle of sacking to Helvi, telling her to keep it warm and quiet for a while—if she was sure that she still wanted a cat.

She felt the oven, still warm though the fire had long died out, then placed the cat on a tray inside, leaving the door open. When her mother went into the cabin to prepare supper and Reino left to milk the cow, Helvi sat cross-legged on the ground by the stove, anxiously chewing the end of one fair braid, watching and waiting. Every now and then she would put her hand into the oven to touch the cat, to loosen the sacking or to stroke the soft fur, which was beginning to pulsate with life under her fingers.

After half an hour she was rewarded: the cat opened his eyes. She leaned over and looked closely into them—their blackness now contracted, slowly, to pinpoints, and a pair of astonishingly vivid blue eyes looked up instead. Presently, under her gentle strok- ing, she felt a throaty vibration, then heard a rusty, feeble purring. Wildly excited, she called to her parents.

Within another half-hour the little Finnish girl held in her lap a sleek, purring, Siamese cat, who had already finished two saucers of milk (which normally he detested, drinking only water), and who had groomed himself from head to foot. By the time the Nurmi family were eating their supper around the scrubbed pine table, he had finished a bowl of chopped meat, and was weaving his way around the table legs, begging in his plaintive, odd voice for more food, his eyes crossed intently, his kinked tail held straight in the air like a banner. Helvi was fascinated by him, and by his gentle- ness when she picked him up.

That night the Nurmis were having fresh pickerel, cooked in the old-country way with the head still on and surrounded by potatoes. Helvi ladled the head with some broth and potatoes into a saucer and put it on the floor. Soon the fishhead had disappeared to the accompaniment of pleased rumbling growls. The potatoes followed; then, holding down the plate with his paw, the cat polished it clean. Satisfied at last, he stretched superbly, his front paws extended so that he looked like a heraldic lion, then jumped onto Helvi's lap, curled himself around and purred loudly.

The parents' acceptance was completed by his action, though there had never before been a time or place in the economy of their lives for an animal that did not earn its keep, or lived anywhere else except the barn or kennel. For the first time in her life Helvi had a pet.

Helvi carried the cat up to bed with her, and he draped himself with familiar ease over her shoulder as she climbed the steep ladder stairs leading up to her little room in the eaves. She tucked him tenderly into an old wooden cradle, and he lay in sleepy contentment, his dark face incongruous against a doll's pillow.

Late in the night she woke to a loud purring in her ear, and felt him treading a circle at her back. The wind blew a gust of cold rain across her face and she leaned over to shut the window, hearing far away, so faint that it died in the second of wind-borne sound, the thin, high keening of a wolf. She shivered as she lay down, then drew the new comforting warmth of the cat closely to her.

When Helvi left in the morning for the long walk and ride to the distant school the cat lay curled on the window sill among the geraniums. He had eaten a large plate of oatmeal, and his coat shone in the sun as he licked it sleepily, his eyes following Mrs. Nurmi as she moved about the cabin. But when she went outside with a basket of washing she looked back to see him standing on his hind legs peering after, his soundless mouth opening and shutting behind the window. She hurried back, fearful of her geraniums, and opened the door—at which he was already scratching— half expecting him to run. Instead he followed her to the washing line and sat by the basket, purring. He followed her back and forth between the cabin and the wood stove, the henhouse and the stable. When she shut him out once by mistake he wailed pitifully.

This was the pattern of his behavior all day—he shadowed the Nurmis as they went about their chores, appearing silently on some point of vantage—the seat of the harrow, a sack of potatoes, the manger or the well platform—his eyes on them constantly. Mrs. Nurmi was touched by his apparent need for companionship: that his behavior was unlike that of any other cat she attributed to his foreign appearance. But her husband was not so easily deceived—he had noticed the unusual intensity in the blue eyes. When a passing raven mocked the cat's voice and he did not

look up, then later sat unheeding in the stable to a quick rustle in the straw behind, Reino knew then that the cat was deaf.

Carrying her schoolbooks and lunch pail, Helvi ran most of the way home across the fields and picked up the cat as well when he came to meet her. He clung to her shoulder, balancing easily, while she performed the routine evening chores that awaited her. Undeterred by his weight she fed the hens, gathered eggs, fetched water, then sat at the table stringing dried mushrooms. When she put him down before supper she saw that her father was right—the pointed ears did not respond to any sound, though she noticed that he started and turned his head at the vibration if she clapped her hands or dropped even a small pebble on the bare floor.

She had brought home two books from the traveling library, and after the supper dishes had been cleared away her parents sat by the stove in the short interval before bed while she read aloud to them, translating as she went. They sat, in their moment of rare relaxation, with the cat stretched out on his back at their feet, and the child's soft voice, flowing through the dark austerity of the cabin, carried them beyond the circle of light from the oil lamp to the warmth and brightness of strange lands. . . .

They heard of seafaring Siamese cats who worked their passages the world over, their small hammocks made and slung by their human messmates, who held them second to none as ship's cats; and of the great proud Siamese Ratting Corps who patrolled the dockyards of Le Havre with unceasing vigilance; they saw, with eyes withdrawn and dreaming, the palace watch-cats of long-ago Siam, walking delicately on long simian legs around the fountained courtyards, their softly padding feet polishing the mosaics to a lustred path of centuries. And at last they learned how these nobly born Siamese acquired the kink at the end of their tails and bequeathed it to all their descendants.

And as they listened, they looked down in wonder, for there on the rag rug lay one of these, stretched out flat on his royal back, his illustrious tail twitching idly, and his jeweled eyes on their daughter's hand as she turned the pages that spoke of his ancestors—the guardian cats of the Siamese princesses. Each princess, when she came down to bathe in the palace lake, would slip her rings for safekeeping on the tail of her attendant cat. So zealous in their charge were these proud cats that they bent the last joint sideways for safer custody, and in time the faithful tails became crooked forever, and their childrens' and their childrens' children. . . .

One after another the Nurmis passed their hands admiringly down the tail before them to feel the truth in its bent bony tip; then Helvi gave him a bowl of milk, which he drank with regal condescension before she carried him up the ladder to bed.

That night, and for one more, the cat lay curled peacefully in Helvi's arms, and in the daytime during her absence he followed her parents everywhere. He trailed through the bush after her mother as she searched for late mushrooms, then sat on the cabin steps and patted the dropped corn kernels as she shucked a stack of cobs. He followed Reino and his work horse across the fields to the wood lot and perched on a newly felled pungent stump, his head following their every movement, and he curled by the door of the stable and watched the man mending harness and oiling traps. And in the late afternoons when Helvi returned he was there waiting for her, a rare and beautiful enigma in the certain routine of the day. He was one of them.

But on the fourth night he was restless, shaking his head and pawing his ears, his voice distressed at her back. At last he lay down, purring loudly, and pushed his head into her hand—the fur below his ears was soaking. She saw their sharp black triangles outlined against the little square of window and watched them flicker and quiver in response to every small night sound. Glad for him in his newfound hearing, she fell asleep.

When she woke, later in the night, aware of a lost warmth, she saw him crouched at the open window, looking out over the pale fields and the tall, dark trees below. His long sinuous tail thrashed to and fro as he measured the distance to the ground. Even as her hand moved out impulsively towards him he sprang, landing with a soft thud.

She looked down and saw his head turn for the first time to her voice, his eyes like glowing rubies as they caught the moonlight, then turn away—and with sudden desolate knowledge she knew that he had no further need of her. Through a blur of tears, she watched him go, stealing like a wraith in the night towards the river that had brought him. Soon the low, swiftly running form was lost among the shadows.

Epilogue

Even though the Siamese found comfort and love with the Nurmi family, he had stronger ties elsewhere. To stay would have been to abandon his "first" family. It didn't take him long to pick up the trail of the dogs, but he had another narrow escape from death before he could reach them. When he finally did, their joy was boundless. All three had lighter hearts as they continued their incredible journey.

◆ LIBRARY LINK ◆

If you'd like to find out whether the Siamese cat finds his real family, read the book The Incredible Journey *by Sheila Burnford, and meet the other two members of a charming trio of pets.*

Reader's Response

Do you think Helvi would have been better off if she had not found the cat?

RIVER RESCUE

Checking Your Comprehension

1. How does the setting explain Helvi's loneliness?
2. What are three words that describe Helvi? Give reasons for your answers.
3. How did Helvi learn more about Siamese cats?
4. Why do you think Helvi was so taken with the Siamese?
5. Was Helvi's father observant? How do you know?
6. Why did the Siamese ultimately leave the Nurmis?

Writing to Learn

THINK AND RECALL Suppose the Nurmi family wanted to find the Siamese cat and decided to place a "Lost Cat" sign on the post office bulletin board. Make a listing of details that describe the cat.

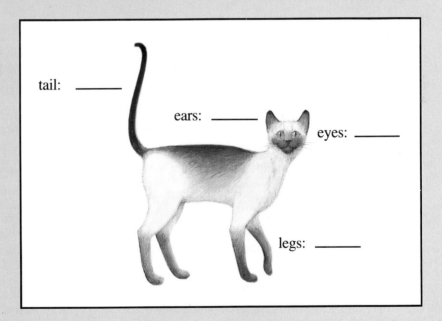

tail: _____

ears: _____

eyes: _____

legs: _____

WRITE Use the details you've listed as you write the "Lost Cat" sign for the Nurmi family.

READING **F**ICTION

Comprehension:

Summarizing

Story Summary

		Where/When
Who		
		Problems
Goals		
		Events
Outcomes		
		Themes

Suppose that a couple of your friends are trying to decide if they should see a movie that you have already seen. To help make up their minds, they ask you what the movie is about. Now, you certainly aren't going to tell them every line of dialogue in the movie (even if you *could* remember it). It would probably take you a few hours, and in that amount of time your friends could have seen the whole movie for themselves! Instead, you would give your friends a *summary* that contains only the most important ideas from the movie.

The same is true for a novel or a story. Summarizing helps you describe what you have read, and it also helps you decide what facts and ideas are important. It also makes it easier to remember those ideas.

When you summarize a story, you briefly state the most important ideas in it. A good summary tells *who* is in the story, *what* happens, *why* it happens, and *where* and *when* the story takes place. It also states the main character's problems and goals, and how the character does or does not reach those goals. Finally, a good summary identifies the *theme* or central idea the author was trying to convey. A good way to identify the information you need for a summary is by using a story map. A story-map outline looks like this:

Where/When:
Who:
Problems:
Goals:
Events:
Outcomes:
Themes:

When you complete the story map, you will have all the information you'll need for a good summary.

Mapping a Story

Create a story map for the story you read recently, "Housekeeper Wanted for Gentleman Cat," using the headings shown above. Begin with "Where/When" (you can fill in the places where the story occurs, but the author does not tell you *when* the story occurs, so you cannot include that information). Next, list the story's characters under "Who." Obviously, the Fur Person is the main character, but who else is in the story?

The next items will require a little more thought. What are the Fur Person's problems? What is his goal? To help you with these items, try thinking about what makes him happy or unhappy and about what makes him act the way he does.

Under "Events," list only the most important events in the story. Do not include unimportant details such as what the Fur Person had for dinner, or what type of flower he attacked.

Under "Outcomes," tell what happens at the end of the story. The outcome of the story relates to the problems and goals you previously described. Did the Fur Person resolve his problems? Did he achieve his goals?

Finally, under "Themes," tell the important ideas the story gets across. What points was the author trying to make about freedom, about finding a home, about the way people behave toward animals, or about what animals might think of humans?

Your finished story map may look something like this:

Where/When: Lady's apartment, kind women's house
Who: Fur Person, lady in apartment, kind women in house
Problems: Likes being cared for, but does not like lady in apartment; cannot get out
Goals: To find a nice home
Events: Lady in apartment interferes with Fur Person's independence. He bites her, and she lets him out. He comes upon house where two kind women live. They feed him and treat him well.
Outcomes: Fur Person moves into house.
Themes: A good home is more than just a place to live; freedom is too important to sacrifice for security.

From Story Map to Story Summary

In a way, the story map is already a summary of the story. However, if you were telling a friend about the story, you would put the information in sentence form. If you use the information from the story map, your summary will tell what the story is about because it will contain the most important ideas. Your summary might go something like this:

"Housekeeper Wanted for Gentleman Cat" is about the Fur Person, a very finicky cat who has been living on his own. He decides that he wants to settle down in a home with a person who will take care of him. He is very careful to choose just the right one, because he knows that a good home provides more than just a place to live. First he stays with a lady in an apartment, but he does not like the way she fusses over him; he doesn't want to sacrifice his freedom to stay in this apartment. He bites the lady and she lets him leave. He comes upon a house where two women live. They feed him and treat him well. He decides to stay with the two women.

When you finish your summary, reread it. Does it tell the important events? Does it express the theme of the story? Did you leave out any important information? Did you include any unimportant details? If necessary, revise the summary.

Guidelines for Summarizing

1. Think about the important parts of the story.
2. Think about what the characters' problems are.
3. Decide what the characters' goals are.
4. Think about the outcome. How does it relate to the characters' problems and goals?
5. Think about the important ideas, or themes, in the story.

Using What You Have Learned

Skim the story "The Wounded Wolf" to refresh your memory. Then write a summary of the story.

As You Read

The next story you will read is called "Only One Woof." As you read, think about the ideas and events in the story. Which of them are important enough to belong in a summary?

In their communication, animals, like people, are not always predictable. Consider Gyp, for instance, a friendly English sheepdog who didn't have much to say for himself.

ONLY ONE WOOF

by James Herriot

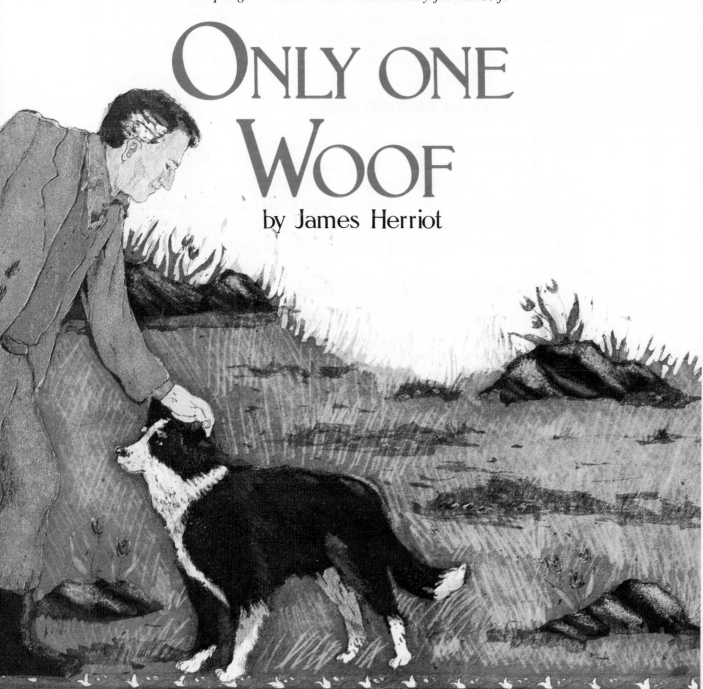

"Is this the thing you've been telling me about?" I asked.

Mr. Wilkin nodded. "Aye, that's it, it's always like that."

I looked down at the helpless convulsions of the big dog lying at my feet; at the staring eyes, the wildly pedalling limbs. The farmer had told me about the periodic attacks which had begun to affect his sheepdog, Gyp, but it was coincidence that one should occur when I was on the farm for another reason.

"And he's all right afterwards, you say?"

"Right as a bobbin. Seems a bit dazed, maybe, for about an hour, then he's back to normal." The farmer shrugged. "I've had lots o' dogs through my hands as you know and I've seen plenty of dogs have attacks. I thought I knew all the causes—worms, wrong feeding, distemper—but this has me beat. I've tried everything."

"Well you can stop trying, Mr. Wilkin," I said. "You won't be able to do much for Gyp. He's got epilepsy."

"Epilepsy? But he's a grand, normal dog most of t' time."

"Yes, I know. That's how it goes. There's nothing actually wrong with his brain—it's a mysterious condition. The cause is unknown but it's almost certainly hereditary."

Mr. Wilkin raised his eyebrows. "If it's hereditary why hasn't it shown up before now? He's nearly two years old and he didn't start this till a few weeks ago."

"That's typical," I replied. "Eighteen months to two years is about the time it usually appears."

Gyp interrupted us by getting up and staggering towards his master, wagging his tail. He seemed untroubled by his experience. In fact the whole thing had lasted less than two minutes.

Mr. Wilkin bent and stroked the rough head briefly. His craggy features were set in a thoughtful cast. He was a big powerful man in his forties and now as the eyes narrowed in that face which rarely smiled he looked almost menacing. I had heard more than one man say he wouldn't like to get on the wrong side of Sep Wilkin and I could see what they meant. But he had always treated me right and since he farmed nearly a thousand acres I saw quite a lot of him.

His passion was sheepdogs. A lot of farmers like to run dogs at the trials but Mr. Wilkin was one of the top men. He bred and trained dogs which regularly won at the local events and occasionally at the national trials. And what was troubling me was that Gyp was his main hope.

He had picked out the two best pups from a litter—Gyp and Sweep—and had trained them with the dedication that had made him a winner. I don't think I have ever seen two dogs enjoy each other quite as much; whenever I was on the farm I would see them together, sometimes peeping nose by nose over the half-door of the loose box where they slept, occasionally slinking devotedly round the feet of their master but usually just playing together. They must have spent hours rolling about in ecstatic wrestling matches, growling and panting, gnawing gently at each other's limbs.

A few months ago George Crossley, one of Mr. Wilkin's oldest friends and a keen trial man, had lost his best dog with nephritis and Mr. Wilkin had let

him have Sweep. I was surprised at the time because Sweep was shaping better than Gyp in his training and looked like he was turning out to be a real champion. But it was Gyp who remained. He must have missed his friend but there were other dogs on the farm and if they didn't quite make up for Sweep he was never really lonely.

As I watched, I could see the dog recovering rapidly. It was extraordinary how soon normality was restored after that frightening convulsion. And I waited with some apprehension to hear what his master would say.

The cold, logical decision for him to make would be to have Gyp put down and, looking at the friendly, tail-wagging animal, I didn't like the idea at all. There was something very attractive about him. The big-boned, well-marked body was handsome but his most distinctive feature was his head, where one ear somehow contrived to stick up while the other lay flat, giving him a lop-sided, comic appeal. Gyp, in fact, looked a bit of a clown. But a clown who radiated goodwill and camaraderie.

Mr. Wilkin spoke at last. "Will he get any better as he grows older?"

"Almost certainly not," I replied.

"Then he'll always have these attacks?"

"I'm afraid so. You say he has them every two or three weeks—well it will probably carry on more or less like that with occasional variations."

"But he could have one any time?"

"Yes."

"In the middle of a trial, like." The farmer sunk his head on his chest and his voice rumbled deep. "That's it, then."

In the long silence which followed, the fateful words became more and more inevitable. Sep Wilkin wasn't the man to hesitate in a matter which concerned his ruling passion. Ruthless culling of any animal which didn't come up to standard would be his policy. When he finally cleared his throat I had a sinking premonition of what he was going to say.

But I was wrong.

"If I kept him, could you do anything for him?" he asked.

"Well I could give you some pills for him. They might decrease the frequency of the attacks." I tried to keep the eagerness out of my voice.

"Right . . . right . . . I'll come into t' surgery and get some," he muttered.

I didn't say any more because I felt intuitively that he did not want to be detected in a weakness; that he was prepared to keep the dog simply as a pet. It was funny how events began to slot into place and suddenly make sense. That was why he had let Sweep, the superior trial dog, go. He just liked Gyp. In fact Sep Wilkin, hard man though he may be, had succumbed to that off-beat charm.

So I shifted to some light chatter about the weather as I walked back to the car, but when I was about to drive off the farmer returned to the main subject.

"There's one thing about Gyp I never mentioned," he said, bending to the window. "I don't know whether it has anything to do with his problem or not. He has never barked in his life."

I looked at him in surprise. "You mean never, ever?"

"That's right. Not a single bark. T'other dogs make a noise when strangers come on the farm but I've never heard Gyp utter a sound since he was born."

"Well that's very strange," I said. "But I can't see that it is connected with his condition in any way."

And as I switched on the engine I noticed for the first time that while a dog and two half-grown pups barked to see me on my way, Gyp merely regarded me in his comradely way, mouth open, tongue lolling, but quiet. A silent dog.

The thing intrigued me. So much so that whenever I was on the farm over the next few months I made a point of watching the big sheepdog at whatever he was doing. But there was never any change. Between the convulsions, which had settled down to around three-week intervals, he was a normal active happy animal. But soundless.

I saw him, too, in Darrowby when his master came in to market. Gyp was often seated comfortably in the back of the car, but if I happened to speak to Mr. Wilkin on these occasions I kept off the subject because, as I said, I had the feeling that he more than most farmers would hate to be exposed in keeping a dog for other than working purposes.

And yet I have always entertained a suspicion that most farm dogs were more or less pets. The dogs on sheep farms were of course indispensable working animals and on other establishments they no doubt performed a function in helping to bring in the cows. But watching them on my daily rounds I often wondered. I saw them rocking along on carts at haytime, chasing rats among the stooks at harvest, pottering around the buildings or roaming the fields at the side of the farmer; and I wondered . . . what did they really do?

My suspicions were strengthened at other times—as when I was trying to round up some cattle into a corner and the dog tried to get into the act by nip-

ping at a hock or tail. There was invariably a hoarse yell of "Siddown, dog!" or "Gerrout, dog!"

So right up to the present day I still stick to my theory: most farm dogs are pets and they are there mainly because the farmer just likes to have them around. You would have to put a farmer on the rack to get him to admit it but I think I am right. And in the process those dogs have a wonderful time. They don't have to beg for walks, they are out all day long, and in the company of their masters. If I want to find a man on a farm I look for his dog, knowing the man won't be far away. I try to give my own dogs a good life but it cannot compare with the life of the average farm dog.

There was a long spell when Sep Wilkin's stock stayed healthy and I didn't see either him or Gyp; then I came across them both by accident at a sheepdog trial. It was a local event run in conjunction with the Mellerton Agricultural Show and since I was in the district I decided to steal an hour off.

I took my wife Helen with me, too, because these trials have always fascinated us. The wonderful control of the owners over their animals, the intense involvement of the dogs themselves, the sheer skill of the whole operation always held us spellbound.

She put her arm through mine as we went in at the entrance gate to where a crescent of cars was drawn up at one end of a long field. The field was on the river's edge and through a fringe of trees the afternoon sunshine glinted on the tumbling water of the shallows and turned the long beach of bleached stones to a dazzling white. Groups of men, mainly competitors, stood around chatting as they watched. They were quiet, easy, bronzed men and as they seemed to be drawn from all social strata, from prosperous farmers to working men, their garb was varied: cloth caps, trilbies, deerstalkers or no hat at all; tweed jackets, stiff best suits, open-necked shirts, fancy ties, sometimes neither collar nor tie. Nearly all of them leaned on long crooks with the handles fashioned from rams' horns.

The dogs waiting their turn were tied up to a fence with a hedge growing over it. There were about seventy of them and it was rather wonderful to see that long row of waving tails and friendly expressions. They were mostly strangers to each other but there wasn't even the semblance of disagreement, never mind a fight. It seemed that the natural obedience of these little creatures was linked to an amicable disposition.

This appeared to be common to their owners, too. There was no animosity, no resentment at defeat, no unseemly display of triumph in victory. If a man overran his time he ushered his group of

sheep quietly in the corner and returned with a philosophical grin to his colleagues. There was a little quiet leg-pulling but that was all.

We came across Sep Wilkin leaning against his car at the best vantage point about thirty yards away from the final pen. Gyp, tied to the bumper, turned and gave me his crooked grin while Mrs. Wilkin on a camp stool by his side rested a hand on his shoulder. Gyp, it seemed, had got under her skin too.

Helen went over to speak to her and I turned to her husband. "Are you running a dog today, Mr. Wilkin?"

"No, not this time, just come to watch. I know a lot o' the dogs."

I stood near him for a while watching the competitors in action, breathing in the clean smell of trampled grass. In front of us next to the pen the judge stood by his post.

I had been there for about ten minutes when Mr. Wilkin lifted a pointing finger. "Look who's there!"

George Crossley with Sweep trotting at his heels was making his way unhurriedly to the post. Gyp suddenly stiffened and sat up very straight, his cocked ears accentuating the lop-sided look. It was many months since he had seen his brother and companion; it seemed unlikely, I thought, that he would remember him. But his interest was clearly intense, and as the judge waved his white handkerchief and the

three sheep were released from the far corner he rose slowly to his feet.

A gesture from Mr. Crossley sent Sweep winging round the perimeter of the field in a wide, joyous gallop and as he neared the sheep a whistle dropped him on his belly. From then on it was an object lesson in the cooperation of man and dog. Sep Wilkin had always said Sweep would be a champion and he looked the part, darting and falling at his master's commands. Short piercing whistles, shrill plaintive whistles; he was in tune with them all.

No dog all day had brought his sheep through the three lots of gates as effortlessly as Sweep did now and as he approached the pen near us it was obvious that he would win the cup unless some disaster struck. But this was the touchy bit; more than once with other dogs the sheep had broken free and gone bounding away within feet of the wooden rails.

George Crossley held the gate wide and extended his crook. You could see now why they all carried those long sticks. His commands to Sweep, huddled flat along the turf, were now almost inaudible but the quiet words brought the dog inching first one way then the other. The sheep were in the entrance to the pen now but they still looked around them irresolutely and the game was not over yet. But as Sweep wriggled towards them almost imperceptibly they turned and entered and Mr. Crossley crashed the gate behind them.

As he did so he turned to Sweep with a happy cry of *"Good lad!"* and the dog responded with a quick jerking wag of his tail.

At that, Gyp, who had been standing very tall, watching every move with the most intense concentration, raised his head and emitted a single resounding bark.

"Woof!" went Gyp as we all stared at him in astonishment.

"Did you hear that?" gasped Mrs. Wilkin.

"Well, by gaw!" her husband burst out, looking open-mouthed at his dog.

Gyp didn't seem to be aware that he had done anything unusual. He was too preoccupied by the reunion with his brother and within seconds the two dogs were rolling around, chewing playfully at each other as of old.

I suppose the Wilkins as well as myself had the feeling that this event might start Gyp barking like any other dog, but it was not to be.

Six years later I was on the farm and went to the house to get some hot water. As Mrs. Wilkin handed me the bucket she looked down at Gyp who was basking in the sunshine outside the kitchen window.

"There you are, then, funny fellow," she said to the dog.

I laughed. "Has he ever barked since that day?"

Mrs. Wilkin shook her head. "No he hasn't, not a sound. I waited a long time but I know he's not going to do it now."

"Ah well, it's not important. But still, I'll never forget that afternoon at the trial," I said.

"Nor will I!" She looked at Gyp again and her eyes softened in reminiscence. "Poor old lad, eight years old and only one woof!"

 Reader's Response

What was it about this selection that made it seem especially real to you?

ONLY ONE WOOF

Checking Your Comprehension

1. What was wrong with Gyp?
2. Why was Mr. Wilkin likely to be very upset at the news of Gyp's special condition?
3. Describe the narrator's theory about most farm dogs.
4. Why did the narrator feel that farm dogs had a much better life than his own dog?
5. Tell why, in your opinion, the narrator originally misjudged what Wilkin would do with Gyp after discovering the dog's condition. What steps did you go through in forming this opinion?
6. Why do you think Gyp barked only that one time?
7. At what points in the story was the narrator surprised or amused by what occurred? Give reasons for your answer.

Writing to Learn

THINK AND RECALL Pet owners see their pets as special kinds of friends. This cluster shows information about Gyp. Make a cluster of information about your pet or another animal you know.

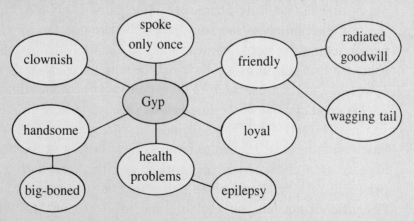

WRITE Share a real or imaginary encounter with the animal that you've described above. Use some of the information you noted in your cluster to write a brief narrative.

279

Literature:

Narrative Point of View

If you've ever tried to write a story, then you already know that a writer must make several important decisions before beginning to write. One of the most important decisions is the choice of the story's *point of view.* In other words, an author must decide from which perspective the story will be told. Will it be told from the point of view of one of the characters in the story, or will it be told by an anonymous narrator?

First-Person Point of View

In the *first-person point of view,* the story is told from the perspective of one of the characters in the story. Everything that you, the reader, learn about the story is filtered through the mind of the person telling the story—the narrator. You can tell that an author is using the first-person point of view if the narrator uses words such as *I*, *we*, *me*, *my*, *mine*, and *our* in the narrative parts of the story.

A good example of the first-person point of view is the story you just read, "Only One Woof." James Herriot writes stories that are based on things that happen to him in his work as a veterinarian. He appears as a character in his stories, and they are told from his perspective. He tells only about things that he sees, hears, or thinks. Herriot does not tell you anything that happened on Mr. Wilkins's farm unless he was there when it happened or heard about it later. As the narrator, Herriot's feelings color his perceptions and descriptions of everything that happens in the story. If a different character—Mr.

Wilkins, for example—told the story, the events might seem different because they would be colored by *his* perceptions.

Third-Person Point of View

Authors may choose to tell their story from the *third-person point of view,* in which case the narrator is a voice from outside the story. All the characters are referred to with words such as *she*, *he*, *her*, *him*, *they*, and *them*. "Housekeeper Wanted for Gentleman Cat" and "River Rescue" both use the third-person point of view, but each uses a slightly different method of narration.

"Housekeeper Wanted for Gentleman Cat" is told by a narrator who is outside the story, but the narrator tells the story through the Fur Person's eyes. It is as if the author has attached a camera to the Fur Person so the reader can get a cat's-eye view of the world. This way of telling a story is called *third-person limited narration* because it is confined to one character's thoughts and perceptions.

In "River Rescue," the narrator tells you what all the different characters think and feel. The narrator is like a movie director, shifting the camera freely from scene to scene. The narrator can put you inside the mind of each character in the story. This is called *third-person omniscient narration. Omniscient* means "all-knowing"; that is, nothing in the story is hidden from the narrator.

Sometimes an author may decide that it is important for the reader to understand the perspective of one of the characters in the story and will choose to use the first-person point of view. Other times the author may decide it is more important to understand all the characters in the story and will opt for the third-person point of view.

Read and Enjoy

The next story, "The Black Stallion," is written from the third-person limited point of view. As you read, notice how this point of view allows you to share in the boy's feelings of despair and hope and to admire his resourcefulness.

It's one thing to learn to communicate with a dog, a cat, or a monkey, but a wild black stallion is another story!

MAROONED
by Walter Farley
from The Black Stallion

The ship Alec was on sank not far from a tropical island. Also on board the ship was a beautiful, but very wild, stallion. By holding onto the stallion as it swam to shore, Alec was saved from drowning, and Alec and the stallion are alone on a desert island. Now what?

The days passed and the boy strove desperately to find food to keep himself alive; he caught only one more fish—it would be impossible for him to depend upon the sea for his living. He turned again to the berries, but they were fast diminishing. He managed to keep his fire going as the heat made the dry fuel plentiful. However, that was of little use to him as he had nothing to cook.

One day as Alec walked along the beach, he saw a large red shell in the distance. He grabbed his spear tighter; it looked like a turtle. Then hunger made him lose all caution and he rushed forward, his spear raised. He threw himself upon the shell, his knife digging into the opening where he believed the turtle's head to be. Desperately he turned the huge shell over—it was empty, cleaned out; only the hollow shell met Alex's famished gaze. He stood still, dazed. Then slowly he turned and walked back to camp.

The Black was drinking from the spring. His large body too was beginning to show signs of starvation. Alec no longer felt any fear of him. The stallion raised his proud head and looked at the boy. Then he turned and trotted off. His mane, long and flowing, whipped in the wind. His whistle filled the air.

Alec watched him, envying his proud, wild spirit. The horse was used to the hardships of the desert; probably he would outlive him. The boy's subconscious thought rose to the surface of his mind: "There's food, Alec, food—if you could only find some way of killing him!" Then he shook his head, hating himself. Kill the animal that had saved his life? Never—even if he could, he would die of starvation first! The stallion reached the top of the hill and stood there, like a beautiful black statue, his gaze upon the open sea.

One morning Alec made his way weakly toward the rocky side of the island. He came to the huge rocks and climbed on top of one of them. It was more barren than any other part of the island. It was low tide and Alec's eyes wandered over the stony shore, looking for any kind of shellfish he might be able to eat. He noticed the mosslike substance on all the rocks at the water's edge, and on those that extended out. What was that stuff the biology teacher had made them eat last term in one of their experiments? Hadn't he called it *carragheen*?[1] Yes, that was it. A sort of seaweed, he had said, that grew abundantly along the rocky parts of the Atlantic coast of Europe and North America. When washed and dried, it was edible for humans and livestock. Could the moss on the rocks below be it? Alec scarcely dared to hope.

Slowly Alec made the dangerous descent. He reached the water level and scrambled across the rocks. He took a handful of the soft greenish-yellow moss which covered them and raised it to his lips. It smelled the same. He tasted it. The moss was terribly salty from the sea, but it was the same as he had eaten that day in the classroom!

[1]carragheen (kar' ə gēn): dark purple branching seaweed

Eagerly he filled his pockets with it, then removed his shirt and filled it full. He climbed up again and hurried back to camp. There he emptied the moss onto the ground beside the spring. The next quarter of an hour he spent washing it, and then placed it out in the sun to dry. Hungrily he tasted it again. It was better—and it was food!

When he had finished eating, the sun was falling into the ocean, and the skies were rapidly growing dark. In the distance Alec saw the stallion coming toward the spring. Quickly he picked up some of the moss for himself and left the rest on the ground beside the pool. Would the Black eat it? Alec hurried to his shelter and stood still, watching intently.

The stallion rushed up, shook his long neck and buried his mouth into the water. He drank long. When he had finished he looked toward the boy, then his pink nostrils quivered. The Black put his nose to the ground and walked toward the moss which Alec had left. He sniffed at it. Then he picked a little up and started eating. He chewed long and carefully. He reached down for more.

That night Alec slept better than he had since he had been on the island. He had found food—food to sustain him and the Black!

The next day Alec set out to obtain more of the carragheen. As he neared the rocks, he saw the stallion standing silently beside a huge boulder. Not a muscle twitched in his black body—it was as if an artist had painted the Black on white stone.

Alex climbed down into a small hollow and paused to look out over the rocks below. Suddenly he heard the stallion's scream, more piercing, more blood-curdling than he had ever heard it before. He looked up.

The Black was on his hind legs, his teeth bared. Then with a mighty leap, he shot away from the boulder toward Alec. Swiftly he came—faster with every magnificent stride. He was almost on top of him when he thundered to a halt and reared again. Alec jumped to one side, tripped on a stone and fell to the ground. High above him the Black's legs pawed the air, and then descended three yards in front of him! Again he went up and down—again and again he pounded. The ground on which Alec lay shook from the force of his hoofs. The stallion's eyes never left the ground in front of him.

Gradually his pounding lessened and then stopped. He raised his head high and his whistle shrilled through the air. He shook his head and slowly moved away, his nostrils trembling.

Alec regained his feet and cautiously made his way toward the torn earth, his brain flooded with confusion. There in front of him he saw the strewn parts of a long yellowish-black body, and the venomous head of a snake, crushed and lifeless. He stood still—the suddenness of discovering life, other than the Black and himself on the island, astounding him! Sweat broke out on his forehead as he realized what a poisonous snake bite would have meant—suffering and perhaps death! Dazed, he looked at the stallion just a few feet away. Had the Black killed the snake to save him? Was the stallion beginning to understand that they needed each other to survive?

Slowly the boy walked toward the Black. The stallion's mane swept in the wind, his muscles twitched, his eyes moved restlessly, but he stood his ground as the boy approached. Alec wanted the horse to understand that he would not hurt him. Cautiously he reached a hand toward the stallion's head. The Black drew it back as far as he could without moving. Alec stepped closer to the side of him. Gently he touched him for an instant. The stallion did not move. Again Alec attempted to touch the savage head. The Black reared and shook a little. Alec said soothingly, "Steady, Black fellow, I wouldn't hurt you." The stallion quivered, then reared again and broke. One hundred yards away he suddenly stopped and turned.

Alec gazed at him, standing there so still—his head raised high in the air. "We'll get out of this somehow, Black—working together," he said determinedly.

Alec walked back to the top of the rocks and again began his descent. He made his way carefully down to the water level. Cautiously he looked before he stepped—where there was one snake there might be more. Reaching the bottom, he once again filled his shirt full of the moss and made his way back. High above him he could see the Black looking out over the cliffs, his mane whipping in the wind. When he reached the top the stallion was still there. He followed a short distance behind as Alec went back to the spring.

Days passed and gradually the friendship between the boy and the Black grew. The stallion now came at his call and let Alec stroke him while he grazed. One night Alec sat within the warm glow of the fire and watched the stallion munching on the carragheen beside the pool. He wondered if the stallion was as tired of the carragheen as he. Alec had found that if he boiled it in the turtle shell it formed a gelatinous substance which tasted a little better than the raw moss. A fish was now a rare delicacy to him.

The flame's shadows reached out and cast eerie ghostlike patterns on the Black's body. Alec's face became grim as thoughts rushed through his brain. Should he try it tomorrow? Did he dare attempt to ride the Black? Should he wait a few more days? Go ahead—tomorrow. *Don't do it!* Go ahead—

The fire burned low, then smoldered. Yet Alec sat beside the fire, his eyes fixed on that blacker-than-night figure beside the spring.

The next morning he woke from a fitful slumber to find the sun high above. Hurriedly he ate some of the carragheen. Then he looked for the Black, but he was not in sight. Alec whistled, but no answer came. He walked toward the hill. The sun blazed down and the sweat ran from his body. If it would only rain! The last week had been like an oven on the island.

When he reached the top of the hill, he saw the Black at one end of the beach. Again he whistled, and this time there was an answering whistle as the stallion turned his head. Alec walked up the beach toward him.

The Black stood still as he approached. He went cautiously up to him and placed a hand on his neck. "Steady," he murmured, as the warm skin quivered slightly beneath his hand. The stallion showed neither fear nor hate of him; his large eyes were still turned toward the sea.

For a moment Alec stood with his hand on the Black's neck. Then he walked toward a sand dune a short distance away. The stallion followed. He stepped up the side of the dune, his left hand in the horse's thick mane. The Black's ears pricked forward, his eyes followed the boy nervously—some of the savageness returned to them, his muscles twitched. For a moment Alec was undecided what to do. Then his hands gripped the mane tighter and he threw himself on the Black's back. For a second the stallion stood motionless, then he snorted and plunged; the sand went flying as he doubled in the air. Alec felt the mighty muscles heave, then he was flung through the air, landing heavily on his back. Everything went dark.

Alec regained consciousness to find something warm against his cheek. Slowly he opened his eyes. The stallion was pushing him with his head. Alec tried moving his arms and legs, and found them bruised but not broken. Wearily he got to his feet. The wildness and savageness had once more disappeared in the Black; he looked as though nothing had happened.

Alec waited for a few minutes—then once again led the stallion to the sand dune. His hand grasped the horse's mane. But this time he laid only the upper part of his body on the stallion's back, while he talked soothingly into his ear. The Black flirted his ears back and forth, as he glanced backward with his dark eyes.

"See, I'm not going to hurt you," Alec murmured, knowing it was he who might be hurt. After a few minutes, Alec cautiously slid onto his back. Once again, the stallion snorted and sent the boy flying through the air.

Alec picked himself up from the ground—slower this time. But when he had rested, he whistled for the Black again. The stallion moved toward him. Alec determinedly stepped on the sand dune and once again let the Black feel his weight. Gently he spoke into a large ear, "It's me. I'm not much to carry." He slid onto the stallion's back. One arm slipped around the Black's neck as he half-reared. Then like a shot from a gun, the Black broke down the beach. His action shifted, and his huge strides seemed to make him fly through the air.

Alec clung to the stallion's mane for his life. The wind screamed by and he couldn't see! Suddenly the Black swerved and headed up the sand dune; he reached the top and then down. The spring was a blur as they whipped by. To the rocks he raced, and then the stallion made a wide circle—his speed never diminishing. Down through a long ravine he rushed. Alec's blurred vision made out a black object in front of them, and as a flash he remembered the deep gully that was there. He felt the stallion gather himself; instinctively he leaned forward and held the Black firm and steady with his hands and knees. Then they were in the air, sailing over the black hole. Alec almost lost his balance when they landed but recovered himself in time to keep from falling off! Once again the stallion reached the beach, his hoofbeats regular and rhythmic on the white sand.

The jump had helped greatly in clearing Alec's mind. He leaned closer to the stallion's ear and kept repeating, "Easy, Black. Easy." The stallion seemed to glide over the sand and then his speed began to lessen. Alec kept talking to him. Slower and slower ran the Black. Gradually he came to a stop. The boy released his grip from the stallion's mane and his arms encircled the Black's neck. He was weak with exhaustion—in no condition for such a ride! Wearily he slipped to the ground. Never had he dreamed a horse could run so fast! The stallion looked at him, his head held high, his large body only slightly covered with sweat.

That night Alec lay wide awake, his body aching with pain, but his heart pounding with excitement. He had ridden the Black! He had conquered this wild, unbroken stallion with kindness. He felt sure that from that day on the Black was his—his alone! But for what—would they ever be rescued? Would he ever see his home again? Alec shook his head. He had promised himself he wouldn't think of that any more.

The next day he mounted the Black again. The horse half-reared but didn't fight him. Alec spoke softly in his ear, and the Black stood still. Then Alec touched him lightly on the side, and he walked—a long, loping stride. Far up the beach they went, then Alec tried to turn him by shifting his weight, and gently pushing the stallion's head. Gradually the horse turned. Alec took a firmer grip on his long mane and pressed his knees tighter against the large body. The stallion broke out of his walk into a fast canter. The wind blew his mane back into the boy's face. The stallion's stride was effortless, and Alec found it easy to ride. Halfway down the beach, he managed to bring him back again to a walk, then to a complete stop. Slowly he turned him to the right, then to the left, and then around in a circle.

Long but exciting hours passed as Alec tried to make the Black understand what he wanted him to do. The sun was going down rapidly when he walked the stallion to the end of the beach. The Black turned and stood still; a mile of smooth, white sand stretched before them.

Suddenly the stallion bolted, almost throwing Alec to the ground. He picked up speed with amazing swiftness. Faster and faster he went. Alec hung low over his neck, his breath coming in gasps. Down the beach the stallion thundered. Tears from the wind rolled down Alec's cheeks. Three-quarters of the way, he tried to check the Black's speed. He pulled back on the flowing mane. "Whoa, Black," he yelled, but his words were whipped away in the wind. Swiftly the stallion neared the end of the beach, and Alec thought that his breathtaking ride of yesterday was to be repeated. He pulled back harder on the mane. Suddenly the Black's pace lessened. Alec flung one arm around the stallion's neck. The Black shifted into his fast trot, which gradually became slower and slower, until Alec had him under control. Overjoyed, he turned him, and rode him over the hill to the spring. Together they drank the cool, refreshing water.

With the days that followed, Alec's mastery over the Black

grew greater and greater. He could do almost anything with him. The savage fury of the unbroken stallion disappeared when he saw the boy. Alec rode him around the island and raced him down the beach, marveling at the giant strides and the terrific speed. Without realizing it, Alec was improving his horsemanship until he had reached the point where he was almost a part of the Black as they tore along.

One night Alec sat beside his campfire and stared into the flames that reached hungrily into the air; his knees were crossed and his elbows rested heavily upon them, his chin was cupped in his two hands. He was deep in thought. The *Drake* had left Bombay on a Saturday, the fifteenth of August. The shipwreck had happened a little over two weeks later, perhaps on the second of September. He had been on the island exactly—nineteen days. That would make it approximately the twenty-first of September. By now his family must think him dead! He doubled his fists. He had to find a way out; a ship just had to pass the island sometime. Daily he had stood on top of the hill peering out to sea, frantically hoping to sight a boat.

For the first time, Alec thought of the approaching cold weather. The heat had been so intense upon the island since his arrival that it had never entered his mind that it would soon get cold. Would his shelter offer him enough protection? He had used every available piece of wood on the island to reinforce it, but would that be enough? How cold would it get? Alec looked up at the clear, starlit sky.

He rose to his feet and walked toward the hill. The Black, standing beside the spring, raised his head and whistled when he saw him. He followed Alec as he climbed to the top. The boy's eyes swept the dark, rolling sea. White-crested swells rushed in and rolled up the beach. The stallion, too, seemed to be watching—his eyes staring into the night, his ears pricking forward. An hour passed, then they turned and made their way back to camp.

A wind started blowing from out of the west. Alec stoked the fire for the night, then crawled wearily into his shelter. He was tired, for he had spent most of the day gathering carragheen. He stretched out and was soon asleep.

He didn't know how long he had been sleeping, but suddenly the Black's shrill scream awakened him. Sleepily he opened his eyes; the air had grown hot. Then he heard a crackling noise above; his head jerked upward. The top of the shelter was on fire! Flames were creeping down the sides. Alec leaped to his feet and rushed outside.

A gale was sweeping the island and instantly he realized what had happened. Sparks from his campfire had been blown upon the top of the shelter and had easily set fire to the dry wood. He grabbed the turtle shell and ran to the spring. Filling it, he ran back and threw the water on the flames.

The Black pranced nervously beside the spring, his nostrils quivering, while Alec rushed back and forth with his little turtle shell full of water, trying to keep the fire from spreading. But it had a good start and soon it had enveloped the whole shelter. Smoke filled the air. The boy and the horse were forced to move farther and farther back.

Soon the two nearby trees caught. Alec knew that the fire could not spread much farther—the island was too barren of any real fuel. But now the flames were devouring everything in sight. They roared and reached high into the air. There was nothing that Alec could do. The one thing he really needed— his shelter—was gone. And there was no more wood.

The fire burned a long time before it started to die down. Then the wind too began to diminish. Alec sat beside the spring, watching the flames, until the first streaks of dawn appeared in the sky. He blinked his smoke-filled eyes, gritted his teeth—he wasn't licked yet! He'd find some way to make a shelter, and if that wasn't possible, then he'd sleep outside like the Black.

Determinedly he set out for the beach. Perhaps some wood had been swept ashore during the night. The Black trotted ahead of him. Then Alec saw him snort and rear as he reached the top of the hill, and plunge back down again. Alec hurried forward.

From the crest of the hill, he looked down. Below him was a ship anchored four hundred yards off the island!

He heard voices. He saw a rowboat being drawn up on the beach by five men. Incredulous, unable to shout, he rushed down the hill.

"You were right, Pat, there is someone on this island!" he heard one of the men shout to the other.

And the other replied in a thick Irish brogue, "Sure, and I knew I saw a fire reaching into the heavens!"

Alec's eyes blurred; he couldn't see. He stumbled and fell and then clambered to his feet. Again he rushed forward. Then they had their arms around him.

"For the love of St. Patrick," the man called Pat groaned, "he's just a boy!"

Words jumbled together and stuck in Alec's throat as he looked into the five pairs of eyes staring at him. Then he found his voice. "We're saved!" he yelled. "We're saved, Black, we're saved!"

The sailors looked at him—he was a strange sight! His red hair was long and disheveled, his face and body so brown that they would have taken him for a native had it not been for the torn remnants of his clothing, which hung loosely on him.

One of the men stepped forward. From his uniform he was obviously the captain of the ship. "Everything is going to be all right, son," he said as he placed an arm around Alec and steadied him.

Slowly Alec gained control of himself. "I'm okay now, sir," he said.

The sailors gathered around him. "Is there someone else with you on this island?" the captain asked.

"Only the Black, sir."

The men looked at one another, and then the captain spoke again, "Who's the Black, son?" he asked.

"He's a horse, sir," Alec answered.

And then he told them his story—of the storm and the shipwreck, the hours spent in the raging sea holding desperately to the rope tied to the stallion's neck, their fight against starvation on the island, his conquest of the Black, and the fire which that night had reduced his shelter to ashes. Sweat broke out on his forehead as he once again lived through the twenty days of hardships and suffering since the *Drake* had gone down.

When he had finished there was a moment of silence, and then one of the men spoke. "This lad is imagining things, Captain. What he needs is some hot food and a good bed!"

Alec looked from one face to another and saw that they didn't believe him. Rage filled him. Why should they be so stupid? Was his story so fantastic? He'd prove it to them, then—he'd call the Black.

He raised his fingers to his lips and whistled. "Listen," he shouted. "Listen!" The men stood still. A minute passed, and then another—only the waves lapping on the beach could be heard in the terrifying stillness of the island.

Then the captain's voice came to him, "We have to go now, son. We're off our course and way behind schedule."

Dazed, Alec's eyes turned from the island to the freighter lying at anchor, smoke belching from its two stacks. It was larger than the *Drake*.

The captain's voice again broke through his thoughts. "We're bound for South America—Rio de Janeiro is our first stop. We can take you there and radio your parents from the ship that you're alive!"

The captain and Pat had him by the arms; the others were in the boat ready to shove off. Desperately Alec tried to collect his thoughts. He was leaving the island. He was leaving the Black. The Black—who had saved his life! He jerked himself free; he was running up the beach.

Their mouths wide open, the sailors watched him as he stumbled up the hill. They saw him reach the top and raise his fingers to his lips. His whistle reached them—then there was silence.

Suddenly, an inhuman scream shattered the stillness—a wild, terrifying call! Stunned, they stood still and the hairs on the back of their necks seemed to curl. Then as if by magic, a giant black horse, his mane waving like a flame, appeared beside the boy. The horse screamed again, his head raised high, his ears pricked forward. Even at this distance they could see that he was a tremendous horse—a wild stallion.

Alec flung his arms around the Black's neck and buried his head in the long mane. "We're leaving together, Black—together," he said.

◆ LIBRARY LINK ◆

To find out more about Alec and the Black, read The Black Stallion *by Walter Farley, the first in a series about this special horse.*

Reader's Response

Does this story of friendship between a boy and a wild horse seem believable to you?

WRITING
—ABOUT—
READING

Writing an Interview

In this unit you read about human and animal communication. One of the most widely used forms of communication is the interview. An interview is conducted to obtain information and to find out a person's thoughts and feelings about a particular topic. Although information from an interview is sometimes put into paragraph form, interviews are also printed word for word in a question-and-answer format. You can create both the questions and the answers for an interview with an animal researcher.

Prewriting

Prepare for writing by reviewing "The Wounded Wolf" and "Keeping in Touch." As you review, think of questions you would ask if you were interviewing a researcher on wolf communication. Also record information that will give you ideas for the answers to your questions.

Now read the interview form that follows.

—————— An Interview with a Wolf Researcher ——————
by Chris King

Time of Interview: 2:00 P.M. June 7, 1990
Place of Interview: The lobby of the Wolf Research Center

    Chris King: I know that wolves can communicate by howling. What other ways can wolves communicate?

Researcher:	Wolves have many forms of communication. In addition to howls, they use a variety of other sounds. They also communicate by scent, body position, and specialized behavior.

Writing

Continue this interview with the researcher. Construct five additional questions, and then put yourself in the place of the researcher and answer the questions. Be sure your questions are brief and to the point. Answers need not be long, but they should completely answer the questions.

Revising

Ask yourself if the interview questions are direct and concise. Answers should contain a variety of sentence structures. Orally read and answer the questions. Listen for answers that are complete. If you need more details, add them.

Proofreading

Correct any spelling, grammar, and punctuation mistakes. Be sure that your format is consistent. Did you remember to use a colon after each speaker's name?

Publishing

Bind the interviews together and make a class book. Think of an interesting title and work together to create a design for the book jacket.

WORKING TOGETHER

HELP WANTED:
Applicant should have
the following qualities:

*Writing an Advertisement for
an Animal Trainer*

Many stories and articles in this unit are about relationships between people and animals. For example, "Helping Hands" describes how trained capuchin monkeys help quadriplegics. People need certain qualities in order to train animals successfully. Your group will decide what those qualities are and will write a "Help Wanted" advertisement for a person who has those qualities.

As a group, assign responsibility for one or more of these tasks:

◆ Recalling selections that show the qualities needed by animal trainers

◆ Encouraging everyone to listen carefully to each other's ideas

◆ Recording the ideas in a list

◆ Showing appreciation for other people's ideas

Discuss the qualities that would make a person a good animal trainer. Together, decide how important each characteristic is. Which characteristics are really essential? Discuss what you know about people who work with animals. Talk about how they communicate with animals and how they train them. Describe the kind of person an animal needs in order to learn. What qualities would she or he need to have?

Everyone should suggest ideas. Make a list of all the ideas. Then agree on four qualities that your group feels are most important. Together, write a "Help Wanted" advertisement that would attract the kind of person you might want to hire.

BOOKS TO ENJOY

The Call of the Wild by Jack London *(Macmillan, 1963)* Buck, a dog stolen from a warm home, is forced to work as a sled dog in the Klondike. Eventually, Buck runs away and becomes the leader of a wolf pack.

The Talking Earth by Jean Craighead George *(Harper & Row, 1983)* A young Seminole girl, Billie Wind, no longer believes in her people's legends. She is sent alone to spend several days in the Florida Everglades, where she learns to rely upon the earth and animals she has distrusted.

The Dog Who Wouldn't Be by Farley Mowat *(Bantam, 1981)* Mutt's refusal to recognize that he is a dog leads him and the Mowat family into a variety of hilarious escapades.

The Wolfling by Sterling North *(Dutton, 1969)* In this documentary novel of the 1870s, young Robbie Trent saves the life of a wolf pup and raises it with loving care. Robbie's interest in wildlife is sparked by his neighbor, a great naturalist who knows every bird, beast, flower, and insect.

Animal Partners: Training Animals to Help People by Patricia Curtis *(Lodestar, 1982)* Seven young people narrate their personal experiences with training animals to help the disabled. The book presents an exciting career choice for people who love animals.

ON
DREAMERS'
WINGS

One of humanity's
great dreams is to
soar above it all.

What kinds of
adventures have
been inspired by
this age-old dream?

BATTERSEA BOX, *lithograph, England*

In this ancient Greek myth, Daedalus, a brilliant and proud inventor, dares to soar beyond all human boundaries.

DAEDALUS
and
ICARUS
by
Penelope Farmer

In ancient Greece, the great inventor Daedalus has been banished from Athens, his home, for committing a serious crime. With his beloved son, Icarus, Daedalus has taken refuge on the island of Crete, where the great King Minos rules. Minos asked Daedalus to construct an inescapable stronghold for the Minotaur, a monstrous creature with the head of a huge black bull and a cavernous mouth. To contain the deadly creature, Daedalus created a maze of tunnels and passages so intricate that a hundred people might wander in it for years without ever meeting one another.

In the labyrinth then lived the Minotaur, its roar confined in rock still heard dimly through the palace. People trembled hearing it. Minos, they knew, sent those who had angered him to feed his son, and to the Minotaur all alike were men of tender flesh to tear and devour—Cretan, Spartan, Athenian, none could withstand its furious charge from some dark winding of the labyrinth.

Daedalus, meanwhile, exiled from the city of his birth, lived on at Cnossus enjoying the hospitality of the king. He had with him his young son, Icarus. He idolized the boy so much you'd think he invented him, not merely fathered him. Daedalus seemed to grow more clever, more ingenious than ever. He copied in iron a fish's backbone with its row of little teeth; this made the first saw ever seen. He fitted together two pointed rods of iron to make compasses with which a perfect circle could be drawn. His fame grew, all over Greece, all round the Aegean Sea. His pride also burned and puffed itself up till he thought his skill equal to a god's. The sun of Minos' favour[1] shone on him more brilliantly each day, and nothing seemed likely to move him from the favour of the king.

But then one day guards came to seize Daedalus and Icarus and drag them before Minos the king. And he was wrathful, furious, bellowing like a bull himself, like his son the Minotaur.

"So you boasted, Daedalus, that no one could escape your labyrinth. But the Minotaur is dead. A man has killed our son and deciphered the plan of the maze and sailed away unharmed from Crete. Now you and your son shall be cast into the maze, and if you too escape from there, you'll get no further, we swear to it. We, Minos, do not swear in vain. We rule not merely Crete but all the sea about. Without ships no man can escape from Crete, and you, O subtle architect, clever as you are, you command no ships upon our Aegean Sea."

[1]Some words in this selection are spelled in the British style.

So Daedalus, with Icarus his son, was cast into the prison he had made. He took with him there a ball of golden thread, which looked in such darkness like an image of the golden sun. This was the device he'd made secretly to guide himself to the far end of the labyrinth. He tied one end to the entrance place, and slowly the ball began to unroll ahead of them, through all the turns and windings, the confusions of entrances and alleyways. After a while Daedalus smelt a familiar, farmyard reek, but it had a fouler, sicklier note to it, and the stench went on growing all the time till they reached the cave at the heart of the labyrinth where the corpse of the Minotaur lay rotting on dirty straw.

It seemed feeble now, and foolish and puny. Its red eyes were closed, its limbs flaccid and limp. Only the yellow horns still looked dangerous.

Daedalus gazed beyond it, shuddering, holding up his little lamp till its light reached the farthest corners of the cave where human bones and skulls lay scattered everywhere. There were feathers also from birds devoured by the Minotaur. He picked up one and examined minutely its shaft and quill.

"Minos rules the land of Crete," he said. "He may rule the sea that surrounds it too. But remember, Icarus my son, remember that great King Minos does not rule the sky."

Icarus did not know what his father meant by this. He watched Daedalus lay feathers overlapping in four separate rows, each diminishing in size from one end to the other. Then Daedalus brought from his tunic a cake of wax, a needle, and some fine strong thread. He joined the larger feathers with the needle and thread. He softened the wax in the warmth of the lamp and used it to unite the smaller feathers.

Icarus watched his father's patient hands, watched small feathers waver in the heat above the lamp and the wax drip down in slow, dull drops. Sometimes Daedalus made him hold feathers or pull on an end of thread, and he was eager to help, too eager perhaps, jogging his father's arm or letting his shadow fall across the light.

At last Daedalus took the completed rows, bent them and curved them into shape, and then his son could see what they were meant to be; how from the wings of birds, his father Daedalus had made wings for men, one pair each for himself and Icarus.

The oil of the lamp was all burned now. As they left the cave the wick flickered and went out so that the only light was in the guiding thread in the diminishing golden ball, which unrolled ahead of them towards the secret entrance of the labyrinth where no guard would stand in wait. The sound of their breathing magnified itself. On and on they went. Even when they neared the end, there was still no light, not the narrowest rim or chink. The thread doubled round and back again, and they twisted confusedly to follow it.

The light broke suddenly, burst upon them. They had to bury their eyes against the blinding, burning sun. The air rushed at them too, strong air full of honey and wild thyme, for this entrance to the labyrinth lay on the hillside by Cnossus, within sight of the glittering sea.

When Daedalus's eyes accepted the light at last, he took some leather thongs and fixed the smaller pair of wings to the arms of Icarus. He fixed the larger to his own, explaining all the while what they had to do. They would have to use their arms just as the wing bones of a bird, making the feathers gently rise and fall.

"But mind, mind, Icarus my son, don't fly too low, too near the sea, for the feathers once wet will not carry you. But then do not fly too high, too near the sun, for the sun's heat like the lamps, will melt the wax, make the feathers fall away."

Icarus heard his father out. But he was already impatient to begin, moving his arms experimentally, so that the air caught the feathers on the wings.

Daedalus started to run along the hillside. When he had gained some speed he jumped into the air, shouting at Icarus to follow him. Both moved their arms with awkward, chopping strokes; they did not soar as they had expected to, but struggled jerkily, not far above the rock. Daedalus kept close to Icarus, instructing him, but made no more elegant a bird himself. If an even stroke did make him soar, he would lose the knack at once and slip down again. Once Icarus, shooting up, met Daedalus struggling down, their wings entangled and both fell hard onto the bruising stone.

Icarus caught it first, the rhythm, the pattern of flight. He swept into the air and away, filled with joyfulness, shouting with delight, and almost at once Daedalus followed his

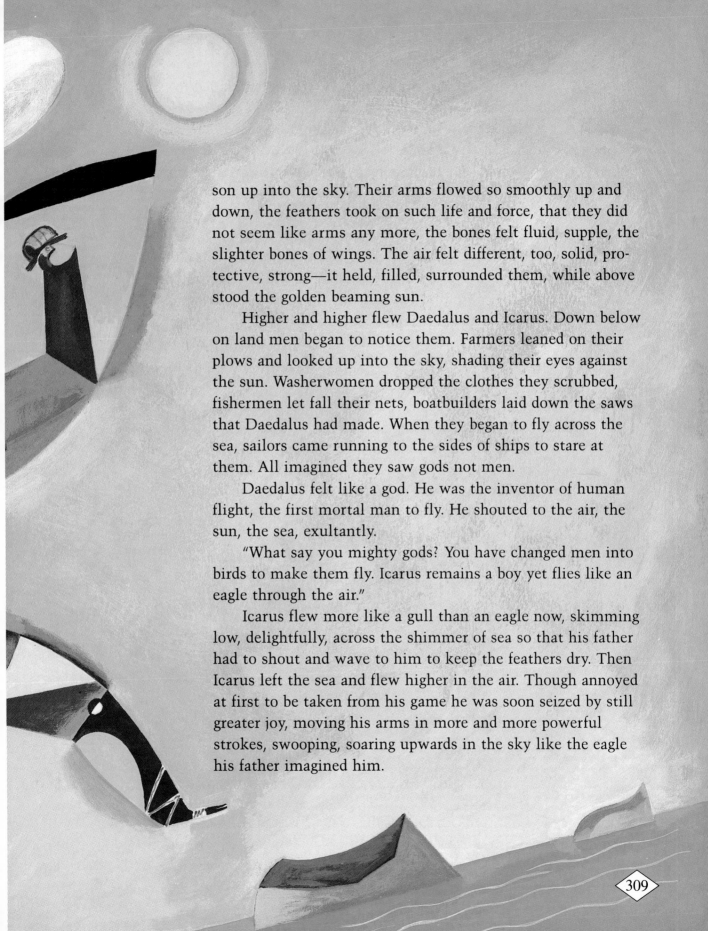

son up into the sky. Their arms flowed so smoothly up and down, the feathers took on such life and force, that they did not seem like arms any more, the bones felt fluid, supple, the slighter bones of wings. The air felt different, too, solid, protective, strong—it held, filled, surrounded them, while above stood the golden beaming sun.

Higher and higher flew Daedalus and Icarus. Down below on land men began to notice them. Farmers leaned on their plows and looked up into the sky, shading their eyes against the sun. Washerwomen dropped the clothes they scrubbed, fishermen let fall their nets, boatbuilders laid down the saws that Daedalus had made. When they began to fly across the sea, sailors came running to the sides of ships to stare at them. All imagined they saw gods not men.

Daedalus felt like a god. He was the inventor of human flight, the first mortal man to fly. He shouted to the air, the sun, the sea, exultantly.

"What say you mighty gods? You have changed men into birds to make them fly. Icarus remains a boy yet flies like an eagle through the air."

Icarus flew more like a gull than an eagle now, skimming low, delightfully, across the shimmer of sea so that his father had to shout and wave to him to keep the feathers dry. Then Icarus left the sea and flew higher in the air. Though annoyed at first to be taken from his game he was soon seized by still greater joy, moving his arms in more and more powerful strokes, swooping, soaring upwards in the sky like the eagle his father imagined him.

Daedalus returned to his godlike dreams and failed to watch the flight of Icarus.

"Other men need gods to make them fly. Icarus has only his mortal father Daedalus."

Higher and higher flew Icarus, towards the strengthening sun. The air grew hotter, the sun more brilliant, dazzling to his eyes. He had forgotten all warnings now, flying nearer as if drawn to it, like a moth towards a lamp.

And slowly the wax on his wings began to melt. It softened gently, then dripped a little, in slow, thick drops. A feather slipped from it, fell drifting, turning, down towards the sea. Other feathers followed, singly at first, but then more and more of them at once. And suddenly, though the ecstatic Icarus as confidently moved his wings, there were not enough feathers left to hold the air, to keep him up in flight.

His father looked back, to see his son plunge headlong, faster than the feathers, passing every one. Straight as a gull he fell towards the sea, but did not swerve in safety like a gull above the glittering waves. He plunged right into the heart of them, and their startled waters closed above his head. All that remained of Icarus were some feathers floating on the sea, while his father flew, weeping, in the sky, alone.

Reader's Response

Do you think that Daedalus was or was not responsible for the death of Icarus?

DAEDALUS *and* ICARUS

Checking Your Comprehension

1. Why did King Minos allow Daedalus to remain on the island of Crete?
2. What two inventions did Daedalus create while he lived on Cnossus?
3. Might it have been possible for someone to enter the labyrinth and escape after killing the Minotaur? How did you think of your answer?
4. When do you think Daedalus got the idea for making wings?
5. What are two figures of speech the author uses in describing the flight of Daedalus and Icarus?
6. How did Daedalus's cleverness bring him grief?
7. Do you think that the death of Icarus changed Daedalus? Explain your answer.

Writing to Learn

THINK AND IMAGINE At the end of this story we see Daedalus sad and alone, yet the story could have had another ending. Imagine that Icarus escaped death. Use a flowchart to identify three incidents that could have happened to him. Read the example below.

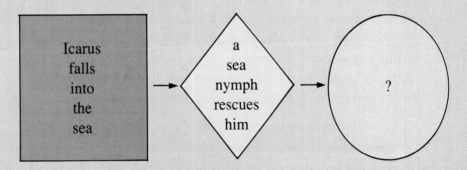

WRITE Add one more incident to the flowchart and write a new ending for this famous story.

A Strategy for Thinking:

Pulling Information Together

When you read fiction or nonfiction, you usually have to keep track of a lot of information that may seem scattered and unconnected. Sometimes an author will make a concluding statement that will bring all of this information together for you. Often, though, it is up to you to think through the information and make a conclusion or unifying statement of your own. How do you do this? First, read the material. As you read, look for pieces of information that are similar to one another and think about what they have in common. When you pull information together this way, you often can see connections in the writing that were not apparent to you before.

Learning the Strategy

One technique to help you pull information together is an evidence chart. In an evidence chart, you list information about a subject on one side of the chart, then pull the information together in a unifying statement on the other side. For example, read the following sentences from "Daedalus and Icarus." As you read, look for common elements in all of the sentences.

> Sailors came running to the sides of ships to stare at them. All imagined they saw gods not men.
>
> Daedalus felt like a god.
>
> Daedalus returned to his godlike dreams and failed to watch the flight of Icarus.

Now look at the evidence chart below. Notice the evidence that is taken from the sentences and then read the sentence on the right that pulls this evidence together.

EVIDENCE CHART FOR "DAEDALUS AND ICARUS"

Evidence:	Pulling it together:
"they saw gods not men" "felt like a god" "returned to his godlike dreams"	The ability to fly unaided has always been seen as a superhuman feat.

The evidence chart lets you see the information clearly so you can draw a conclusion or make a unifying statement more easily.

Using the Strategy

Now make an evidence chart of your own. Based on the following sentences from "Daedalus and Icarus," list common elements in each sentence. Then pull this information together in a unifying statement.

♦ He swept into the air and away, filled with joyfulness, shouting with delight, and almost at once Daedalus followed his son up into the sky.

♦ He shouted to the air, the sun, the sea, exultantly.

♦ Icarus flew more like a gull than an eagle now, skimming low, delightfully, across the shimmer of the sea. . . .

Applying the Strategy to the Next Selection

The next selection, "Wings to Fly," is also about attempts to fly. As you read, keep track of clues by using an evidence chart. At the end of the selection, you will be asked to write a sentence that pulls together all of the clues.

The writing connection can be found on page 381.

WINGS TO FLY

BY JAY WILLIAMS

The dream of Daedalus lived on through the ages. During the Renaissance, this dream took hold in the imagination of Leonardo da Vinci, the great Italian artist and inventor.

His passion for research and his respect for knowledge mark Leonardo da Vinci unmistakably as a man of the Renaissance[1]—even more, as a man of Florence. For it was in that rich and thriving Renaissance city, where old ways were being questioned and new ideas were coming into life, that Leonardo's artistic talent had flourished and his philosophical ideas had matured. It was there too that Leonardo's inventive genius began to assert itself. As he probed deeper into the mysteries of nature in order to understand them better as an artist and a thinker, he found he was spending more time on tinkering than on painting. Gradually, he abandoned art for technology and science and became specifically absorbed in a problem that had fascinated him for years—the problem of flight.

From his early youth he had dreamed of flying, and he was determined to make his dream a reality. Typically, he began by watching closely the flight of birds and then writing down his findings in his notebooks. After studying the structure of birds' wings, he made experiments with models and noted the results. He proposed to gather his observations into a book on the flight of birds. The book would be divided into four parts, the first of which "treats of their flight by beating their wings; the second of flight without beating their wings, and with the help of the wind; the third of flight in general, such as that of birds, bats, fishes, animals, and insects; the last of the mechanism of this movement." He watched the way birds used their tails as rudders and how they make gentle landings by stalling—lowering their tails and spreading the tailfeathers, flapping their wings quickly to cut down their speed, and changing their center of gravity by moving their heads. He dissected countless birds and bats to learn how the wing opens and closes and how its muscles move it. The end of all of his work was to be an attempt at actual flight. ◆◆◆

◆◆◆
You may want to use information from this sentence in your evidence chart.

[1]Renaissance (ren′ ə säns)

315

Leonardo's parachute, though pyramidal, operated in exactly the same way as the modern version; it was to be built of specially treated cloth.

Others, it happened, had made attempts before Leonardo. One, an Italian mathematician and engineer named Giovanni Danti, had made a short glide over—and into—Lake Trasimeno around 1490; later he made a second attempt at gliding, which resulted in a broken leg. Leonardo was certain he could succeed where Danti had failed.

"A bird," he wrote, "is an instrument working according to mathematical law, which instrument it is within the capacity of man to reproduce . . ." His investigations were spread over a long period of time, during which he watched and studied birds and invented various contraptions that would demonstrate how different surfaces are affected by the movement of air. Among his notes is a drawing of a parachute, made of starched linen, with which, wrote Leonardo, a man would be able "to throw himself down from any great height without sustaining any injury." Another drawing shows a kind of helicopter with a note that a model could be made of pasteboard with a steel-wire spring. "I find that if this instrument . . . be well made . . . and be turned swiftly . . . it will rise high."

His final plan was to build a great bird on which a man could ride, a device lacking, as he wrote, ". . . in nothing except the life of the bird, and this life must needs be supplied from that of man."

Leonardo's helicopter had a screw-shaped rotor operated by four men (to be workable, a powerful engine would, of course, have been necessary).

He knew that a bird's wings were moved by powerful chest muscles. The driving force for the wings of his bird machine, he felt, could be supplied by man's powerful leg muscles, which, he said, were twice as strong as was needed for bearing his weight. He never discovered, unfortunately, that in proportion to its size a bird's bones are much lighter than a man's, and thus he never realized how much power it would take to raise both a man and his machine into the air. He did, however, calculate fairly accurately how large a wing would be needed to support a man in glider flight, and he was far ahead of anyone of his own time—or for centuries to come—in recognizing the effect of air on the surfaces of wings.

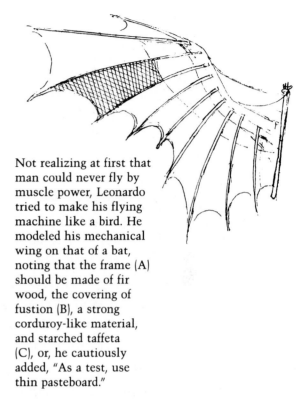

Not realizing at first that man could never fly by muscle power, Leonardo tried to make his flying machine like a bird. He modeled his mechanical wing on that of a bat, noting that the frame (A) should be made of fir wood, the covering of fustion (B), a strong corduroy-like material, and starched taffeta (C), or, he cautiously added, "As a test, use thin pasteboard."

With particular care he studied the ways in which birds use the wind to rise and descend and their methods of balancing themselves in flight; how hawks rise on air currents, and the way in which they slant their wings and tails so as to take advantage of the wind. He wrote: "The man in a flying machine (has) to be free from the waist upward in order to be able to balance himself as he does in a boat, so that his center of gravity and that of his machine may . . . change where necessity requires . . ." Many of his notes show his startling powers of vision. He was able to observe, for instance, how a bird prevents itself from being turned over in the air when it is struck from underneath by the wind. He noted that "[the bird] lowers the right or left wing, for this will cause it to turn to the right or left, dropping down in a half circle." ◄❖►

◄❖►

You may want to use information from this sentence in your evidence chart.

Elsewhere he noted that "when the bird wishes suddenly to turn on one of its sides, it pushes out swiftly, toward its tail, the point of the wing on that side, and since every movement tends to maintain itself, or rather every body that is moved continues to move as long as the impression of the force of its mover is retained in it, therefore the movement of this wing . . . in the direction of the tail . . . will come to move the whole bird with it . . ." ◄◆►

◄◆►

You may want to use information from this sentence in your evidence chart.

On the basis of such close scrutiny and such precise piecing together of observations, Leonardo built many models, some of them fairly large. He worked on them in great secrecy, for he writes, "Close up with boards the large room above, and make the model large and high, and you will have space upon the roof above . . . if you stand upon the roof at the side of the tower, the men at work upon the cupola will not see you." Later, he made a note to himself to try a small model over the Arno, and he added, "See tomorrow to all these matters and the copies, and then efface the originals and leave them at Florence so that if you lose those that you take with you, the invention will not be lost." He tried all sorts of materials: light fir wood and cane for the framework of the wings, and starched cloth, paper, or parchment for the skin. Joints were padded with leather, springs were made of ox horn or steel wire, and bindings were of strong raw silk.

Leonardo drew plans for several different types of machines. His earliest device had the wings attached to the flier's body. Then, he developed a machine in which the pilot would lie flat on his face, pedaling at stirrups that made the wings rise and fall. Finally, he decided that the best position for the pilot was upright, both because it was more natural and because the machine would then never turn upside down. By this time the "bird" had become very complicated. It consisted of a kind of basket in which the pilot stood, pumping treadles with his feet, and with his hands turning a windlass to operate two pairs of huge wings. Each pair would move "crosswise after the manner of the gait of the horse." Two long retractable ladders were fastened under the machine to act as legs so that the wings could clear the ground when beating,

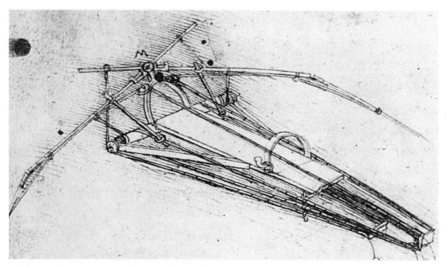

The "Orthopter" was designed so the pilot would lie flat, pedaling at stirrups that made the wings rise and fall.

and Leonardo mentions that some birds such as the martin, or swift, are not able to rise flying from the ground because their legs are so short.

Even while he was still in Milan, Leonardo seems to have tried out one of his inventions, probably a model of a larger machine, for among his records is an entry that speaks of making thongs of oxhide to hold the joints: "Tomorrow morning on the second day of January, 1496, I will make the thong and the attempt."

It is possible that some time in the year 1505 he put his "bird" to the test. Among his papers from about this time there is a page on which is written, "From the mountain which takes its name from the great bird, the famous bird will take its flight, which will fill the world with its great renown." The mountain is believed to be Mount Ceceri, not far from Florence, for the Italian word *cecero* means "swan." This is made surer by a sentence written on the cover of the same notebook: "The great bird will take its first flight upon the back of the great swan, filling the whole world with amazement and filling all records with its fame; and it will bring eternal glory to the nest where it was born."

And then there is silence. No one can say whether the complex machine with four wings was trundled up to a cliff on Mount Ceceri, or whether it was a kind of glider that was tried. Did Leonardo himself make the attempt, or some daring young apprentice? All that is known is summed up in the words of the philosopher and mathematician Geronimo Cardano, writing nearly fifty years later. In his book *De Subtilitate Rerum*, he remarks, "It has turned out badly for the two who have recently made a trial of it [flying]: Leonardo da Vinci also attempted to fly, but he was not successful."

Not for another four hundred years was man to conquer the air, and then only when a power source, the gasoline engine, had been developed which could give enough power to lift the weight of a man and his "bird"—and only when the principles of lateral balance and steering, first noted by Leonardo, had been rediscovered. Although Leonardo failed, his careful and inventive researches in aerodynamics make him the true forerunner of modern flying. ◄◆►

◄◆►
Complete your evidence chart by writing a sentence that pulls together the information drawn from the article.

Did the evidence chart help you collect your thoughts? How?

♦ LIBRARY LINK ♦

You can learn more about the life of this fascinating genius by reading the book from which this excerpt was taken, Leonardo da Vinci, *by Jay Williams.*

Reader's Response

Do you agree with the author that Leonardo da Vinci's research made him "the true forerunner of modern flying"?

WINGS TO FLY

Checking Your Comprehension

1. What qualities describe Leonardo da Vinci?
2. How did Leonardo use the study of birds to help him build a flying machine?
3. List three inventions or devices with which Leonardo investigated the problems of flight.
4. How did people's thinking change during the Renaissance?
5. What was the main reason Leonardo's flying machine failed?
6. Leonardo da Vinci is famous as both an artist and an inventor. What qualities do you think artists and inventors have in common? How did you decide on your answer?

Writing to Learn

THINK AND QUESTION If you could interview Leonardo da Vinci, what questions would you ask him? Read the questions below, and then write two original additional questions.

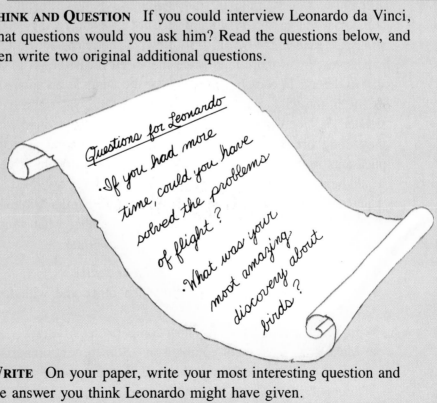

Questions for Leonardo
• If you had more time, could you have solved the problems of flight?
• What was your most amazing discovery about birds?

WRITE On your paper, write your most interesting question and the answer you think Leonardo might have given.

READING SCIENCE TEXTBOOKS

Understanding Comparisons in Science

Scientists frequently make comparisons when they study the physical and biological world. As a result, science writing often includes important descriptions that point out similarities and differences. For example, in studying birds, scientists might note that herons have large wings, while pheasants have short wings. The large wingspan enables the heron to fly slowly. The pheasant, on the other hand, must fly at more than twice the speed of the heron in order to stay in the air. In each bird, the size of the wings is an adaptation for its life in the wild. Herons hunt for food in the water and have long slender legs for wading. Large wings enable them to land slowly so they don't break their legs when they touch down. By contrast, pheasants search for food in shrubs and bushes where large wings would be a disadvantage.

Comparisons like the ones you just read are important in science writing. You will better understand and remember what you read if you recognize and focus on comparisons. To do this:

♦ Look for signal words such as *similar* and *alike*.
♦ Try to compare new facts with each other and with facts you already know.
♦ Look for graphic aids that show comparisons.
♦ Make a list or chart of comparisons. Sometimes comparisons are stated, and sometimes you need to make those comparisons yourself.

How to Read for Comparisons in Science

Read the following paragraph from a science textbook. Notice how the writer makes comparisons.

> In most coldblooded vertebrates, the parents do not take care of the eggs after they are laid. In some warmblooded animals like birds, however, the eggs are usually protected by the parents. Either the male or the female parent sits on the eggs until they hatch. In some bird species the male and female take turns sitting on the eggs. Sitting on the eggs not only protects them but also warms them. A bird embryo can develop only if incubation occurs. **Incubation** is the warming of an egg to a certain temperature over a period of time while the embryo develops.

The first two sentences of the paragraph set up a comparison between coldblooded vertebrates, such as fish and frogs, and birds, which are warmblooded. The word *however* is one indication that a comparison is being made. You learn that most coldblooded vertebrates do not care for their eggs, while birds do.

The writer also presents the parenting styles of different types of birds. No key word tells you a comparison is being made. Nonetheless, you learn that in some bird species only one parent sits on the eggs, while in others, the male and female take turns. You make the comparison yourself.

New Facts and What You Know

To help you remember what you read, you might compare new information to what you already know. If you have seen frog eggs in a pond, for example, you probably have not seen a parent frog hovering over them. However, you probably have seen a bird sitting on eggs in a nest, or at least seen this in a picture.

Toward the end of the paragraph, the writer introduces a word that may be unfamiliar to you—*incubation.* Can you think of a word you know that is like the word *incubation?* Perhaps you have heard of an incubator, a piece of equipment that provides an even temperature for a premature infant.

Graphic Aids

Photographs help make comparisons. To accompany the science paragraph below, the textbook provides a visual comparison.

The length of incubation varies with the species of a bird. In general, the shorter the period of incubation, the less developed are the baby birds when they hatch. Small birds, such as sparrows, wood thrushes, and robins are incubated for 10−20 days. Photograph A shows newly hatched wood-thrush chicks. These baby birds are weak, blind, and have few or no feathers. They are dependent on their parents. Larger birds, such as ducks and geese, incubate their eggs for 21−28 days. These birds are strong and independent soon after they hatch. They can feed themselves, walk, and swim. How do the baby ducks and wood-thrushes shown in the photographs differ?

The incubating habits of small birds are compared with those of larger birds. Using the written material and the graphic aids, you could make a chart, like the one below, showing the comparisons.

	long incubation	born blind	born with feathers	born dependent
wood thrushes	−	+	−	+
ducks	+	−	+	−

As You Read Read the following pages from a science textbook, and look for comparisons. Answer the questions on page 329.

WARM-BLOODED VERTEBRATES

As you watch a bird in flight, you may be reminded of the way an airplane or a glider flies. But one type of bird moves like a helicopter. Not only can the hummingbird fly backward, it can also hover, or remain in one place, in midair!

Due to their rapid movement, the wings of the hummingbird may appear as a blur. The wings beat so rapidly — up to 70 times per second — that they give off a humming sound. The hummingbird is named for this sound.

- *What traits of birds are helpful for flight?*
- *In what ways are birds like mammals?*
- *How do mammals differ from other animals?*

13-1 TRAITS OF BIRDS

Though birds and mammals do not appear to have much in common, they share some important traits. Unlike all other animals, birds and mammals are *warm-blooded*. A warm-blooded animal is able to maintain a constant body temperature, even when the outside temperature changes. Besides being warm-blooded, birds and mammals both have well-developed body systems.

A **bird** is a warm-blooded vertebrate that has wings and a body covering of feathers. Recall that a vertebrate is an animal that has a backbone. There are over 8500 species of birds. Birds are found all over the world, in a variety of environments. They live on land, and even in water. Since birds are warm-blooded, they are able to live in places where there are wide temperature ranges. Some species of birds live in places where the temperatures are extreme. For example, penguins live in the cold, ice-covered Antarctic. Other birds live in hot, humid jungles or in hot, dry deserts. Differences among birds enable them to live in these many kinds of places.

After completing this section, you will be able to

- **describe** traits of birds and **identify** traits that are adaptations for flight.
- **compare** down and contour feathers.
- **relate** the structure of beaks and feet to their functions.
- **define** the term *migration*.

The key terms in this section are

air sac   down feather
bird   migration
contour feather
crop

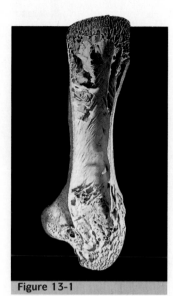

Figure 13-1

The crisscross structure of a bird bone.

LOW WEIGHT AND HIGH ENERGY

The most unique feature of birds is flight. Flight requires a low body weight compared with the size of the animal's body. Flight also requires a great amount of energy. Although birds differ in many ways, most birds have certain traits in common. Many of these traits are adaptations for flight. Recall that an adaptation is a trait that makes an organism better able to survive in its environment. The front limbs of birds are wings, and the hind limbs are legs. Most birds use their wings for flying. The legs are used for walking and for perching.

There are several traits of birds that result in their having a low body weight. Compared with the size of its body, the skeleton of a bird is very light. Many of the bones are filled with air spaces. Notice the crisscross structure inside the bird bone shown in Figure 13-1. This structure makes the bone strong but adds little weight.

Large amounts of oxygen are needed for flight. The oxygen is supplied by a complex respiratory system. Birds have well-developed lungs. Birds also have a series of air sacs. An **air sac** is a structure that is connected to the lungs of a bird and that helps to supply oxygen used in respiration. When a bird inhales, or takes in air, air enters the lungs and the air sacs. When a bird exhales, air goes out of its lungs. At the same time, air also moves from the air sacs to the lungs. Thus the lungs fill with air both when the bird inhales and when it exhales. Look at Figure 13-2 to see how much the air sacs increase the amount

Figure 13-2

The structure of a pigeon. How do air sacs affect the supply of air to the lungs?

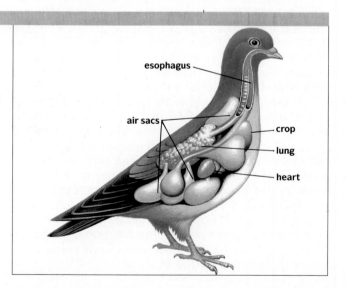

of air that is available to the lungs. The air sacs also function in cooling the bird's body during flight. The air sacs bring cool external air into close contact with the organs inside the body.

As you have learned, animals need food and oxygen for energy. Birds are able to eat large amounts of food at one time. After it is eaten, the food is stored in the crop. The **crop** is an organ in which food is moistened and stored before digestion. Locate the crop in Figure 13-2.

Birds have a well-developed circulatory system with a four-chambered heart. Look at the bird heart in Figure 13-3. Notice that in a four-chambered heart, there is a complete separation of oxygen-rich and oxygen-poor blood. The separation of oxygen-rich and oxygen-poor blood is an important feature. Because of it, the blood that is pumped throughout the body contains the large amounts of oxygen needed for flight.

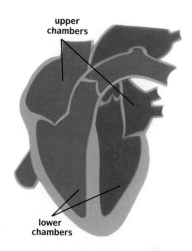

upper chambers

lower chambers

Figure 13-3

A bird heart has four chambers.

FEATHERS

Birds are aided in flight by the streamlined shape of their body. Overlapping feathers cover a bird's body and help to give it this shape. There are two main types of feathers: contour (KAHN tawr) feathers and down feathers. A **contour feather** is one of the large feathers that help to give a bird its streamlined shape. Contour feathers also cover the wings. In flight the wings cut through the air

---

ACTIVITY   How Do Contour and Down Feathers Differ?

OBJECTIVE
Compare contour and down feathers.

MATERIALS
contour feather, scissors, hand lens, down feather

PROCEDURE
A. Examine a contour feather and locate the long central shaft.
B. Feel the vane along either side of the central shaft. Use scissors to cut about 2 cm off the end of the shaft. Look at the cut end. Record your observations.
C. Notice that the vane is soft yet firm. Hold the feather by the shaft and fan yourself. Describe what you feel.

D. Examine a down feather. Note the shape of the feather and how it feels. Hold the feather by the shaft and fan yourself. Describe what you feel.

RESULTS AND CONCLUSIONS
1. How is the shaft of the contour feather an adaptation for flight?
2. Does the down feather fan the air in the same way as the contour feather? Explain any differences you observed in the way the feathers fan the air.
3. As you have learned, down feathers function in insulation. How does the structure of a down feather serve this function?

or glide on air currents. The light weight and smooth shape of contour feathers make them a good covering for the wings. Notice in Figure 13-4 that a contour feather has a main stem called a *shaft*. The flat part of the feather attached to the shaft is the *vane*.

A **down feather** is a short, fluffy feather found close to a bird's body. Compare the contour and down feathers shown in Figure 13-4. Down feathers are the main covering of young birds. In mature birds the down feathers are found between the bird's body and the contour feathers. Down feathers insulate the bird, or keep heat from being lost from the bird's body. These feathers trap air, which is then warmed by the bird's body. This warm layer of air helps to insulate the bird.

BEAKS AND FEET

Although birds lack teeth, they have a strong beak. The beak is used to pick up food, such as seeds. The structure of a bird's beak is adapted to the kind of food the bird eats. The shape of its beak can provide clues to the kind of food that a bird eats. Look at Figure 13-5. Notice the long, pointed beak of the woodpecker. This beak is used to bore into the trunks of trees as the woodpecker searches for insects. The cardinal breaks open seeds with its strong, thick beak. The meat-eating hawk tears the flesh of other animals by using its sharp, hooked beak.

Different types of birds' feet can also be seen in Figure 13-5. The structure of a bird's feet shows adaptations for food getting and for moving about in its environment. Most birds' feet have four toes—three in the front and one in the back. You can see this type of foot in the cardinal.

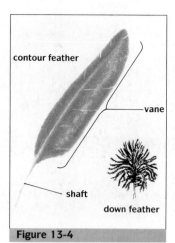

Figure 13-4

Contour and down feathers.

Figure 13-5

Notice the differences among the beaks and feet of the woodpecker, cardinal, hawk, and duck. Based on the shape of its beak, or bill, what kind of food might the duck eat?

Using What You Have Learned

1. In the first paragraph on page 325, what signal words tell you a comparison is being made? What is compared?

2. How does the size of a bird's body compare with the weight of its skeleton? Does the writer tell you this comparison is being made, or do you have to make the comparison yourself?

3. Use the paragraphs on down and contour feathers to complete this chart. Copy the chart on your own paper, and fill in each box with a plus sign for yes or a minus sign for no.

	light weight	large size	insulates	smooth	main stem
down feather					
contour feather					

4. In the paragraph on birds' beaks on page 328, what types of beaks does the author compare?

5. Using the pictures on page 328, write a brief comparison of the feet of ducks and hawks.

6. Compare what you know about penguins with the birds described in the reading selection. Why do you think penguins can't fly?

The excerpt is from *Silver Burdett & Ginn Life Science,* © 1987.

When I Heard the Learn'd Astronomer

When I heard the learn'd astronomer,
When the proofs, the figures, were ranged in columns before
    me,
When I was shown the charts and diagrams, to add, divide, and
    measure them.
When I sitting heard the astronomer where he lectured with
    much applause in the lecture room,
How soon unaccountable I became tired and sick,
Till rising and gliding out I wander'd off by myself,
In the mystical moist night air, and from time to time,
Look'd up in perfect silence at the stars.

Walt Whitman

EAGLE FLIGHT

An eagle wings gracefully
through the sky.
On the earth I stand
and watch.
My heart flies with it.

Alonzo Lopez

The Great
Balloon Craze

by Ann Hodgman
&
Rudy Djabbaroff

The dream of flight finally came true in the 1800s, with the invention of the hot-air balloon. Many of the early balloonists were women who showed daring, skill, humor, and, above all, courage, through all their ups and downs.

In 1751 a strange and fanciful book was published. It was called *The Life and Adventures of Peter Wilkins*, and it told the tale of a shipwrecked sailor who met and married an enchanting woman named Youwarkee.[1] Youwarkee could fly. As the story went, she lived in a kingdom whose inhabitants all flew: each member of her race possessed a "graundee,"[2] a silky skin, which could be spread to create a set of wings. Explaining how it felt to fly, Youwarkee said: "If you had but the graundee, flying would rest you, after the greatest labour[3] . . . once you are upon the graundee at a proper height, all the rest is play, a mere trifle; you need only to think of your way, and incline to it, your graundee directs you as readily as your feet obey you on the ground without thinking of every step you take; it does not require labour, as your boat does, to keep you a-going."

Less than fifty years later came the first actual flight ever made by a woman. This flight took place in one of the most famous inventions of the century: a balloon. Flying in a balloon was not nearly as simple as the mythical flights made by Youwarkee. But the first women who flew in balloons would certainly have agreed with Youwarkee that flight was the perfect way to travel.

The story of the first woman who flew in balloons must start with the story of the first balloons themselves. It all began simply enough. In the eighteenth century, two French brothers, Joseph and Etienne Montgolfier, lived in a town near Lyons called Annonay. Papermakers by trade, they were really more interested in science, and especially in the forces at work in the atmosphere. They had noticed and remembered what many people have noticed and ignored: that bits of ash in a fire are often carried aloft by the smoke. What caused this? the brothers wondered. What made smoke itself rise? They placed little paper bags in the smoke; these miniature balloons also rose gently into the air. Perhaps smoke and hot air could be trapped. If a small fire could lift ash, perhaps a larger one could lift something heavier.

Joseph Montgolfier tried this in 1782, in Avignon. He borrowed some silk from his landlady and sewed it into a bag. Next he set fire to some scraps of paper in his room and held the bag over them. He was delighted, and his patient landlady was astounded, to see the bag swell and float up to bob against the ceiling. "Prepare promptly a supply of taffeta and ropes," Joseph wrote rapturously to Etienne, "and you will see one of the most astonishing sights in the world!" The brothers tried the same experiment outside at Annonay, and the silken bag was lifted almost 100 feet.

By June 1783, the Montgolfiers had advanced from small silk bags to huge tethered balloons, or, as they called them, "acrostatic machines." They went on to greater fame with the help of a duck, a rooster, and a sheep—the world's

[1]Youwarkee (yo͞o wôr′ kē)
[2]graundee (gron dē′)
[3]Some words in this selection are spelled in the British style.

unwilling first three air passengers, who lifted off from Versailles in a balloon on September 19, 1783. (The three travelers landed safely in a tree.) A month later, the first human balloon passenger ascended eighty feet in a tethered balloon; this honor belonged to a young man named Francois Pilatre de Rozier.

The public became fascinated with ballooning. It had suddenly become possible for humanity to do what it had dreamed about for centuries. Everyone wanted to fly now, and perhaps it was because ballooning was so wildly popular that women began to travel in balloons as early as they did. In fact, the first women to go up in a balloon did so only seven months after Francois Pilatre de Rozier had made his own first ascent. Four of them went up at once, in a tethered-balloon exhibition on May 20, 1784. The Marchioness[4] de Montalembert, the Countess de Montalembert, the Countess de Podenas, and Mademoiselle de Lagarde were the daring noblewomen.

Less than a month later, the first woman ever actually to travel in a balloon went aloft from Lyons on June 4—one year after the Montgolfiers had made their first public balloon demonstration at Annonay. She was Madam Thible, another Frenchwoman and a very popular opera singer. A watercolor painted at the time shows Madam Thible and her companion, a painter named Fleurant, riding in state in a dashing pink balloon, with a tremen-

[4]Marchioness (mär sha nes′)

dous crowd to cheer them on. An onlooker remarked that Madame Thible seemed much more courageous than Monsieur Fleurant. She certainly showed no stage fright: at one point in her voyage she entertained the crowds with a comic-opera song called "Oh, To Travel in the Clouds!"

A year later came the voyage of the first English woman to fly in a balloon. Like Madame Thible's ascent, Mrs. Letitia Ann Sage's had a picturesque quality about it. For one thing, Mrs. Sage weighed 200 pounds, a fact not revealed in the flattering painting of *her* trip. This painting shows Mrs. Sage and her two male companions, Vincent Lunardi and George Biggin, aloft in a blue balloon with a crimson chamber for the passengers. Vincent Lunardi wears the uniform of the British Redcoats and waves a tricornered hat; Mrs. Sage wears a most unsuitable traveling dress and a hat with huge ostrich plumes (which would have blown off instantly in real life), and she reclines on a little fringed sofa.

The painting is flattering. It is also inaccurate. When all three riders were in the balloon chamber, it was discovered that the balloon could not possibly lift such a load. Vincent Lunardi graciously stepped out and let George Biggin and Mrs. Sage ride alone. Their trip was very pleasant. They took off from London with no difficulty; Mrs. Sage did crush the barometer by accident, but otherwise there were no problems on the voyage. The travelers lunched off ham and chicken before land-

ing in a field near Harrow School. A farmer who owned the field tried to destroy the balloon. It had landed on his vegetables. He was unsuccessful, however, Mrs. Sage wrote later, because "the heroic boys of Harrow School saved the balloon from destruction."

Back in France, respectable citizens were beginning to worry about women and ballooning. Were women over-stepping their bounds? The Chief of Police of Paris evidently thought so: in 1795 he decided that there were to be no more Parisian women in balloons. Women could not possibly stand up to the strain of riding in balloons, he felt, and for their own sakes they should be protected from the temptation to fly.

Nevertheless, it was in France that the next ballooning heroine was found. Sophie Blanchard's fascination with balloons began when her husband, Jean-Pierre Blanchard, became interested in them himself. Blanchard's specific interest was in developing a balloon that could be controlled and propelled by its rider. He was totally unsuccessful, as it turned out. The balloon he developed was equipped with meaningless "airscrews," and also with a pair of "air oars" with which to row through the skies. However, Blanchard's failure at balloon design was soon forgotten, for in January, 1785, he and a partner became the first people ever to cross the English Channel in a balloon. Later Blanchard, now internationally famous, would make the

335

M.S. Blanchard Célèbre Aéronaute au moment de son ascension aérienne suivie à Turin Le Soir du 26 avril 1812

first balloon voyage in the United States, in the presence of George Washington.

After Jean-Pierre's death, Madame Blanchard—who had also become a skilled balloonist herself during her husband's life—decided to make his career her own. Her many exhibition voyages, during which she parachuted fireworks out of her balloon, brought her great fame. More important, they gave her a reputation for bravery and coolheadedness. In 1804, Napoleon himself named Madame Blanchard to the post of chief of France's new Aeronautic Corps. (The previous chief had been fired when a balloon he'd designed to celebrate Napoleon's coronation had landed ignominiously on the corner of Nero's tomb.)

Madame Blanchard brought great zest to her new job. When the new King of Rome was born in 1811, she dropped birth announcements from her balloon. She was in charge of many other public festivals as well. In all, she made more than fifty balloon voyages. Many of them were terribly dangerous, but Madame Blanchard was as much of a showman as her husband had been—and the more dangerous the act, the larger the crowd.

Her final flight came on July 6, 1819, at the Tivoli Gardens in Paris. For this flight, Madame Blanchard had the idea of setting off fireworks, not by parachuting them but by fastening them to the balloon itself, lighting them with a long torch, and then cutting them loose. As an onlooker in the crowd later wrote: "The balloon rose splendidly, to the sound of music and the shoutings of the people. A rain of gold and thousands of stars fell from the car as it ascended. A moment of calm, and then an unexpected light appeared . . . increased, then disappeared suddenly; then appeared again, in the form of an immense jet of blazing gas. The spectators cried 'Brava! Viva Madame Blanchard!' thinking she was giving them an unexpected treat."

What had actually happened was that the torch's fire had ignited the hydrogen balloon. Thousands of spectators, unaware of any danger, watched as the flaming balloon flew down through the air, smashing against a rooftop. Madame Blanchard died of a broken neck. The crowds were still cheering as she died.

It took a comparatively long time for American women to begin ballooning. Not until 1825 did a Mrs. Johnson make an ascent in the United States. Little is known about this first ascent. The New York *Evening Post* reported that Mrs. Johnson was about thirty-five years old and was dressed in a white satin dress and a short red jacket. "She gave the word to let go, bade her friends farewell, waved her flags, and rose with great rapidity, amidst the shouts of the surrounding multitude." Her balloon took Madame Johnson across the East River and Brooklyn and dumped her unceremoniously in a marsh, which must have done some damage to the white satin dress.

In 1855 another American woman, Lucretia Bradley from Pennsylvania, made an ascent which was considerably more dramatic. Eager to make a name for herself, Bradley bought a secondhand balloon from the famous American balloonist John Wise. She quickly put together a hydrogen-producing system for the old balloon and made the ascent in January.

The balloon rose easily, and Lucretia Bradley was amazed by the wonderful view it gave her of the countryside—so amazed that she forgot to check the balloon's progress until she was two miles up in the air. When she did glance up, Bradley realized suddenly that the balloon had swollen almost as far as it could go without exploding. She pulled the safety valve to release some of the balloon's hydrogen, pulled it again, and watched in terror as the balloon continued to swell and to float relentlessly higher. Finally she pulled the safety valve as hard as she could, and at last the balloon slowed down as the gas began to escape. It could not escape fast enough. Two or three seconds later the balloon exploded and began to drop at the rate of 100 feet a second.

By miraculous luck, Lucretia Bradley did not die in the accident. In fact she landed unhurt, though breathless: the falling balloon had formed a parachute. Bradley walked away from the scene and later wrote a letter to John Wise. She wondered if he could sell her another balloon.

Ballooning remained the only way to travel by air for more than a century after the first balloon had flown. The fact that balloons were impossible to steer, controllable only by capricious winds, meant that no balloon flight could ever be completely safe. This, of course, made the flights more interesting to the public. Ballooning in the nineteenth century was mostly a spectator sport, popular with crowds at circuses and fairs. Balloonists were looked on as entertainers, and never more so than in 1874, when the first aerial wedding in the world took place.

Miss Mary Elizabeth Walsh was the bride. The balloon, appropriately, was the "P. T. Barnum." The bride—an equestrienne with Barnum's Roman Hippodrome—wore "a delicate pearl-colored silk, with bias folds and heavy trimmings of fringe and puffing in the back." The bridesmaid wore black. The balloon was specially decorated with bouquets, flags, and ribbons to make it look as romantic as possible. The wedding party rose more than a mile before the ceremony was over. The minister announced weightily after the ceremony that, since marriage is "an institution above those of the world, merely, it is, then, most fitting that its solemnization should be celebrated far above the earth." The whole event is worth remembering as one of the most frivolous in the history of ballooning.

To the modern mind, balloons may seem like fickle, ridiculously fragile contraptions useful only for providing adventure. But that is because the twentieth century takes flight for granted. It is hard to realize what ballooning meant in its early days. Balloons embodied one of history's oldest dreams. Those flimsy contraptions proved that objects heavier than air could become lighter than air, that people were not tied to the sober earth. Whether they flew for adventure, for the public, or for romance, the women who traveled in balloons should be remembered for more than their courage. Like the balloon itself, they started a new age.

◆ LIBRARY LINK ◆

This selection is taken from Skystars: The History of Women in Aviation *by Ann Hodgman and Rudy Djabbaroff. To learn more about ballooning, you may also enjoy* Balloons: The First Two Hundred Years *by Antonio Sotomayor.*

 Reader's Response

Why do you think flying in hot-air balloons held such an appeal for the people described in this selection?

The Great
Balloon Craze

Checking Your Comprehension

1. Describe briefly how the Montgolfier brothers invented the hot-air balloon.
2. How did the public react to Madame Blanchard's feats as a balloonist?
3. Did the public understand the dangers of ballooning? How do you know?
4. How would you characterize the first female balloonists?
5. What generalization does the author make about the safety of ballooning?
6. In the nineteenth century, the balloon represented people's dream of flight. What do you think represents our dream of flight today?

Writing to Learn

THINK AND PREDICT Copy the time line below and add dates and important events in the history of flight from "The Great Balloon Craze." Then add to the chart one more balloon flight, a flight you predict may happen in the future.

1782	1783	1784	1785

Montgolfier sees silks rise in air

WRITE Compose a news story for a newspaper of the future about the balloon flight you predicted, above. Report *when* (in the future) it took place, *who* did it, *what* they did, *where* they went, and *why* they went there.

AIRY-GO-ROUND

written and illustrated by
William Pène du Bois

Professor William Sherman considers himself to have a pioneering spirit when it comes to hot-air balloons. But his spirit of adventure is sorely tested by a balloon ride that he couldn't have imagined in his wildest dreams!

Professor William Waterman Sherman, a mathematics professor, flew off from San Francisco in a giant balloon. He intended to stay aloft for one year, but seven days later his balloon descended into the water. Professor Sherman was washed ashore to the Pacific island of Krakatoa. Sherman soon learned that the volcanic island contained the world's richest diamond mines, a fact known only to the twenty families who lived on the island. These inhabitants, identified only by letter names, shared equally in the wealth from the mines. Since the people had all the wealth one could possibly desire, they spent their time designing very unusual inventions. After he returned to San Francisco, Professor Sherman described one of these unusual inventions to an interested audience.

The packed auditorium wasn't making a sound. It was waiting anxiously to hear Professor Sherman's extraordinary story. He turned to the audience, cleared his throat, and began his talk:

Mr. F. led me to the first invention he had promised to show me, the Balloon Merry-Go-Round. On our way I told Mr. F. that the name of the invention suggested something at an amusement park. "Just what is this invention for?"

"It is part of an amusement park," said Mr. F., "which the children of Krakatoa are planning for themselves. You see, our children now are between the ages of ten and fifteen. When we return from our trips to other countries, they help us unload our freighter with great interest. It suddenly dawned on them a year or so ago that it would be an excellent idea if a few boatloads were brought back full of supplies exclusively for them; for after all they do own a share in the mines, too. We agreed to give them two boatloads a year, so all of the children held a meeting to decide how best to fill their freighters. This amusement park they have started to build is the result of their planning. The Balloon Merry-Go-Round is their own invention, designed with but little help from us."

"Is there any school here?" I asked.

"The children have no formal schooling. We have taught them how to read and write, and we have tried to teach them a little arithmetic. They have all taken part in the building of our international houses—which is most educating in itself. But all in all, a school is sorely needed here. You aren't by any chance a teacher, are you? Just what does the title Professor stand for in your case?"

"Professor of, uh, Aeronautics," I stuttered. "I teach Balloon Theory at, uh, San Francisco Lighter than Air School." I felt a flush of heat in my cheeks as I waded through this fabulous lie. I had no intention of getting involved again in teaching, the very thing from which this trip of mine was intended to take me.

"How interesting," said Mr. F. "That goes to show how quickly one gets out of touch with one's native city. I can't say that I even recall hearing of such an institution."

"It's one of the latest," I muttered, "practically brand-new." Then quickly changing the subject, I asked what other forms of amusement could be found at the park.

"So far, they have just had time to design and build the Merry-Go-Round, but they have a lot more planned. Most of the usual rides found at amusement parks are impractical for Krakatoa because they are higher than the jungle life on the Island and would be visible from the sea. As a matter of fact, we only take rides on the Balloon Merry-Go-Round after thoroughly scanning the horizon for passing ships. We never use it if anything is in sight. Do you see that tall pole in the distance?"

"Yes, I do," I said. The pole was straight and the same width at the bottom as at the top. It was threaded like a gigantic screw and it was about seventy-five feet tall.

"That's part of the Balloon Merry-Go-Round, the axle around which it revolves to give it its spin when it is gaining altitude."

"Can't that be seen from the ocean?" I asked.

"Yes, it can. But one lone pole isn't enough to attract much attention from passing ships."

We came to a little forest of palm trees, the same sort of neatly kept little forest I had seen the day before, with freshly cut lawn instead of the usual jungle underbrush. We walked through this forest for a hundred yards or so and then came upon a clearing. In the middle of this clearing was what was apparently the Balloon Merry-Go-Round. There were eight little boats around the base of the pole, all joined together bow to stern. In the place of oarlocks, there were two brass rings on these boats, and through these rings passed poles which all met at the main vertical pole of the Merry-Go-Round where they were screwed into the hub of another large brass ring around the pole, forming spokes of a giant wheel. Each boat was covered with a protective tarpaulin. Mr. F. removed one of the tarpaulins and showed me one. They were nice little centerboard sailboats, sturdy and quite seaworthy. The sails were neatly stowed in trim lockers. I didn't notice any masts, but there was definitely a place for them. Alongside of each of these boats was a large deflated balloon painted a pale sky-blue. Off to one side in the clearing there was a little shack made of bamboo which reminded me very much of my basket house. On its walls outside, eight silk hoses were hanging, neatly coiled up and in line. There was a bell on top of this little shack, which could be reached by climbing a ladder.

Mr. F. walked over to the shack, went

inside, and came out again with a spy-glass. He climbed up the ladder to the roof of the shack and carefully looked over the horizon around him, apparently for ships. "Would you care to risk a trip in it?" he asked me. "The weather today is ideal."

"As an ardent balloonist, I accept with enthusiasm; but as a sixty-six-year-old man I must confess that I accept with some trepidation. Is it safe?"

"Absolutely," answered Mr. F. "You don't believe that we would allow our children to make ascensions in danger-ous contraptions, do you?"

"I guess not," I said, reassured. "I am sure that any invention using bal-loons and wind as motive power cannot but be enjoyable."

"Very well, then," said Mr. F. He then loudly rang the bell on top of the shack. This sound produced the same reaction, only considerably happier and more excited, as a school bell back home. We were shortly surrounded by children. These children didn't seem to need to be explained anything either; as soon as they arrived in the clearing they made them-selves extremely busy readying the Bal-loon Merry-Go-Round. They took the tar-paulins off all the boats and rolled them up neatly. Four of the children ran into the shack where they prepared the hydrogen machine and pumps. Another eight each grabbed a silk hose, attached it to the hydrogen machine in the shack

on one end, and to one of the balloons on the other. The balloons were all care-fully unfolded and laid out flat on the ground, and the nets and ropes which attached them to the boats were care-fully placed around and beside them so that they wouldn't get tangled up when the balloons were filled with gas. Slowly the balloons started to fill with hydrogen, the ones nearest the pumps filling faster than the others. They lazily lifted them-selves off the ground with the children watching them carefully, constantly straightening the ropes so they wouldn't get tangled. Soon they were all full of hydrogen and straining at the boats, which were roped to the ground. All forty children were present, working effi-ciently on the Merry-Go-Round, although it was apparent that there was only room for fourteen of them on this trip. There was room for two in each boat, making a total of sixteen seats, but Mr. F. and I were going to occupy two of the seats. There was no arguing among the chil-dren as to whose turn it was; they must have had some sort of passenger sched-ule they followed closely. I sat in a boat with Mr. F.'s son, F-1, and Mr. F. sat with a child in a boat which was on the oppo-site side of the big pole from ours. "This will make the Merry-Go-Round balance better," said F-1.

There were two children on the ground near each boat. When we were all aboard, they detached the silk hydrogen hoses and rolled them back up to the shack where they carefully hung them up. They then returned to us and one held a rope at the bow of each boat and the other held a rope at the boat's stern. One of the children passengers had a blank pistol, the sort used for starting races at track meets. He stood up and yelled in a high clear voice. *"Is everybody ready?"*

A shrill and deafening "yes" was heard, mixed with the deeper voices of Mr. F. and myself. At this signal, the children standing near the boats all gave their ropes a sharp pull, which seemed to unhook the boats from the ground, and they all ran around the pole in the direction we were heading, giving us a good fast start.

The boats were joined together to form the rim of a wheel. The poles going through the brass oarlocks of the boats formed the spokes of this wheel. The spokes were attached to a big brass ring, or hub of the wheel, and this whole gigantic Merry-Go-Round revolved around the seventy-five-foot pole which was pointing straight up to the sky and was threaded like a screw. The balloons lifted the boats around and around the huge screw up into the air. The Balloon Merry-Go-Round gained speed as it gained altitude. The pole was well greased so that by the time we neared the top we were going very fast. I asked F-1 what happened when we reached the top of the pole. "Do we quickly deflate the balloons and revolve back down to the ground around the pole in the opposite direction?"

"Of course not," said F-1. "We fly right off the pole into the air."

"How do we keep the wheel straight when it's in the air?"

"You'll see," he said.

We soon reached the top and the Merry-Go-Round lunged upward as it lost its grip on the pole. The wind immediately started to carry us over the Island. We were gaining altitude fast and, of course, still spinning around at great speed. I must admit this was a truly delightful and exciting ride, unlike any other balloon experience I have ever had. I saw now how the boats were kept level. A child in each boat held the ripcord of his boat's balloon. Whenever a boat went a little higher than the others, the ripcord would be pulled releasing a little hydrogen until the boat was again on the same level.

"You must only be able to take short trips," I told F-1, "if you constantly have to release gas to keep the Merry-Go-Round level."

"That's right," he answered. "The length of our trips depends on many things such as the calmness of the weather, how well we distribute the weight in the boats, and how skillfully we control the ripcords. But you understand," he added, "the Balloon Merry-Go-Round wasn't built for travel but rather for short pleasure trips."

"Oh, of course," I said.

The Balloon Merry-Go-Round was heading directly for the mountain. I saw that we were going to fly over it. I asked F-1 if this were not dangerous.

"It isn't dangerous, but it's rather unfortunate because it always means a short trip."

"Why?" I asked.

"Because the huge crater of the volcanic mountain is full of hot air which forms sort of a vacuum. When we fly over the crater, the Merry-Go-Round is sucked downward rather violently and we always use up a lot of gas controlling it and keeping it level."

"Isn't this hazardous?" I asked.

"No," said F-1, "by the time we reach the mountain, we will be high enough to clear it by a great distance. The only danger in taking a ride in this is landing on the ground or on the mountain, or worst of all, in the mountain when the wind is calm. Krakatoa is a small island, and if there is any wind at all, it will carry the Merry-Go-Round out to sea. Once when we first got it, we took a trip on a very calm day. We went straight up, spun around a while, and gradually lost altitude, landing in a forest of palm trees. No one was hurt, but some of the boats were damaged and one of the balloons was torn. Since then, we have only risked trips when there is wind."

We were nearing the mountain and I leaned over the side of my boat to look

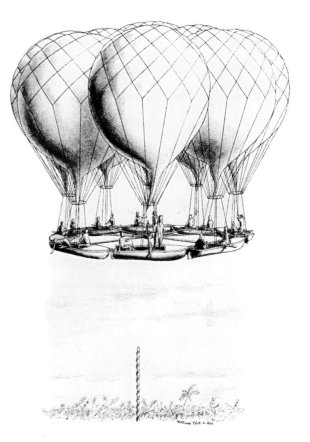

down at the crater. There was a thick gray smoke crawling around inside. It was like looking into a horrible pit full of elephants. When we were directly over the mountain there was a sickening atmosphere of hot air permeated with sulphurous gases. The Merry-Go-Round started tossing around violently over the pit, and the children with the ripcords kept a careful watch directly across our giant wheel at opposite boats to keep the Merry-Go-Round as steady and level as possible. Hanging on tightly, I leaned over the side of the boat in order to have a direct look into the volcanic crater itself. In places where the smoke had cleared

could hear the rumbling of the mountain beneath me mixed with the hissing noise of hydrogen being released from the balloons. I think I was as close to being sick then as it is possible for anyone to be. We were soon over the mountain and in fresh, calm air again and I sat up feeling considerably better.

"To tell you the truth, Sir," said F-1, who apparently could well see that I had nearly lost my breakfast, "I was nearly sick myself that time. The mountain seems unusually violent this morning. I hope this isn't a bad sign."

I took this to be the remark of a younger balloonist comforting an older one who had nearly made a fool of himself. I told him that my behavior was quite inexcusable.

Flying over water in this spinning airship was completely enjoyable. The magnificent seascape of the Pacific Ocean passed before your eyes half of the time, and Krakatoa in its entirety was beneath you for your careful observation with each turn of the Merry-Go-Round. The Island looked beautiful from the air. Its vegetation was so rich, warm, and soft-looking. The mountain looked so fearful and exciting.

After a flight lasting approximately thirty-five minutes we were near the surface of the water. The children, controlling their ripcords like experts, lowered the Merry-Go-Round gently and smoothly

a bit I could see a lake of thick molten lava boiling and bubbling in slow motion. It was a sickening, frightening sight. As I was leaning over, the Merry-Go-Round suddenly plunged downward, then swayed from side to side as the children steadied it. I must have taken a deep gasp of breath, out of fear, I suppose, and my lungs were suddenly filled with hot sulphurous fumes. The Merry-Go-Round was still spinning fast, as well as pitching and rocking in the air. I hastily drew my head back into the boat, shut my eyes, and lay down on the bottom of the boat. I

into the ocean. We made one complete turn in the water and came slowly to a stop. "Well," I exclaimed, "that was undoubtedly the most thrilling and unusual trip I have ever had the pleasure of taking."

The children in the boats, Mr. F., and I then all leaned back and relaxed a while in the sun, looking up at the balloons, which were now half empty and bobbing back and forth with the wind. Suddenly one of the boys, the same one who had fired the starting gun, stood up and said, "All right, everybody, let's go."

At this command, the rest of the children stood up and carefully deflated their balloons and folded them up in their boats without letting any part of them touch water. They folded them lengthwise first, then rolled them from the top toward the bottom where the gas escape was, thus forcing all of the gas out of them and making small neat bundles. They opened the little lockers in the boats, where the sails were, took the sails out, and replaced them with the folded balloons. Each boat had one mainsail.

"How do you sail these boats when they are all attached together like a wheel?" I asked. "And what do you use for masts?" These were foolish questions, I immediately realized, for while I was asking them I managed to figure out these problems myself.

First of all, the children detached the boats one from the other at their bows and sterns. When this was done, they were still attached to each other by the poles which formed the spokes of the giant wheel. These poles were obviously the masts when the boats were used for sailing. The children, two on each pole, all pushed together toward the center hub until the poles slid out through the brass oarlock rings on their boats. Then, still working two on each pole, they unscrewed the poles from the brass hub in the center. They all unscrewed their poles except one boy, the boy who gave the commands. He pulled his pole in with the hub still attached to it, unscrewed the hub in his boat, and put it away in a separate locker. Now that they each had their masts, it was a simple problem to put them into the mast holes. Mr. F. and I did our best to work as efficiently as any of the other crew members. Soon the mainsail was rigged up and we were ready to sail back to the Island. Only the need for a boom was absent from this compact invention. We lowered the centerboards and lined up. It was evidently the custom to race home. The boy who gave the signals took out his gun, fired it, and we were homeward bound as fast as the wind would take us. I am afraid I was more of a hindrance than a capable assistant to young F-1. We finished the race last by about seven minutes. The boats were moored to a dock near the freighter in the hidden inlet and we assembled on shore. F-1 explained to me that the boy who had given the signals was the "Captain of the Day," some sort of honor each child received in turn.

The Captain of the Day told the rest of us that since this was my first trip in the Balloon Merry-Go-Round, the results of the boat race wouldn't count on the Official Scoring Sheet. F-1 let out a whooping cheer at this, which made me feel quite badly. The Captain of the Day then took me aside and told me, in a most polite way, that he thought it would be an excellent idea if I learned a bit about sailing. I assured him that I would.

The Captain of the Day then closed the meeting by saying that the Merry-Go-Round would be reassembled around the flying pole right after supper. "And I want you all to be here and help," he said, looking sternly in my direction.

After forty years of schoolteaching I found myself being ordered about by a child. I couldn't help but find this heretofore impossible turnabout amusing. I was indeed far away from the usual dull school routines I so disliked.

"I'll be there!" I said in a loud voice, as everybody looked at me and laughed.

The whole trip had taken about five hours and we had therefore missed lunch. I devoured an excellent supper at the B.'s chop house, and then Mr. F. and I reported to the flying pole. The Captain of the Day rang the bell on top of the shack assembling all of the children and we were divided into eight groups of five. With five on each boat, we had the Merry-Go-Round reassembled and ready to go in less than half an hour. I will confess, though, that after this busy day on the fabulous Island, I was well ready for bed and slept like a top.

♦ LIBRARY LINK ♦

"Airy-Go-Round" is taken from William Pène du Bois's The Twenty-One Balloons, *winner of the Newbery Award. His other books include* Bear Party *and* Lion, *each of which won the Caldecott Award.*

Reader's Response

What do you think it would be like to grow up on the island of Krakatoa as the author has described it?

AIRY-GO-ROUND

Checking Your Comprehension

1. Who invented the Balloon Merry-Go-Round?
2. Why were the people on Krakatoa worried that passing ships would sight them? How did you decide on the reason?
3. Why did Professor Sherman lie down in the bottom of the boat as they passed over the volcano?
4. Describe how the Balloon Merry-Go-Round worked.
5. What was the only danger in riding the Balloon Merry-Go-Round?

Writing to Learn

THINK AND INVENT William Pène du Bois seems to have enjoyed inventing the Balloon Merry-Go-Round. If you had unlimited resources, what kind of machine would you invent? Sketch and label parts of your new machine, as in the model below.

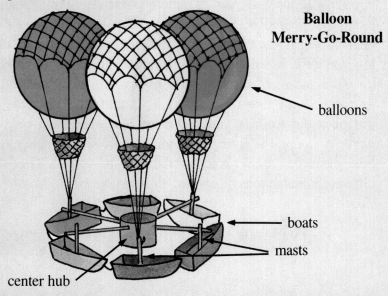

Balloon Merry-Go-Round

balloons

boats

masts

center hub

WRITE Design and write a billboard advertisement for your new machine. Highlight its imaginative features and explain why every person should have one.

READING FICTION

Vocabulary:
Connotations and Denotations

What do you think it would be like to ride on the Balloon Merry-Go-Round? After his ride, Professor Sherman described it as "the most *thrilling* and unusual trip" he had ever taken.

Professor Sherman could have described his trip as amusing, pleasant, or fun. Any one of these words could be used correctly in the above sentence. *Thrilling* is probably the best choice, though, because it gives more of a sense of the excitement involved in the ride.

These four words have similar denotations, but they have different connotations. A word's *denotation* is its literal meaning—the dictionary definition. Sometimes a word will have several different denotations. If you look up the word *run* in an unabridged dictionary, for example, you will find over one hundred different definitions!

The *connotation* of a word goes beyond its dictionary definition. The connotation is the emotional quality the word suggests; it describes the feelings you get when you hear the word. The two words *mutter* and *whisper*, for example, have similar denotations: they both mean "to speak in a lowered tone of voice." They have very different connotations, however. Read this excerpt from "Airy-Go-Round":

> "I can't say that I even recall hearing of such an institution."
> "It's one of the latest," I *muttered*, "practically brand-new."

Because the professor mutters, you get the sense that he is unhappy or uncomfortable with what he is saying. What if he had *whispered*, rather than *muttered*, his remark? Then the connotation would be that he is sharing a secret that he doesn't want overheard.

Sensing Connotations

Good writers are well aware of how important the different connotations of words are, and they will take great care in choosing just the right word for a sentence.

The paragraph below is from "Daedalus and Icarus." In each case, one of the words in parentheses is the one the author used; the other has a similar meaning. See if you can identify the author's words and explain why she chose them.

But then one day guards came to (take, seize) Daedalus and Icarus and (drag, escort) them before Minos the king. And he was (wrathful, sore), furious, (bellowing, yelling) like a (steer, bull). . . .

Did you choose the words with the most powerful, dramatic effect? The author used these words: *seize, drag, wrathful, bellowing,* and *bull.* She carefully chose these words because each one describes the dramatic and threatening nature of the event better than its alternative does.

Using What You Have Learned

Rewrite each sentence using the word in parentheses that has the most powerful, dramatic connotation.

1. We couldn't believe the (ancient, old) plane would fly.
2. Clara covered her ears to block the deafening (noise, roar).
3. The half-starved cat (devoured, ate) the can of food in record time.

As You Read

In the next selection, "Through Skies Never Sailed," notice the words with strong connotations that create certain impressions.

Alberto Santos-Dumont's flying machine was nearly ready, but before it could fly, the daring inventor had to solve a major problem.

THROUGH SKIES NEVER SAILED

by David Fulton

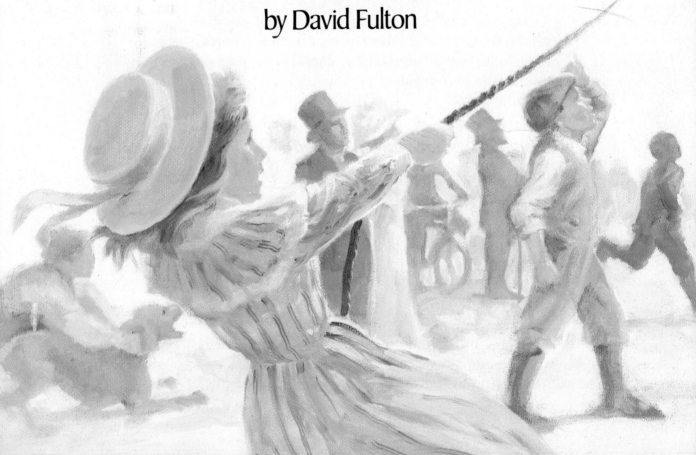

The voice came from out of the sky, "Hey fellows, quick, grab those ropes and pull me into the wind as if I were a kite. Hurry!"

Looking up, the young people were startled to see a man waving wildly at them from a strange banana-shaped flying balloon—a balloon that was about to crash!

Sara reacted quickly and grabbed one of the ropes that dangled near her. But Sara could not even stop the flying contraption, let alone pull it in the other direction. As she attempted to dig her heels into the ground, the balloon nearly toppled her.

"Boys, don't just stand there. Help her," the man in the balloon shouted at Etienne[1] and Louis.

Rushing to help their sister, the boys grabbed other ropes trailing from the balloon and frantically tugged at the runaway flying machine. Finally, the three of them were able to change the direction of the balloon, carrying it into the wind as the aeronaut had requested. The flying machine bobbed up like a kite.

As the young people pulled the balloon down, following the aeronaut's instructions, a crowd began to gather. The

[1]Etienne (ā tyen')

moment the flier was safe on the ground, he was surrounded by a large crowd of curious people, all talking at once.

Sara realized that the man she had rescued was the famous Monsieur Santos-Dumont, the wealthy Brazilian inventor and daredevil who predicted people would someday fly like birds.

"Where are the young people? They are the real heroes of this escape from the jaws of death," she heard him shout over the crowd. Before she knew it, she and her brothers were being thrust toward the aeronaut. "Ah, here they are," he said, and he embraced each of the boys. "You probably saved my life today," he remarked, "and particularly you, young lady, the courageous one. If the balloon had dragged you before your brothers came to your aid, you could have been seriously hurt. I, Alberto Santos-Dumont, am honored to make your acquaintance," he added as he kissed her hand.

Sara blushed and replied, "It is I, Sara Marie Cote, that is honored, Monsieur Santos-Dumont."

"There must be some way I can show my appreciation to you for saving my life," Santos-Dumont said. "How would you like to go for an airborne picnic in one of my balloons?"

Before her stunned brothers could react, the spunky Sara exclaimed eagerly, "I would love that more than anything," for there was no one in Paris who would have appreciated a balloon excursion more than Sara Cote. From the time she was a little girl, Sara had been fascinated by the things of the air. She would often become totally engrossed in watching flocks of pigeons flapping around the Paris church steeples, autumn leaves floating to earth, swirling snowflakes, shooting stars, and—Sara's favorite—kites. Sara had a talent for making kites; her brothers maintained that she was the best kite maker in Paris. Her kites flew higher, they were more maneuverable, and they looked like no others.

Louis and Etienne rehearsed the story of "The Daring Rescue" on the way home, but Sara persuaded them not to tell their parents about her part in the adventure. MaMa often chided Sara for behaving in an unladylike manner, and Sara was sure that being dragged heels first through the park by an experimental flying balloon would not please her. As for the proposed balloon ride, they decided not to bother mentioning it; they knew their parents would never allow it.

When PaPa heard the story later that evening, he noticed Sara's lack of enthusiasm.

"Sara, this account seems to be missing some of your usual influence," he said. Monsieur Cote knew that occasionally Sara intentionally left out her part in such stories to avoid her mother's lecture on ladylike behavior.

"Oh no, she helped," Louis said quickly.

"I'm sure she did," their father said. "But why so glum? It sounds like just your kind of adventure."

"It's nothing, PaPa," Sara replied dejectedly.

"Monsieur Santos-Dumont offered us a ride in a balloon," Etienne said.

"Oh, he did," Monsieur Cote laughed. "In a balloon, you say?"

"Yes," said Sara brightening up, "and I would like to do it."

"Sara," her father said, "you are fearless. I hope you acquire the wisdom to survive being so."

Just then the butler entered the parlor carrying a calling card from a visitor. Sara's father took it, appeared surprised, and then announced, "A Monsieur Alberto Santos-Dumont calls on us this evening. Please show him in, Alphonse."

Alphonse returned with "le petit Santos," as Santos-Dumont was known. Santos-Dumont was a small man with curly black hair, a moustache, and a dark complexion.

"Monsieur Santos-Dumont, we are honored to have this celebrity with us. Knowing of your recent exploits, I marvel that my own children have been involved in one of your daring attempts to fly against the wind. Please join us," Monsieur Cote said as he motioned to a chair.

"Thank you," Monsieur Santos-Dumont said, sitting down. "The press has a tendency to sensationalize my efforts, Monsieur Cote, but indeed your sons, and particularly your courageous daughter, did rescue me this afternoon."

"My daughter?" said Monsieur Cote gazing from his wife to Sara, who focused her eyes on the pattern in the carpet.

"Yes, your daughter was the first one to grab one of my guidelines, although the dirigible was more than she could handle. She was fortunate that the boys joined her as quickly as they did because the dirigible was dragging her."

"Ah, yes, of course. That would be my Sara," Monsieur Cote replied, smiling. Out of the corner of her eye, Sara noticed that her mother wasn't smiling.

"The purpose of my visit in fact is related to the events of this afternoon. I came to invite your family for an excursion in one of my balloons."

Silence filled the Cote parlor as all eyes turned to Sara's father, awaiting his reply. "I don't wish to seem overly conservative or closed minded, Monsieur Santos-Dumont, but I wouldn't consider air travel sufficiently safe to risk my whole family. This afternoon's events are evidence of that."

"I certainly wouldn't ask you to endanger your family, but flying in a balloon, which is merely a big bag filled with hydrogen, has long been demonstrated to be a safe sport.

"I wouldn't suggest taking you in a craft such as the one I was flying this afternoon. That was a 'dirigible.' Its design is the latest breakthrough in the attempt to control the direction of flight. It's a balloon that has a gasoline engine suspended beneath it to direct its movement. Unfortunately, my colleagues and I have yet to work out all the problems. But we will. In any case, the dirigible may soon be obsolete. I recently heard a report at a meeting of the Aero Club, and I understand that some Americans have actually built a glider of some sort that is heavier than the air, and it is said they use a gasoline engine to power it. Now, that is really incredible."

Santos-Dumont could be very persuasive. Sara had

expected PaPa to just say no and put an end to the matter.

That was what her mother had hoped as well. "Frankly, Monsieur," she said, "I am reminded of the story of Icarus when I read of your exploits."

"Icarus's mistake, Madame, was not in the technology but in his ignorance of the limits of the technology. The inventor, Daedalus, was in fact successful because he knew what his invention could and couldn't do. He lived to achieve fame with further feats. I hope I am more like Daedalus than his foolish son.

"Madame, my motto is 'through skies never sailed,' a line I've loosely adapted from Brazil's greatest poet, Luiz Camoes. In describing the exploits of some of our greatest explorers, he wrote that they traveled 'through seas never sailed before.' I intend to go where no one has gone before but I assure you, ballooning is a well-traveled path these days."

"Just how do you figure these Americans are able to lift a glider off the ground if it is heavier than the air?" PaPa asked Monsieur Santos-Dumont.

"I think if you could gain a certain speed in relation to the overall weight and direct the air as it passed over the craft to create loft, that it is very likely that you could lift an object heavier than air," Santos-Dumont replied.

"That's an interesting problem, Monsieur," PaPa concluded. "Would you mind if I visited your workshop one day?"

"I would be truly delighted to have you, and if you are still interested in my little puzzle, perhaps you could check some of my mathematics," Monsieur Santos-Dumont replied.

Monsieur Cote didn't waste any time; he visited the workshop the very next day.

"What happened in St. Cloud?" asked Sara, the moment her father came in the door.

"My experience was very enlightening. This Sunday I propose we all go to St. Cloud for a picnic, a picnic in the air."

MaMa's reaction was not enthusiastic. "Surely, you wouldn't risk your entire family in such a device."

"You are correct, my dear. I wouldn't risk your lives. I believe that there is no risk in a simple balloon ride. Balloons have been with us quite a while and there have been very few accidents with balloons."

"It would only take one, and this Santos-Dumont is a well-known daredevil."

"He's also a very careful man. The risks he takes are well known to him before he takes them. Right now he is building an amazing craft. The mathematics involved in planning the craft are complicated, and I must say he has been extremely careful. I was very impressed," PaPa explained.

"Well, I will trust your judgment, but I can't say I am looking forward to this excursion," MaMa said.

It was a beautiful day, the day they went out to St. Cloud. Light warm breezes blew big fluffy spring clouds across the landscape. Everyone was nervous. A picnic in the air! This would be a day to remember.

On the outskirts of St. Cloud, Louis spotted the top of the balloon over the trees. When they turned the corner, the bright green and yellow balloon loomed over them, bobbing in the wind like an enormous flower. Monsieur Santos-Dumont was standing by the basket directing the workmen.

"Ah, what a perfect day for a balloon ride," the aeronaut exclaimed as the family gathered around him.

Before Sara could catch her breath, they were all in the basket, Santos-Dumont had given orders to have the tether ropes loosened, and the basket had jumped into the air.

Sara watched the objects on the ground become smaller and smaller. She couldn't say a word. It was incredible. She was flying! She wasn't the only one at a loss for words.

"It's something, isn't it?" Monsieur Santos-Dumont said. They all nodded. MaMa looked a little pale. The boys had bug eyes. PaPa was almost laughing.

The breeze caught them, and they floated out over the

country. They could see farms, animals grazing, country roads, ponds, stately villas, gardens, the river as it twisted away south. It was as if they saw these things for the first time. From this vantage point, it was all new. The patterns of the farms were like a crazy quilt embroidered by the paths the animals had made in their pastures. "This is the most wonderful way to view the world," sighed Sara.

They felt so free, being carried by the wind. "Flying is something I want to do the rest of my life," Sara decided. They feasted on the picnic lunch that MaMa had prepared, and eventually it was time to land. Monsieur Santos-Dumont chose a field directly ahead with a road nearby and began to let gas escape from the balloon. Before they knew it, they were down—a perfect landing.

"I must say, Monsieur Santos-Dumont, that you have even won *me* over," MaMa said. "I want to thank you very much for what has been an extraordinary experience."

"The pleasure was all mine," Monsieur Santos-Dumont replied. "And Sara, how did you find ballooning?"

"It was the most wonderful thing in the world," she said.

"Well, perhaps you can accompany your father when he visits my workshop. I've asked him to check my figures from time to time," Santos-Dumont said.

"Could I, PaPa?" Sara pleaded.

"We'll see," her father said.

Several weeks later, Sara stood next to her father in Monsieur Santos-Dumont's workshop, staring at a contraption that looked like an enormous, oddly shaped box kite that had *14 bis* written on its side. "Surely no one expects this thing to fly," she murmured. "It couldn't possibly . . . but then again, why not? It's really not that much different than a giant kite."

Week after week, Sara accompanied her father as he traveled to St. Cloud to go over the figures Santos-Dumont and his colleagues developed from their experiments. They often discussed the exploits of other aeronauts and the amazing flying machines that were being built all over the world. Enormous dirigibles were being built that carried passengers thousands of miles. People were flying in gliders, and it seemed only a matter of time before someone would achieve flight in a glider powered by an internal combustion machine. Santos-Dumont wanted to be that person.

His colleagues thought he was chasing the impossible. The problem of how the craft would lift not just a man but a gas engine as well seemed insurmountable.

"There must be some way," Sara insisted, as she and her father drove home from the workshop one evening. As she watched the city lights grow from a few to several hundred, she pondered the problem of how the craft could gain altitude. In her mind she pictured *14 bis* as it stood in the hangar. It was actually built from box kites. Two boxes on either side of the engine formed the wings and a long narrow structure extended to the front where there was another large box. The air blew through these boxes. How did she get lift with her kites? As she pictured a kite in the air, she could almost feel the tugging of the kite string in her hand. And then suddenly, like the lights in Paris, the answer flashed on in her mind, clear and obvious.

"PaPa," she shouted, "I know what's wrong with *14 bis*!"

"Now how would you know the answer when all those experts don't?" he replied.

"My kites, my kites—that craft is just a big kite."

"Think a minute," PaPa said. "That so-called big 'kite' can carry a human being, possibly our friend, to his death."

Sara momentarily doubted that she could possibly think of something that those scientists had overlooked. But then she remembered a discussion in which some of Monsieur Santos-Dumont's colleagues were bemoaning the fact that so many "amateurs" were now trying their hand at flying. It was felt that these "amateurs" gave aeronauts a bad name. But Santos-Dumont had defended them, asserting that often discoveries that changed history had come from the ranks of such "amateurs."

"PaPa, I know the answer," Sara said, more confidently. She described the kite-like structure of *14 bis* and the parallels she saw with her kites. "There are surfaces," she explained.

"Planes," her father added, "as in geometry."

"Yes, exactly—planes as in geometry. But at an angle that allows the air to push it up."

Sara's father thought for a few seconds. Then he put his head out of the carriage. "Driver!" he shouted, "We'd like to go back to St. Cloud."

Turning to Sara he said, "My dear, I think you've hit upon something very important."

Santos-Dumont thought so, too. "That's it! Of course, that's it exactly! The dihedral angle of the wings provides the extra power to lift the craft. Cote, your daughter is a genius! You must stay and help me work out the computations."

"I am afraid Madame Cote is expecting us, and we are already very late," Monsieur Cote replied.

"No, we must send her a message and explain the situation. Please, Monsieur Cote. This is history!"

Sara's father was finally persuaded and arrangements were made. Soon other scientists began arriving. As the night progressed, there was loud debate over Sara's idea. Sara could hear the arguing late into the night from her cot in the office.

It was dawn when her father woke her. He looked exhausted. Later, as they rode home, he announced, "Next week, after they make the adjustments to the craft, Santos-Dumont plans to fly."

The news swept Paris—Santos-Dumont was going to attempt to be the first human to fly a craft heavier than air.

A tremendous crowd gathered in St. Cloud to watch Santos-Dumont attempt his flight. Sara and her family found a vantage point from which to watch but they could not get close enough to offer any words of encouragement.

The *14 bis* looked awkward and small when Santos-Dumont climbed into position. Sara was afraid that he couldn't possibly survive a crash in such a flimsy craft, but the motor roared and as the glider sped across the field, the Santos-Dumont pennant billowed reassuringly, "Through Skies Never Sailed."

The *14 bis* lumbered across the field, gaining speed, and then suddenly it lurched into the air. The drone of the engine was the only sound as the entire crowd held its breath and watched history being made. The *14 bis* was flying! Then, suddenly, it dipped down and crashed. A tremendous roar went up and the crowd rushed out onto the field.

"Is he all right?" Sara shouted frantically.

Then, there he was—on the shoulders of the crowd—arms raised in victory.

The news astonished the world. Santos-Dumont had flown thirty-six feet at twenty-three miles per hour at a height of ten feet. *The New York Herald* exclaimed, First Mechanical Flight of Man. *Le Monde* in Paris carried the headline, An "Infuriated Grasshopper" Makes History.

Although damaged, *"The Infuriated Grasshopper,"* as the *14 bis* was now known, was repaired and flew again a month later—a little higher, a little longer.

Santos-Dumont became an international celebrity, and the Cotes saw little of him because of the new demands on his time. But one day he arrived to personally deliver invitations to Sara and her father. He was to receive the Legion of Honor from the president of France and they were to attend the ceremony as his special guests.

In his acceptance speech, Santos-Dumont noted that his success represented the hard work and insights of many people.

"From a kite builder to a scientist," he said.

"A kite builder? That's me!" Sara thought proudly and her spirits soared. What a grand affair!

Reader's Response

What did you learn from Sara's determination in this story?

THROUGH SKIES NEVER SAILED

Checking Your Comprehension

1. In the story, the author uses the word *contraption* to describe the dirigible. What is the connotation of *contraption*?
2. How was Santos-Dumont's dirigible different from a balloon?
3. Describe how Madame Cote's attitude toward flying changed.
4. What gave Sara the courage to tell her father her idea of how a heavy flying machine could gain altitude?
5. List three qualities that describe Sara's character. Tell why you chose each quality. How did you decide on these qualities?
6. Do you think Santos-Dumont would have succeeded without Sara's help?

Writing to Learn

THINK AND EVALUATE Imagine that you have the task of selecting *one* balloonist to perform the dangerous feat of crossing the Pacific Ocean in a balloon. Read the characteristics of two applicants below and decide which one you would select for the job.

Applicant 1	Applicant 2
restrained	enthusiastic
intuitive	daring
plodding	exact
self-controlled	hot-tempered
non-social	socially active
reflective	imaginative

WRITE Write a letter to the person you did not select for the job. Tell why you made the decision.

To Beachey, 1912

Riding against the east,
A veering, steady shadow
Purrs the motor-call
Of the man-bird
Ready with the death-laughter
In his throat
And in his heart always
The love of the big blue beyond.

Only a man,
A far fleck of shadow on the east,
Sitting at ease
With his hands on a wheel
And around him the large gray wings.
Hold him, great soft wings,
Keep and deal kindly, O wings,
With the cool, calm shadow at the wheel.

Carl Sandburg

To an
Aviator

You who have grown so intimate with stars
And know their silver dripping from your wings,
Swept with the breaking day across the sky,
Known kinship with each meteor that swings—
You who have touched the rainbow's fragile gold,
Carved lyric ways through dawn and dusk and rain
And soared to heights our hearts have only dreamed—
How can you walk earth's common ways again?

Daniel Whitehead Hicky

WEST WITH THE NIGHT

BY BERYL MARKHAM

By the 1930s, flying machines were no longer a dream—but many frontiers of flight still remained. In 1936, Beryl Markham flew "West with the Night," chasing her own special dream.

There was hardly an adventure that the young British woman Beryl Markham did not attempt. As a young girl, she lived in the plains of East Africa, training horses on her family's ranch and hunting with native tribespeople. Then in the 1920s, she met a veteran flier named Tom Black, and he helped her become the first professional woman pilot in all of Africa, delivering mail and supplies from cities like Cairo, Nairobi, and Kisumu to lonely outposts in the jungle.

I have seldom dreamed a dream worth dreaming again, or at least none worth recording. Mine are not enigmatic dreams; they are peopled with characters who are plausible and who do plausible things, and I am the most plausible amongst them. All the characters in my dreams have quiet voices like the voice of the man who telephoned me at Elstree one morning in September of nineteen-thirty-six and told me that there was rain and strong head winds over the west of England and over the Irish Sea, and that there were variable winds and clear skies in mid-Atlantic and fog off the coast of Newfoundland.

"If you are still determined to fly the Atlantic this late in the year," the voice said, "the Air Ministry suggests that the weather it is able to forecast for tonight, and for tomorrow morning, will be about the best you can expect."

The voice had a few other things to say, but not many, and then it was gone, and I lay in bed half-suspecting that the telephone call and the man who made it were only parts of the mediocre dream I had been dreaming. I felt that if I closed my eyes the unreal quality of the message would be re-established, and that, when I opened them again, this would be another ordinary day with its usual beginning and its usual routine.

But of course I could not close my eyes, nor my mind, nor my memory. I could lie there for a few moments—remembering how it had begun, and telling myself, with senseless repetition, that by tomorrow morning I should either have flown the Atlantic to America—or I should not have flown it. In either case this was the day I would try.

Record flights had actually never interested me very much for myself. There were people who thought that such flights were done for admiration and publicity, and worse. But of all the records—from Louis Blériot's[1] first crossing of the English Channel in nineteen hundred and nine, through and beyond Kingsford Smith's flight from San Francisco to Sydney, Australia—none had been made by amateurs, nor by novices, nor by men or women less hardened to failure, or less than masters of their trade. None of these was false. They were a company that simple respect and simple ambition made it worth more than an effort to follow.

The Carberrys (of Seramai) were in London and I could remember everything about their dinner party—even the menu. I could remember June Carberry and all her guests, and the man named McCarthy, who lived in Zanzibar, leaning across the table and saying, "J.C., why don't you finance Beryl for a record flight?"

I could lie there staring lazily at the ceiling and recall J.C.'s dry answer: "A number of pilots have flown the North Atlantic, west to east. Only Jim Mollison has done it alone the other way—from Ireland. Nobody has done it alone from England—man or woman. I'd be interested in that, but nothing else. If you want to try it, Burl, I'll back you. I think Edgar Percival could build a plane that would do it, provided you can fly it. Want to chance it?"

"Yes."

I could remember saying that better than I could remember anything—except J.C.'s almost ghoulish grin, and his remark that sealed the agreement: "It's a deal, Burl. I'll furnish the plane and you fly the Atlantic—but, gee, I wouldn't tackle it for a million. Think of all that black water! Think how cold it is!"

And I had thought of both.

I had thought of both for a while, and then there had been other things to think about. I had moved to Elstree, half-hour's flight from the Percival Aircraft Works at Gravesend, and almost daily for three months now I had flown down to the factory in a hired plane and watched the Vega Gull they were making for me. I had watched her birth and watched her growth. I had watched her wings take shape, and seen wood and fabric moulded to her ribs to form her long, sleek belly, and I had seen her engine cradled into her frame, and made fast.

The Gull had a turquoise-blue body and silver wings. Edgar

[1] Blériot (ble rēō')

Percival had made her with care, with skill, and with worry—the care of a veteran flyer, the skill of a master designer, and the worry of a friend. Actually the plane was a standard sport model with a range of only six hundred and sixty miles. But she had a special under-carriage built to carry the weight of her extra oil and petrol tanks. The tanks were fixed into the wings, into the centre[2] section, and into the cabin itself. In the cabin they formed a wall around my seat, and each tank had a valve of its own. The valves were important.

"If you open one," said Percival, "without shutting the other first, you may get an airlock. You know the tanks in the cabin have no gauges, so it may be best to let one run completely dry before opening the next. Your motor might go dead in the interval—but she'll start again. She's a De Havilland Gipsy—and Gipsys never stop."

I had watched the building of the plane and I had trained for the flight like an athlete. And now, as I lay in bed, fully awake, I could still hear the quiet voice of the man from the Air Ministry intoning, like the voice of a dispassionate court clerk: ". . . the weather for tonight and tomorrow . . . will be about the best you can expect." I should have liked to discuss the flight once more with Tom before I took off, but he was on a special job up north. I got out of bed and bathed and put on my flying clothes and took some cold chicken packed in a

[2]Some of the words in this selection are spelled in the British style.

cardboard box and flew over to the military field at Abingdon, where the Vega Gull waited for me under the care of the R.A.F. I remember that the weather was clear and still.

Here is a sprig of heather," said Jock Cameron, and I took it and pinned it into a pocket of my flying jacket.

There were press cars parked outside the field at Abingdon, and several press planes and photographers, but the R.A.F. kept everyone away from the grounds except technicians and a few of my friends.

You can live a lifetime and, at the end of it, know more about other people than you know about yourself. You learn to watch other people, but you never watch yourself because you strive against loneliness. If you read a book, or shuffle a deck of cards, or care for a dog, you are avoiding yourself. The abhorrence of loneliness is as natural as wanting to live at all. If it were otherwise, people would never have bothered to make an alphabet, nor to have fashioned words out of what were only animal sounds, nor to have crossed continents—each wishing to see what the other looked like.

Being alone in an aeroplane for even so short a time as a night and a day, irrevocably alone, with nothing to observe but your instruments and your own hands in semi-darkness, nothing to contemplate but the size of your small courage, nothing to wonder about but the beliefs, the faces, and the hopes rooted in your mind—such an experience can be as startling as the first awareness of a stranger walking by your side at night. You are the stranger.

It is dark already and I am over the south of Ireland. There are the lights of Cork and the lights are wet; they are drenched in Irish rain, and I am above them and dry. I am above them and the plane roars in a sobbing world, but it imparts no sadness to me. I feel the security of solitude, the exhilaration of escape. So long as

I can see the lights and imagine the people walking under them, I feel selfishly triumphant, as if I have eluded care and left even the small sorrow of rain in other hands.

It is a little over an hour now since I left Abingdon. England, Wales, and the Irish Sea are behind me like so much time used up. On a long flight distance and time are the same. But there had been a moment when Time stopped—and Distance too. It was the moment I lifted the blue-and-silver Gull from the aerodrome, the moment the photographers aimed their cameras, the moment I felt the craft refuse its burden and strain toward the earth in sullen rebellion, only to listen at last to the persuasion of stick and elevators, the dogmatic argument of blueprints that said she *had* to fly because the figures proved it.

So she had flown, and once airborne, once she had yielded to the argument of the blueprints, she had said, "There: I have lifted the weight. Now, where are we bound?"—and the question had frightened me.

"We are bound for a place thirty-six hundred miles from here—two thousand miles of it unbroken ocean. Most of the way it will be night. We are flying west with the night." So there behind me is Cork; and ahead of me is Berehaven Lighthouse. It is the last light, standing on the last land. I watch it, counting the frequency of its flashes—so many to the minute. Then I pass it and fly out to sea.

The fear is gone now—not overcome nor reasoned away. It is gone because something else has taken its place; the confidence and the trust, the inherent belief in the security of land underfoot—now this faith is transferred to my plane, because the land has vanished and there is no other tangible thing to fix faith upon. Flight is but momentary escape from the eternal custody of earth.

Rain continues to fall, and outside the cabin it is totally dark. My altimeter says that the Atlantic is two thousand feet below me, my Sperry Artificial Horizon says that I am flying level. I judge my drift at three degrees more than my weather chart suggests, and fly accordingly. I am flying blind. A beam to follow would help. So would a radio—but then, so would clear weather. The voice of the man at the Air Ministry had not promised storm.

I feel the wind rising and the rain falls hard. The smell of petrol in the cabin is so strong and the roar of the plane so loud that my senses are almost deadened. Gradually it becomes unthinkable that existence was ever otherwise.

At ten o'clock P.M. I am flying along the Great Circle Course for Harbour Grace, Newfoundland, into a forty-mile headwind at a speed of one hundred and thirty miles an hour. Because of the weather, I cannot be sure of how many more hours I have to fly, but I think it must be between sixteen and eighteen.

At ten thirty I am still flying on the large cabin tank of petrol, hoping to use it up and put an end to the liquid swirl that has rocked the plane since my take-off. The tank has no gauge, but written on its side is the assurance: "This tank is good for four hours."

There is nothing ambiguous about such a guaranty. I believe it, but at twenty-five minutes to eleven, my motor coughs and dies, and the Gull is powerless above the sea.

I realize that the heavy drone of the plane has been, until this moment, complete and comforting silence. It is the actual silence following the last splutter of the engine that stuns me. I can't feel fear; I can't feel anything. I can only observe with a stupid disinterest that my hands are violently active and know that, while they move, I am being hypnotized by the needle of my altimeter.

I suppose that the denial of natural impulse is what is meant by "keeping calm," but impulse has reason in it. If it is night and you are sitting in an aeroplane with a stalled motor, and there are two thousand feet between you and the sea, nothing can be more reasonable than the impulse to pull back your stick in the hope of adding to that two thousand, if only by a little. The thought, the knowledge, the law that tells you that your hope lies not in this, but in a contrary act—the act of directing your impotent craft toward the water—seems a terrifying abandonment, not only of reason, but of sanity. Your mind and your heart reject it. It is your hands—your stranger's hands—that follow with unfeeling precision the letter of the law.

I sit there and watch my hands push forward on the stick and feel the Gull respond and begin its dive to the sea. Of course it is a simple thing; surely the cabin tank has run dry too soon. I need only to turn another valve . . .

But it is dark in the cabin. It is easy to see the luminous dial of the altimeter and to note that my height is now eleven hundred feet, but it is not easy to see a valve that is somewhere near the floor of the plane. A hand gropes and reappears with an electric torch, and fingers, moving with agonizing composure, find the valve and turn it; and I wait.

At three hundred feet the motor is still dead, and I am conscious that the needle of my altimeter seems to whirl like the spoke of a spindle winding up the remaining distance between the plane and the water. There is some lightning, but the quick flash only serves to emphasize the darkness. How high can waves reach—twenty feet, perhaps? Thirty?

It is impossible to avoid the thought that this is the end of my flight, but my reactions are not orthodox; the various incidents of my entire life do not run through my mind like a motion-picture gone mad.

I only feel that all this has happened before—and it has. It has all happened a hundred times in my mind, in my sleep, so that now I am not really caught in terror; I recognize a familiar scene, a familiar story with its climax dulled by too much telling.

I do not know how close to the waves I am when the motor explodes to life again. But the sound is almost meaningless. I see my hand easing back on the stick, and I feel the Gull climb up into the storm, and I see the altimeter whirl like a spindle again, paying out the distance between myself and the sea.

The storm is strong. It is comforting. It is like a friend shaking me and saying, "Wake up! You were only dreaming."

But soon I am thinking. By simple calculation I find that my motor had been silent for perhaps an instant more than thirty seconds.

A lighted ship—the daybreak—some steep cliffs standing in the sea. The meaning of these will never change for pilots. If one day an ocean can be flown within an hour, if planes can be built that so master time, the sight of land will be no less welcome to the pilots of those fantastic craft. They will have cheated laws that the cunning of science has taught them how to cheat, and they will feel their guilt and be eager for the sanctuary of the soil.

I saw the ship and the daybreak, and then I saw the cliffs of Newfoundland wound in ribbons of fog. I felt the elation I had so long imagined, and I felt the happy guilt of having circumvented the stern authority of the weather and the sea. But mine was a minor triumph; my swift Gull was not so swift as to have escaped unnoticed. The night and the storm had caught her and we had flown blind for nineteen hours.

I was tired now, and cold. Ice began to film the glass of the cabin windows and the fog played a magician's game with the island. But the land was there. I could not see it, but I had seen it. I could not afford to believe that it was any land but the land I wanted. I could not afford to believe that my navigation was at fault, because there was no time for doubt.

South to Cape Race, West to Sydney on Cape Breton Island. With my protractor, my map, and my compass, I set my new course, humming the ditty that Tom had taught me: "Variation West—magnetic best. Variation East—magnetic least." A silly rhyme, but it served to placate, for the moment, two warring poles—the magnetic and the true. I flew south and found the lighthouse of Cape Race protruding from the fog like a warning finger. I circled twice and went on over the Gulf of Saint Lawrence.

After a while there would be New Brunswick, and then Maine— and then New York. I could anticipate. I could almost say, "Well, if you stay awake, you'll find it's only a matter of time now"—but there was no question of staying awake. I was tired and I had not moved an inch since that uncertain moment at Abingdon when the Gull had elected to rise with her load and fly, but I could not have closed my eyes. I could sit there in the cabin, walled in glass and petrol tanks, and be grateful for the sun and light, and the fact that I could see the water under me. They were almost the last waves I had to pass. Four hundred miles of water, but then the land again—Cape Breton. I would stop at Sydney to refuel and go on. It was easy now. It would be like stopping at Kisumu and going on.

Success breeds confidence. But who has a right to confidence? I had a following wind, my last tank of petrol was more than three-quarters full, and the world was as bright to me as if it were a new world, never touched. If I had been wiser, I might have known that such moments are, like innocence, short-lived. My engine began to shudder before I saw the land. It died, it spluttered, it started again and limped along. It coughed and spat black exhaust toward the sea.

There are words for everything. There was a word for this— airlock, I thought. This had to be an airlock because there was petrol enough. I thought I might clear it by turning on and turning off all the empty tanks, and so I did that. The handles of the valves were sharp little pins of metal, and when I had opened and closed them a dozen times, I saw that my hands were bleeding and that the blood was dropping on my maps and on my clothes, but the effort wasn't any good. I coasted along on a sick and halting engine. The oil pressure and the oil temperature gauges were normal, the magnetos working, and yet I lost altitude slowly while the realization of failure seeped into my heart. If I made the land, I should have been the first to fly the North Atlantic from England, but from my point of view, from a pilot's point of view, a forced landing was failure because New York was my goal. If only I could land and then take off, I would make it still . . . if only, if only. . . .

The engine cuts again, and then catches, and each time it spurts to life I climb as high as I can get, and then it splutters and stops and I glide once more toward the water, to rise again and descend again, like a hunting sea bird.

I find the land. Visibility is perfect now and I see land forty or fifty miles ahead. If I am on course, that will be Cape Breton. Minute after minute goes by. The minutes almost materialize; they pass before my eyes like links in a long slow-moving chain, and each time the engine cuts, I see a broken link in the chain and catch my breath until it passes.

The land is under me. I snatch my map and stare at it to confirm my whereabouts. I am, even at my present crippled speed, only twelve minutes from Sydney Airport, where I can land for repairs and then go on.

The engine cuts once more and I begin to glide, but now I am not worried; she will start again, as she has done, and I will gain altitude and fly into Sydney.

But she doesn't start. This time she's dead as death; the Gull settles earthward and it isn't any earth I know. It is black earth stuck with boulders and I hang above it on hope and on a motionless propeller. Only I cannot hang above it long. The earth hurries to meet me, I bank, turn, and sideslip to dodge the boulders, my wheels touch, and I feel them submerge. The nose of the plane is engulfed in mud, and I go forward, striking my head on the glass of the cabin front, hearing it shatter, feeling blood pour over my face.

I stumble out of the plane and sink to my knees in muck and stand there foolishly staring, not at the lifeless land, but at my watch.

Twenty-one hours and twenty-five minutes.

Atlantic flight. Abingdon, England, to a nameless swamp—nonstop.

A Cape Breton Islander found me—a fisherman trudging over the bog saw the Gull with her tail in the air and her nose buried, and then he saw me floundering in the embracing soil of his native land. I had been wandering for an hour and the black mud had got up to my waist and the blood from the cut in my head had met the mud halfway.

From a distance, the fisherman directed me with his arms and with shouts toward the firm places in the bog, and for another hour I walked on them and came toward him like a citizen of the underworld blinded by the sun, but it wasn't the sun; I hadn't slept for forty hours.

He took me to his hut on the edge of the coast and I found that built upon the rocks there was a little cubicle that houses an ancient telephone—put there in case of shipwrecks.

I telephoned to Sydney Airport to say that I was safe and to prevent a needless search being made. On the following morning I did step out of a plane at Floyd Bennett Field and there was a crowd of people waiting there to greet me, but the plane I stepped from was not the Gull, and for days while I was in New York I kept thinking about that and wishing over and over again that it had been the Gull, until the wish lost its significance, and time moved on, overcoming many things it met on the way.

Reader's Response

How do you feel about Beryl Markham's final statement in the selection?

WEST WITH THE NIGHT

Checking Your Comprehension

1. Markham says that she was never interested in record flights. Why, then, does she decide to attempt this record flight?
2. How does Markham feel about the *Vega Gull*? How did you figure this out?
3. What does Markham think is the main reason human beings developed language and engaged in exploration?
4. Do you agree with Markham that no matter how easy flight may become, the sight of land will always be welcomed by pilots? Why or why not?
5. What physical and mental qualities does a pilot need in order to fly long distances?
6. What do you think is the main idea of the last paragraph?
7. Why do you think "West with the Night" was written in the present tense? What feelings did Markham want to bring out?

Writing to Learn

THINK AND EVALUATE   Not many people could have accomplished what Beryl Markham did. In fact, Beryl Markham was well-suited to fly across the Atlantic alone. Go back through "West with the Night" and find evidence that supports this statement. Then complete the chart below on your own paper.

Evidence:	Pulling it together:
_____ _____ _____	Beryl Markham was well-suited to fly across the Altantic alone.

WRITE   Write a paragraph based on the evidence chart above. Tell how the evidence supports the idea that Beryl Markham was well-suited to fly across the Atlantic Ocean alone.

381

READING NON-FICTION

Comprehension:

Generalizations

If someone said to you, "People like Beryl Markham risk their lives because they want to be famous," you might respond, "No, they just want to do something that no one else has ever done." Both of these statements are *generalizations*. A generalization is a broad statement based on a number of facts. Authors often make generalizations in their writing. In order to evaluate authors' ideas, you need to be able to recognize and make judgments about their generalizations.

Identifying Generalizations

To spot a generalization, watch for signal words such as *many, most, usually, typically,* and *generally*. Even without signal words, you can identify a generalization by looking for a broad statement that encompasses many specific examples. Both sentences below from "The Great Balloon Craze" contain generalizations.

> Ballooning in the nineteenth century was mostly a spectator sport, popular with crowds at circuses and fairs. Balloonists were looked upon as entertainers. . . .

You know that the first sentence contains a generalization because of the signal word *(mostly).* The second sentence does not have a signal word, but it is a generalization because it tells you about people *in general* rather than one specific balloonist or group of balloonists.

These generalizations are *valid*. That is, they are true for many individual examples. You can test their validity by looking for specific examples they apply to in the selection. You can also use your own knowledge to determine if a generalization is valid.

A generalization is *faulty,* or not valid, if it is not consistent with the facts as we know them, or if it makes a statement that is too broad for the supporting evidence. When you see generalizations that contain words such as *only, all, none, always, never,* and *every* beware! It is rare that something is *always* or *never* the case.

Finding and Judging Generalizations

The following sentences are from "The Great Balloon Craze." Find the one that is a generalization and decide if it is valid or faulty.

1. It took a long time for American women to begin ballooning.
2. Not until 1825 did a Mrs. Johnson make an ascent.
3. In 1855 . . . Lucretia Bradley, from Pennsylvania, made an ascent which was considerably more dramatic.

Did you remember to look for a broad statement? The first sentence is a generalization that makes a broad statement about American women *in general.* The other sentences state facts about particular American women. The generalization is valid because the specific facts given in the selection support it.

Using What You Have Learned

The following statements are from "The Great Balloon Craze." Decide whether each one is a generalization, and, if it is, whether it is valid or faulty.

1. Less than fifty years later came the first actual flight by a woman.
2. Bits of ash in a fire are often carried aloft by smoke.
3. Everyone wanted to fly now.

As You Read

As you read the next selection, "One Bright Star," watch for any generalizations that the author makes.

Modern technology quickly expanded the capabilities of aircraft, and transatlantic flight soon became commonplace. Before long, fliers' dreams began to reach beyond this planet to the vastness of space.

ONE BRIGHT STAR

by Anne Morrow Lindbergh

We wake to the alarm at four thirty and leave our motel at five fifteen. The three astronauts must be already climbing into their seats at the top of their "thirty-six-story" rocket, poised for flight. The pilgrimage of sightseers has started to the Cape. Already the buses have left and lines of cars are on the roads. It is dark, a little chilly, with a sky full of stars. As we approach the Cape we see again the rocket and its launching tower from far off over the lagoon. It is the newest and most perfected creation of a scientific age—hard, weighty metal.

We watch the launching with some of the astronauts and their families, from a site near the Vehicle Assembly Building [VAB]. Our cars are parked on a slight rise of ground. People get out, walk about restlessly, set up cameras, and adjust their binoculars. The launch pad is about three miles away, near the beach. We look across Florida marsh grass and palmettos. A cabbage palm stands up black against

a shadowy sky, just left of the rocket and its launching tower. As dawn flushes the horizon, an egret rises and lazily glides across the flats between us and the pad. It is a still morning. Ducks call from nearby inlets. Vapor trails of a high-flying plane turn pink in an almost cloudless sky. Stars pale in the blue.

With the morning light, Apollo 8 and its launching tower become clearer, harder, and more defined. One can see the details of installation. The dark sections on the smooth sides of the rocket, marking its stages, cut up the single fluid line. Vapor steams furiously off its side. No longer stark and simple, this morning the rocket is complicated, mechanical, earth-bound. Too weighty for flight, one feels.

People stop talking, stand in front of their cars, and raise binoculars to their eyes. We peer nervously at the launch site and then at our wrist watches. Radio voices blare unnaturally loud from car windows: "Now only thirty minutes to launch time . . . fifteen minutes

. . . six minutes . . . thirty seconds to go . . . twenty . . . T minus fifteen . . . fourteen . . . thirteen . . . twelve . . . eleven . . . ten . . . nine . . . Ignition!"

A jet of steam shoots from the pad below the rocket.

"Ahhhh!" The crowd gasps, almost in unison. Now great flames spurt, leap, belch out across the horizon. Clouds of smoke billow up on either side of the rocket, completely hiding its base. From the midst of this holocaust, the rocket begins to rise—slowly, as in a dream, so slowly it seems to hang suspended on the cloud of fire and smoke. It's impossible—it can't rise. Yes, it rises, but heavily, as if the giant weight is pulled by an invisible hand out of the atmosphere, like the lead on a plumb line from the depths of the sea. Slowly it rises and—because of our distance—silently, as in a dream.

Suddenly the noise breaks, jumps across our three separating miles—a shattering roar of explosions, a trip hammer over one's head, under one's feet, through one's body. The earth shakes; cars rattle; vibrations beat in the chest. A roll of thunder, prolonged, prolonged, prolonged.

I drop the binoculars and put my hands to my ears, holding my head to keep it steady. My throat tightens—am I going to cry?—my eyes are fixed on the rocket, mesmerized by its slow ascent.

The foreground is now full of birds; a great flock of ducks, herons, small birds, rise pell-mell from the marshes at the noise. Fluttering in alarm and confusion, they scatter in all directions as if it were the end of the world. In the seconds I take to look at them, the rocket has left the tower.

It is up and away, a comet boring through the sky, no longer the vulnerable untried child, no longer the earth-bound machine, or the weight at the end of a line, but sheer terrifying force, blasting upward on its own titanic power.

It has gone miles into the sky. It is blurred by a cloud. No, it has made its own cloud—a huge vapor trail, which hides it. Out of the cloud something falls, cartwheeling down, smoking. "The first-stage cutoff," someone says. Where is the rocket itself?

There, above the cloud now, reappears the rocket, only a very bright star, diminishing every second. Soon out of sight, off to lunar space.

One looks earthward again. It is curiously still and empty. A cloud of brown smoke hangs motionless on the horizon. Its long shadow reaches us across the grass. The launch pad is empty. The abandoned launching tower is being sprayed with jets of water to cool it down. It steams in the bright morning air. Still dazed, people stumble into cars and start the slow, jammed trek back to town. The monotone of radio voices continues. One clings to this last thread of contact with something incredibly beautiful that has vanished.

"Where are they—where are they now?" In eleven minutes we get word. They are in earth orbit. They "look good" in the laconic space talk that comes down from over a hundred miles above earth. And one realizes again that it is the people above all that matter, the individuals who man the machine, give it heart, sight, speech, intelligence, and direction; and the people on earth who are backing them up, monitoring their every move, even to their heartbeats. This is not sheer power, it is power under the control of man.

We drive slowly back to town. Above us the white vapor trail of the rocket is being scattered by wind into feathery shapes of heron's wings—the only mark in the sky of the morning's launching.

Afternoon—Merritt Island Refuge

The long afternoon stretches before us. Instinctively we want to touch earth again, to drench ourselves in nature. The desire is as strong as sleep, or the thirst to plunge into the sea. We must find our human base, after the superhuman sight of this morning. Several astronauts have told us that the Cape is a wildlife refuge and, rather incredulous, we want to see what is left of the quiet coast we remember. The greatest rocket site on earth, with its noise, mechanization, buildings, and roads, hardly seems the place for a wildlife sanctuary. What could be further from primitive wilderness than this pinnacle of scientific civilization, this last reach of humanity, this rocket to leave the earth itself?

But actually NASA has preserved over fifty thousand acres of wild land, surrounding the central base of activity. The launching sites and Industrial Area are buffered from the mainland by a broad belt of wilderness. Here now, as before, migratory birds and water fowl, as well as birds and animals native to Florida, find sanctuary. The Cape, angling out into the Atlantic, has always been a crucial flyway for migrating birds. Without NASA's protection, it might well have gone the way of much of Florida's coastline, slashed by highways, cut up for real estate, and cluttered by roadside stands. Fortunately, it has been saved, not only for wildlife but also for man.

"Doesn't the blast-off frighten the birds?" I ask the refuge director, remembering the distracted flight this morning. "It does," he answers, "but they come right back." There aren't enough launchings, he explains, to frighten them away permanently, as might happen near a commercial airport. "And also," he adds, hesitating, as though it might sound extravagant, "before launchings we try to go around with a helicopter and herd the wildlife to another area."

Out of sight of the rocket towers, we begin to realize, are wide stretches of jungle growth, fresh-water marshes and salt-water creeks, where great flocks of ducks and coots winter, and even occasional blue and snow geese find shelter. In the mangrove thickets, herons, ibis, and egrets hunt and nest. Hidden in the pinewoods and palmetto brush are white-tailed deer, bobcats, wild hogs, and opossums, as well as the raccoons we used to see.

Our pace eases as we drive over some of the same roads we covered on our tour of the Space Center yesterday, or even on our way to the launching this morning. Only a few hours ago, it seems days removed, another world. This afternoon we are looking for wildlife, not for launching towers and rockets. We have passed into a different frame of reference. The veil of civilization has become almost invisible. Instead of the mammoth gray-and-white VAB on the horizon, our eyes pick up white herons, standing in the ditches, poised motionless for prey. Instead of staring at the bulky simulators, we watch armadillos, small armor-plated animals, rooting back into the ages, nosing for insects in the turf. Instead of gazing at vapor trails, we sigh with delight as great blue herons lazily shake out their wings and glide to another bank. Like an umbrella, they unfurl their feathers for flight, and then abruptly telescope into a rigid walking stick to stalk for food.

Pushing to outer reaches of the Cape, we refind the kind of territory we camped on years ago. The same bumpy sand roads are there behind the rolling bulwark of dunes. On the beach beyond, pelicans still sail downwind and sandpipers eternally chase the shining edge of foam. Behind the dunes are saw-grass marshes where flocks of ducks beat the water white, taking off for flight, or, braking the air with their wings, make a great "whoosh" when they land, like a long sigh of contentment. Here a white-breasted osprey hides in the crook of a dead tree, waiting for the flicker of a fish in the pool below. Kingfishers dart across the streams like blue lightning.

Our eyes, quickened now to nature, find hidden surprises. That dark mass of sticks in a tall pine is a bald eagle's nest. That water-

soaked log on a muddy bank is a sleeping alligator. His eye is glassy, but his crenellated tail twitches occasionally like a mechanical toy. Wild hogs scurry through palmettos and a red-tailed hawk spreads his wings as we pass. We stop to watch a water turkey, swimming noiselessly downstream, bowing its snaky black neck rhythmically with each stroke before it dives into the safety of the dark water below.

At sunset, refreshed by our deep plunge into the green silence of wilderness and the white stillness of beach and water, we turn back to the jangling lights of town. In a faint pink sky above us, we see the moon, a thin silver crescent with the shadow of the full moon between its horns. "The new moon, with the old moon in its arms," I think. There is a single bright star above it. Not ours, though—not our star of this morning. Invisible to our eyes, somewhere between us and that moon is Apollo 8 speeding ahead with its three passengers perhaps seeing the same moon, or looking back at us. The vast emptiness of celestial space becomes alive because three mortal men are in it. I remember how, in my early days of flying across desert stretches of the West, the slightest touch of a human would light up a landscape. A dusty track or the round ring of an abandoned corral caught my eye as a scrap of glass on a road reflects sunlight. Here too, the dead wastes of the universe have been touched by the spark of life.

Reader's Response

How were you affected by Anne Morrow Lindbergh's description of the takeoff of Apollo 8?

ONE BRIGHT STAR

Checking Your Comprehension

1. In what way was going to Cape Canaveral a "pilgrimage"?
2. Lindbergh stated that the rocket was "the newest and most perfected creation of the scientific age." What details, if any, did she provide to support this generalization?
3. What is the main idea of the first part of the essay (the description of the rocket launch)?
4. Why did Lindbergh go to the wildlife refuge after the launching?
5. Why are the animals herded to another area before launches?
6. Do you agree with the author that the emptiness of space comes alive when we know people are traveling in it? What are your reasons for agreeing or disagreeing?

Writing to Learn

THINK AND CREATE Anne Morrow Lindbergh brings a sense of poetry to her prose. Read the personification examples below and notice how the author gives *life* to *nonliving* things like vapor, the crowd, and flames. Review the article and copy three additional examples of personification on your paper.

The crowd gasps, almost in unison

Great flames spurt, leap, belch out across horizon

Vapor steams ferociously

WRITE Observe and write. Give life to nonliving objects and things you select by creating five examples of personification. Use your examples in five different sentences.

DARK THEY WERE, AND GOLDEN-EYED

by Ray Bradbury

*The Bittering family has traveled all the way from Earth to Mars.
They wonder how they will be affected by a world that is so different.*

The rocket metal cooled in the meadow winds. Its lid gave a bulging *pop*. From its clock interior stepped a man, a woman, and three children. The other passengers whispered away across the Martian meadow, leaving the man alone among his family.

The man felt his hair flutter and the tissues of his body draw tight as if he were standing at the center of a vacuum. His wife, before him, seemed almost to whirl away in smoke. The children, small seeds, might at any instant be sown to all the Martian climes.

The children looked up at him, as people look to the sun to tell what time of their life it is. His face was cold.

"What's wrong?" asked his wife.

"Let's get back on the rocket."

"Go back to Earth?"

"Yes! Listen!"

The wind blew as if to flake away their identities. At any moment the Martian air might draw his soul from him, as marrow comes from a white bone. He felt submerged in a chemical that could dissolve his intellect and burn away his past.

They looked at Martian hills that time had worn with a crushing pressure of years. They saw the old cities, lost in their meadows, lying like children's delicate bones among the blowing lakes of grass.

"Chin up, Harry," said his wife. "It's too late. We've come over sixty million miles."

The children with their yellow hair hollered at the deep dome of Martian sky. There was no answer but the racing hiss of wind through the stiff grass.

He picked up the luggage in his cold hands. "Here we go," he said—a man standing on the edge of a sea, ready to wade in and be drowned.

They walked into town.

Their name was Bittering. Harry and his wife Cora; Dan, Laura, and David. They built a small white cottage and ate good breakfasts there, but the fear was never gone. It lay with Mr. Bittering and Mrs. Bittering, a third unbidden partner at every midnight talk, at every dawn awakening.

"I feel like a salt crystal," he said, "in a mountain stream, being washed away. We don't belong here. We're Earth people. This is Mars. It was meant for Martians. For heaven's sake, Cora, let's buy tickets for home!"

But she only shook her head. "One day the atom bomb will fix Earth. Then we'll be safe here."

"Safe and insane!"

Tick-tock, seven o'clock sang the voice-clock; *time to get up.* And they did.

Something made him check everything each morning—warm hearth, potted blood-geraniums—precisely as if he expected something to be amiss. The morning paper was toast-warm from the 6 A.M. Earth rocket. He broke its seal and tilted it at his breakfast place. He forced himself to be convivial.

"Colonial days all over again," he declared. "Why, in ten years there'll be a million Earthmen on Mars. Big cities, everything! They said we'd fail. Said the Martians would resent our invasion. But did we find any Martians? Not a living soul! Oh, we found their empty cities, but no one in them. Right?"

A river of wind submerged the house. When the windows ceased rattling Mr. Bittering swallowed and looked at the children.

"I don't know," said David. "Maybe there're Martians around we don't see. Sometimes nights I think I hear 'em. I hear the wind. The sand hits my window. I get scared. And I see those towns way up in the mountains where the Martians lived a long time ago. And I think I see things moving around those towns, Papa. And I wonder if those Martians *mind* us living here. I wonder if they won't do something to us for coming here."

"Nonsense!" Mr. Bittering looked out the windows. "We're clean, decent people." He looked at his children. "All dead cities have some kind of ghosts in them. Memories, I mean." He stared at the hills. "You see a staircase and you wonder what Martians looked like climbing it. You see Martian paintings and you wonder what the painter was like. You make a little ghost in your mind, a memory. It's quite natural. Imagination." He stopped. "You haven't been prowling up in those ruins, have you?"

"No, Papa." David looked at his shoes.

"See that you stay away from them. Pass the jam."

"Just the same," said little David, "I bet something happens."

Something happened that afternoon.

Laura stumbled through the settlement, crying. She dashed blindly onto the porch.

"Mother, Father—the war, Earth!" she sobbed. "A radio flash just came. Atom bombs hit New York! All the space rockets blown up. No more rockets to Mars, ever!"

"Oh, Harry!" The mother held onto her husband and daughter.

"Are you sure, Laura?" asked the father quietly.

Laura wept. "We're stranded on Mars, forever and ever!"

For a long time there was only the sound of the wind in the late afternoon.

Alone, thought Bittering. Only a thousand of us here. No way back. No way. No way. Sweat poured from his face and his hands and his body; he was drenched in the hotness of his fear. He wanted to strike Laura, cry, "No, you're lying! The rockets will come back!" Instead, he stroked Laura's head against him and said, "The rockets will get through someday."

"Father, what will we do?"

"Go about our business, of course. Raise crops and children. Wait. Keep things going until the war ends and the rockets come again."

The two boys stepped out onto the porch.

"Children," he said, sitting there, looking beyond them, "I've something to tell you."

"We know," they said.

In the following days, Bittering wandered often through the garden to stand alone in his fear. As long as the rockets had spun a silver web across space, he had been able to accept Mars. For he had always told himself: Tomorrow, if I want, I can buy a ticket and go back to Earth.

But now: The web gone, the rockets lying in jigsaw heaps of molten girder and unsnaked wire. Earth people left to the strangeness of Mars, the cinnamon dusts and wine airs, to be baked like gingerbread shapes in Martian summers, put into harvested storage by Martian winters. What would happen to him, the others? This was the moment Mars had waited for. Now it would eat them.

He got down on his knees in the flower bed, a spade in his nervous hands. Work, he thought, work and forget.

He glanced up from the garden to the Martian mountains. He thought of the proud old Martian names that had once been on those peaks. Earthmen, dropping from the sky, had gazed upon hills, rivers, Martian seas left nameless in spite of names. Once Martians had built cities, named cities; climbed mountains, named mountains; sailed seas, named seas. Mountains melted, seas drained, cities tumbled. In spite of this, the Earthmen had felt a silent guilt at putting new names to these ancient hills and valleys.

Nevertheless, man lives by symbol and label. The names were given.

Mr. Bittering felt very alone in his garden under the Martian sun, an anachronism bent here, planting Earth flowers in a wild soil.

Think. Keep thinking. Different things. Keep your mind free of Earth, the atom war, the lost rockets.

He perspired. He glanced about. No one watching. He removed his tie. Pretty bold, he thought. First your coat off, now your tie. He hung it neatly on a peach tree he had imported as a sapling from Massachusetts.

He returned to his philosophy of names and mountains. The Earthmen had changed names. Now there were Hormel Valleys, Roosevelt Seas, Ford Hills, Vanderbilt Plateaus, Rockefeller Rivers, on Mars. It wasn't right. The American settlers had shown wisdom, using old Indian prairie names: Wisconsin, Minnesota, Idaho, Ohio, Utah, Milwaukee, Waukegan, Osseo. The old names, the old meanings.

Staring at the mountains wildly, he thought: Are you up there? All the dead ones, you Martians? Well, here we are, alone, cut off! Come down, move us out! We're helpless!

The wind blew a shower of peach blossoms.

He put out his sun-browned hand, gave a small cry. He touched the blossoms, picked them up. He turned them, he touched them again and again. Then he shouted for his wife.

"Cora!"

She appeared at a window. He ran to her.

"Cora, these blossoms!"

She handled them.

"Do you see? They're different. They've changed! They're not peach blossoms any more!"

"Look all right to me," she said.

"They're not. They're *wrong!* I can't

395

tell how. An extra petal, a leaf, something, the color, the smell!"

The children ran out in time to see their father hurrying about the garden, pulling up radishes, onions, and carrots from their beds.

"Cora, come look!"

They handled the onions, the radishes, the carrots among them.

"Do they look like carrots?"

"Yes . . . no." She hesitated. "I don't know."

"They're changed."

"Perhaps."

"You know they have! Onions but not onions, carrots but not carrots. Taste: the same but different. Smell: not like it used to be." He felt his heart pounding, and he was afraid. He dug his fingers into the earth. "Cora, what's happening? What is it? We've got to get away from this." He ran across the garden. Each tree felt his touch. "The roses. The roses. They're turning green!"

And they stood looking at the green roses.

And two days later Dan came running. "Come see the cow. I was milking her and I saw it. Come on!"

They stood in the shed and looked at their one cow.

It was growing a third horn.

And the lawn in front of their house very quietly and slowly was coloring itself like spring violets. Seed from Earth but growing up a soft purple.

"We must get away," said Bittering.

"We'll eat this stuff and then we'll change—who knows to what? I can't let it happen. There's only one thing to do. Burn this food!"

"It's not poisoned."

"But it is. Subtly, very subtly. A little bit. A very little bit. We mustn't touch it."

He looked with dismay at their house. "Even the house. The wind's done something to it. The air's burned it. The fog at night. The boards, all warped out of shape. It's not an Earthman's house any more."

"Oh, your imagination!"

He put on his coat and tie. "I'm going into town. We've got to do something now. I'll be back."

"Wait, Harry!" his wife cried.

But he was gone.

In town, on the shadowy step of the grocery store, the men sat with their hands on their knees, conversing with great leisure and ease.

Mr. Bittering wanted to fire a pistol in the air.

What are you doing, you fools! he thought. Sitting here! You've heard the news—we're stranded on this planet. Well, move! Aren't you frightened? Aren't you afraid? What are you going to do?

"Hello, Harry," said everyone.

"Look," he said to them. "You did hear the news, the other day, didn't you?"

They nodded and laughed. "Sure. Sure, Harry."

"What are you going to do about it?"

"Do, Harry, do? What *can* we do?"

"Build a rocket, that's what!"

"A rocket, Harry? To go back to all that trouble? Oh, Harry!"

"But you *must* want to go back. Have you noticed the peach blossoms, the onions, the grass?"

"Why, yes, Harry, seems we did," said one of the men.

"Doesn't it scare you?"

"Can't recall that it did much, Harry."

"Idiots!"

"Now, Harry."

Bittering wanted to cry. "You've got to work with me. If we stay here, we'll all change. The air. Don't you smell it? Something in the air. A Martian virus, maybe; some seed, or a pollen. Listen to me!"

They stared at him.

"Sam," he said to one of them.

"Yes, Harry?"

"Will you help me build a rocket?"

"Harry, I got a whole load of metal and some blueprints. You want to work in my metal shop on a rocket, you're welcome. I'll sell you that metal for five hundred dollars. You should be able to construct a right pretty rocket, if you work alone, in about thirty years."

Everyone laughed.

"Don't laugh."

Sam looked at him with quiet good humor.

"Sam," Bittering said. "Your eyes—"

"What about them, Harry?"

"Didn't they used to be grey?"

"Well now, I don't remember."

"They were, weren't they?"

"Why do you ask, Harry?"

"Because now they're kind of yellow-colored."

"Is that so, Harry?" Sam said, casually.

"And you're taller and thinner—"

"You might be right, Harry."

"Sam, you shouldn't have yellow eyes."

"Harry, what color eyes have *you* got?" Sam said.

"My eyes? They're blue, of course."

"Here you are, Harry." Sam handed him a pocket mirror. "Take a look at yourself."

Mr. Bittering hesitated, and then raised the mirror to his face.

There were little, very dim flecks of new gold captured in the blue of his eyes.

"Now look what you've done," said Sam a moment later. "You've broken my mirror."

Harry Bittering moved into the metal shop and began to build the rocket. Men stood in the open door and talked and joked without raising their voices. Once in a while they gave him a hand on lifting something. But mostly they just idled and watched him with their yellowing eyes.

"It's suppertime, Harry," they said.

His wife appeared with his supper in a wicker basket.

"I won't touch it," he said. "I'll eat only food from our Deepfreeze. Food that came from Earth. Nothing from our garden."

His wife stood watching him. "You can't build a rocket."

"I worked in a shop once, when I was twenty. I know metal. Once I get it started, the others will help," he said, not looking at her, laying out the blueprints.

"Harry, Harry," she said, helplessly.

"We've got to get away, Cora. We've *got* to!"

The nights were full of wind that blew down the empty moonlit sea meadows past the little white chess cities lying for their twelve-thousandth year in the shallows. In the Earthmen's settlement, the Bittering house shook with a feeling of change.

Lying abed, Mr. Bittering felt his bones shifted, shaped, melted like gold. His wife, lying beside him, was dark from many sunny afternoons. Dark she was, and golden-eyed, burnt almost black by the sun, sleeping, and the children metallic in their beds, and the wind roaring forlorn and changing through the old peach trees, the violet grass, shaking out green rose petals.

The fear would not be stopped. It had his throat and heart. It dripped in a wetness of the arm and the temple and the trembling palm.

A green star rose in the east.

A strange word emerged from Mr. Bittering's lips.

"*Iorrt. Iorrt.*" He repeated it.

It was a Martian word. He knew no Martian.

In the middle of the night he arose and dialed a call through to Simpson, the archaeologist.

"Simpson, what does the word *Iorrt* mean?"

"Why that's the old Martian word for our planet Earth. Why?"

"No special reason."

The telephone slipped from his hand.

"Hello, hello, hello, hello," it kept saying while he sat gazing out at the green star. "Bittering? Harry, are you there?"

The days were full of metal sound. He laid the frame of the rocket with the reluctant help of three indifferent men. He grew very tired in an hour or so and had to sit down.

"The altitude," laughed a man.

"Are you *eating*, Harry?" asked another.

"I'm eating," he said, angrily.

"From your Deepfreeze?"

"Yes!"

"You're getting thinner, Harry."

"I'm not!"

"And taller."

"Liar!"

His wife took him aside a few days later. "Harry, I've used up all the food in the Deepfreeze. There's nothing left. I'll have to make sandwiches using food grown on Mars."

He sat down heavily.

"You must eat," she said. "You're weak."

"Yes," he said.

He took a sandwich, opened it, looked at it, and began to nibble at it.

"And take the rest of the day off," she said. "It's hot. The children want to swim in the canals and hike. Please come along."

"I can't waste time. This is a crisis!"

"Just for an hour," she urged. "A swim'll do you good."

He rose, sweating. "All right, all right. Leave me alone. I'll come."

"Good for you, Harry."

The sun was hot, the day quiet. There was only an immense staring burn upon the land. They moved along the canal, the father, the mother, the racing children in their swim suits. They stopped and ate meat sandwiches. He saw their skin baking brown. And he saw the yellow eyes of his wife and his children, their eyes that were never yellow before. A few tremblings shook him, but were carried off in waves of pleasant heat as he lay in the sun. He was too tired to be afraid.

"Cora, how long have your eyes been yellow?"

She was bewildered. "Always, I guess."

"They didn't change from brown in the last three months?"

She bit her lips. "No. Why do you ask?"

"Never mind."

They sat there.

"The children's eyes," he said. "They're yellow, too."

"Sometimes growing children's eyes change color."

"Maybe *we're* children, too. At least to Mars. That's a thought." He laughed. "Think I'll swim."

They leaped into the canal water, and he let himself sink down and down to the bottom like a golden statue and lie there in green silence. All was water-quiet and deep, all was peace. He felt the steady, slow current drift him easily.

If I lie here long enough, he thought, the water will work and eat away my flesh until the bones show like coral. Just my skeleton left. And then the water can build on that skeleton—green things, deep water things, red things, yellow things. Change. Change. Slow, deep, silent change. And isn't that what it is up *there*?

He saw the sky submerged above him, the sun made Martian by atmosphere and time and space.

Up there, a big river, he thought, a Martian river, all of us lying deep in it, in our pebble houses, in our sunken boulder houses, like crayfish hidden, and the water washing away our old bodies and lengthening the bones and—

He let himself drift up through the soft light.

Dan sat on the edge of the canal, regarding his father seriously.

"*Utha,*" he said.

"What?" asked his father.

The boy smiled. "You know. *Utha's* the Martian word for 'father.' "

"Where did you learn it?"

"I don't know. Around. *Utha!*"

"What do you want?"

The boy hesitated. "I—I want to change my name."

"Change it?"

"Yes."

His mother swam over. "What's wrong with Dan for a name?"

Dan fidgeted. "The other day you called Dan, Dan, Dan. I didn't even hear. I said to myself, That's not my name. I've a new name I want to use."

Mr. Bittering held to the side of the canal, his body cold and his heart pounding slowly. "What is this new name?"

"Linnl. Isn't that a good name? Can I use it? Can't I, please?"

Mr. Bittering put his hand to his head. He thought of the silly rocket, himself working alone, himself alone even among his family, so alone.

He heard his wife say, "Why not?"

He heard himself say, "Yes, you can use it."

"Yaaa!" screamed the boy. "I'm Linnl, Linnl!"

Racing down the meadowlands, he danced and shouted.

Mr. Bittering looked at his wife. "Why did we do that?"

"I don't know," she said. "It just seemed like a good idea."

They walked into the hills. They strolled on old mosaic paths, beside still pumping fountains. The paths were covered with a thin film of cool water all summer long. You kept your bare feet cool all the day, splashing as in a creek, wading.

They came to a small deserted Martian villa with a good view of the valley. It was on top of a hill. Blue marble halls, large murals, a swimming pool. It was refreshing in this hot summertime. The Martians hadn't believed in large cities.

"How nice," said Mrs. Bittering, "if we could move up here to this villa for the summer."

"Come on," he said. "We're going back to town. There's work to be done on the rocket."

But as he worked that night, the thought of the cool blue marble villa entered his mind. As the hours passed, the rocket seemed less important.

In the flow of days and weeks, the rocket receded and dwindled. The old fever was gone. It frightened him to think he had let it slip this way. But somehow the heat, the air, the working conditions—

He heard the men murmuring on the porch of his metal shop.

"Everyone's going. You heard?"

"All going. That's right."

Bittering came out. "Going where?" He saw a couple of trucks, loaded with children and furniture, drive down the dusty street.

"Up to the villas," said the man.

"Yeah, Harry. I'm going. So is Sam. Aren't you, Sam?"

"That's right, Harry. What about you?"

"I've got work to do here."

"Work! You can finish that rocket in the autumn, when it's cooler."

He took a breath. "I got the frame all set up."

"In the autumn is better." Their voices were lazy in the heat.

"Got to work," he said.

"Autumn," they reasoned. And they sounded so sensible, so right.

"Autumn would be best," he thought. "Plenty of time, then."

No! cried part of himself, deep down, put away, locked tight, suffocating. No! No!

"In the autumn," he said.

"Come on, Harry," they all said.

"Yes," he said, feeling his flesh melt in the hot liquid air. "Yes, in the autumn. I'll begin work again then."

"I got a villa near the Tirra Canal," said someone.

"You mean the Roosevelt Canal, don't you?"

"Tirra. The old Martian name."

"But on the map—"

"Forget the map. It's Tirra now. Now I found a place in the Pillan mountains—"

"You mean the Rockefeller range," said Bittering.

"I mean the Pillan mountains," said Sam.

"Yes," said Bittering, buried in the hot, swarming air. "The Pillan mountains."

Everyone worked at loading the truck in the hot, still afternoon of the next day.

Laura, Dan, and David carried packages. Or, as they preferred to be known, Ttil, Linnl, and Werr carried packages.

The furniture was abandoned in the little white cottage.

"It looked just fine in Boston," said

the mother. "And here in the cottage. But up at the villa? No. We'll get it when we come back in the autumn."

Bittering himself was quiet.

"I've some ideas on furniture for the villa," he said after a time. "Big, lazy furniture."

"What about your encyclopedia? You're taking it along, surely?"

Mr. Bittering glanced away. "I'll come and get it next week."

They turned to their daughter. "What about your New York dresses?"

The bewildered girl stared. "Why, I don't want them any more."

They shut off the gas, the water, they locked the doors and walked away. Father peered into the truck.

"Gosh, we're not taking much," he said. "Considering all we brought to Mars, this is only a handful!"

He started the truck.

Looking at the small white cottage for a long moment, he was filled with a desire to rush to it, touch it, say good-by to it, for he felt as if he were going away on a long journey, leaving something to which he could never quite return, never understand again.

Just then Sam and his family drove by in another truck.

"Hi, Bittering! Here we go!"

The truck swung down the ancient highway out of town. There were sixty others traveling the same direction. The town filled with a silent, heavy dust from their passage. The canal waters lay blue in the sun, and a quiet wind moved in the strange trees.

"Good-by, town!" said Mr. Bittering.

"Good-by, good-by," said the family, waving to it.

They did not look back again.

Summer burned the canals dry. Summer moved like flame upon the meadows. In the empty Earth settlement, the painted houses flaked and peeled. Rubber tires upon which children had swung in back yards hung suspended like stopped clock pendulums in the blazing air.

At the metal shop, the rocket frame began to rust.

In the quiet autumn Mr. Bittering stood, very dark now, very golden-eyed, upon the slope above his villa, looking at the valley.

"It's time to go back," said Cora.

"Yes, but we're not going," he said quietly. "There's nothing there any more."

"Your books," she said. "Your fine clothes.

"Your *llles* and your fine *ior uele rre*," she said.

"The town's empty. No one's going back," he said. "There's no reason to, none at all."

The daughter wove tapestries and the sons played songs on ancient flutes and pipes, their laughter echoing in the marble villa.

Mr. Bittering gazed at the Earth settlement far away in the low valley. "Such odd, such ridiculous houses the Earth people built."

"They didn't know any better," his wife mused. "Such ugly people. I'm glad they've gone."

They both looked at each other, startled by all they had just finished saying. They laughed.

"Where did they go?" he wondered. He glanced at his wife. She was golden and slender as his daughter. She looked at him, and he seemed almost as young as their eldest son.

"I don't know," she said.

"We'll go back to town maybe next year, or the year after, or the year after that," he said, calmly. "Now—I'm warm. How about taking a swim?"

They turned their backs to the valley. Arm in arm they walked silently down a path of clear-running spring water.

Five years later a rocket fell out of the sky. It lay steaming in the valley. Men leaped out of it, shouting.

"We won the war on Earth! We're here to rescue you! Hey!"

But the American-built town of cottages, peach trees, and theaters was silent. They found a flimsy rocket frame rusting in an empty shop.

The rocket men searched the hills. The captain established headquarters in an abandoned building. His lieutenant came back to report.

"The town's empty, but we found native life in the hills, sir. Dark people. Yellow eyes. Martians. Very friendly. We talked a

bit, not much. They learn English fast. I'm sure our relations will be most friendly with them, sir."

"Dark, eh?" mused the captain. "How many?"

"Six, eight hundred, I'd say, living in those marble ruins in the hills, sir. Tall, healthy. Beautiful women."

"Did they tell you what became of the men and women who built this Earth-settlement, Lieutenant?"

"They hadn't the foggiest notion of what happened to this town or its people."

"Strange. You think those Martians killed them?"

"They look surprisingly peaceful. Chances are a plague did this town in, sir."

"Perhaps. I suppose this is one of those mysteries we'll never solve. One of those mysteries you read about."

The captain looked at the room, the dusty windows, the blue mountains rising beyond, the canals moving in the light, and he heard the soft wind in the air. He shiv-

ered. Then, recovering, he tapped a large fresh map he had thumbtacked to the top of an empty table.

"Lots to be done, Lieutenant." His voice droned on and quietly on as the sun sank behind the blue hills. "New settlements. Mining sites, minerals to be looked for. Bacteriological specimens taken. The work, all the work. And the old records were lost. We'll have a job of remapping to do, renaming the mountains and rivers and such. Calls for a little imagination.

"What do you think of naming those mountains the Lincoln Mountains, this canal the Washington Canal, those hills—we can name those hills for you, Lieutenant. Diplomacy. And you, for a favor, might name a town for me. Polishing the apple. And why not make this the Einstein Valley, and further over . . . are you *listening*, Lieutenant?"

The lieutenant snapped his gaze from the blue color and the quiet mist of the hills far beyond the town.

"What? Oh, *yes*, sir!"

Reader's Response

Did you feel that you were on Mars with the Bittering family?

DARK THEY WERE, AND GOLDEN-EYED

Checking Your Comprehension

1. Why did Harry want to return home just after arriving on Mars?
2. Why did Cora want to stay on Mars?
3. Tell how the war on Earth changed everything for the Bitterings.
4. At what point did Harry first notice that things were changing?
5. Why did Harry feel so impatient with the people in town?
6. How might the story have differed if the rocket flights to Mars had not been disrupted?
7. What do you think happened to the original Martians? What questions did you ask yourself to reach your conclusion?

Writing to Learn

THINK AND IMAGINE Ray Bradbury excels in the use of dialogue. Find a short passage of dialogue that you enjoyed reading in this story. Copy it on your paper. Now imagine that you were on Mars and you entered the scene.

WRITE Use your sample of dialogue as a model for form and punctuation. Then write a brief dialogue between yourself and the Bitterings. You may enter the story at the time and place you select.

THE WORLD OF READING

Astronomy in Print

For centuries, people have looked at the stars and planets in the night sky and asked questions about the universe. In the past five or six thousand years, people have recorded their astronomical observations in a variety of ways. The ancient monuments at Stonehenge, clay tablets, records in papyrus, and books written centuries ago help modern scientists learn about early observations of the heavens.

The early astronomer Galileo was the first person to use a telescope effectively to study the sky. In 1610, he recorded his discovery of four moons circling Jupiter, thereby supporting the Copernican theory that not all bodies revolved around Earth.

Another scientist whose writings are still widely read and studied was Sir Isaac Newton of Britain, who explained the principles of gravity. It was British astronomer Edmond Halley who persuaded Newton to publish his theories about the gravitational force in 1687.

▲ Books are a key source of information about astronomy.

The appearance of Halley's comet in 1680 is illustrated in this woodcut from the seventeenth century. ▼

Maria Mitchell (1818–1889) an American astronomer, was famous for her studies of comets and sunspots. She published her findings in many articles for professional astronomers. ◄

This computer-enhanced image of Halley's comet is based on a 1910 photograph of the comet. ►

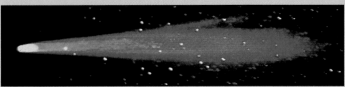

A

B

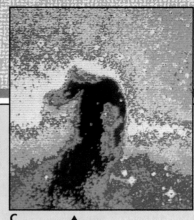

C

▲
A. This is a photograph of the nebula Horsehead in the constellation Orion.

B. A computer helps show the heights of different parts of Horsehead.

C. A computer-aided image shows dust and gases surrounding Horsehead.

The same Edmond Halley who helped Newton was the man for whom Halley's comet was named. A fascinating astronomical phenomenon, Halley's comet appears every seventy-six years as it passes Earth in its orbit. This recurring phenomenon has been observed, feared, recorded, and studied for at least two thousand years. During its most recent return in 1985 and 1986, Halley's comet was visible to the naked eye. At that time, accounts of historical sightings as well as contemporary reports and speculations about the comet appeared in hundreds of books, newspapers, and magazines.

In recent years, computer data banks have become the main means of storing data gathered by telescopes and astronomers. Despite the growing role of computers in astronomy, however, astronomers still rely heavily on books and other printed material. They continue to refer to the classic works by Galileo, Newton, and other early astronomers; they publish their findings in professional journals read by other astronomers; and they communicate their research to the general public through books and popular magazines.

People who pursue astronomy as a hobby, or who just find it fascinating, turn to books and magazines to find out about the latest theories and discoveries or to learn which kind of telescope is best for their purposes, how to locate stars and planets, or how to set up experiments. In fact, books and journals about astronomy are more popular with the reading public than ever before.

An astronomer gathers data about the planets and the stars. ▶

Literature:

Conflict, Turning Point, Resolution

Have you ever met a really *great* storyteller? Most of us know someone who has a true gift for telling stories—the kind of stories that excite us, that make us laugh or cry, that may even teach us something about ourselves. Whether the story was about their childhood or about a pet they once had or about a fantastic trip they took somewhere, it probably had the three elements you usually find in a great story: conflict, turning point, and resolution.

A *conflict* is a struggle between two opposing forces. There are, of course, all different kinds of conflicts, but they can usually be divided into two types: external conflicts and internal conflicts.

An *external conflict* is one that occurs between a character and an outside force. There are many kinds of outside forces—the outside force may be another character or group of characters, or it may be nature or technology. Think about the selection you read recently, "West with the Night," in which Beryl Markham sets out to fly alone across the Atlantic, from England to the United States. To achieve this goal, Markham must struggle with the forces of nature and the limitations of her own plane. These are external conflicts.

Sometimes the most difficult conflict is an *internal conflict*—the kind of conflict that pits a character against him- or herself. This kind of conflict usually takes place within a character's mind, between opposing ideas, feelings, or desires. In the case of Beryl Markham, for instance, the internal conflict is between her will and her body: she must will herself to stay awake even when her body is tired, to do what is necessary for her own survival.

Very often in a story, the conflict keeps building until it reaches a *turning point*, the decisive event that brings about a major change. In "West with the Night," the turning point occurs when Beryl Markham is forced to crash-land her plane on Cape Breton. The crash landing is the most exciting moment in the story; after that, the tension is broken and you can relax.

The turning point leads to the *resolution*, which is the event that clarifies the direction the story will take to its end. In "West with the Night," the resolution occurs when Markham is rescued by the fisherman. At this point, it is clear that she will survive her journey without serious injury, although she will not exactly achieve her original goal.

Most of the stories and novels you will come across follow this pattern. The conflict is introduced early on, and the tension it causes builds throughout the story. The turning point comes late in the story and brings about the resolution. The resolution clears up the original conflict and leads to the ending.

Noticing the conflict, turning point, and resolution in the stories you read will help you to understand their plots and the reasons for the characters' behavior. If you can keep these elements in mind when you plan the stories you write or tell, you may find the finished stories sharper and more compelling, so that when your friends think about the great storytellers they know, they will think about you.

Read and Enjoy

The story you are about to read, "The Wind from the Sun," is about a race. Of course, the hero is in conflict with the other contestants, all of whom want to win. But that is not all. As you read, look for other conflicts and watch them build toward the turning point and resolution.

THE WIND FROM THE SUN

by Arthur C. Clarke

In this story, set two hundred years into the next century, John Merton sets off in a fantastic race from Earth to the Moon.

John Merton, the captain of the ship Diana, *is in a race from the Earth to the Moon. He is racing against six other ships:* Gossamer, Santa Maria, Sunbeam, Woomera, Lebedev, *and* Arachne. *These unique vehicles are equipped with fifty million square feet of sails that capture energy from the sun.*

It seemed a strange thing to do, now that the race had just started, but it might be a good idea to get some sleep. The two-man crews on the other boats could take it in turns, but Merton had no one to relieve him. He must rely on his physical resources—like that other solitary seaman, Joshua Slocum, in his tiny

Spray. The American skipper had sailed *Spray* single-handed around the world; he could never have dreamt that, two centuries later, a man would be sailing single-handed from Earth to Moon—inspired, at least partly, by his example.

Merton snapped the elastic bands of the cabin seat around his waist and legs, then placed the electrodes of the sleep-inducer on his forehead. He set the timer for three hours, and relaxed.

Very gently, hypnotically, the electronic pulses throbbed in the frontal lobes of his brain. Colored spirals of light expanded beneath his closed eyelids, widening outward to infinity. Then—nothing. . . .

The brazen clamor of the alarm dragged him back from his dreamless sleep. He was instantly awake, his eyes scanning the instrument panel. Only two hours had passed—but above the accelerometer, a red light was flashing. Thrust was falling; *Diana* was losing power.

Merton's first thought was that something had happened to the sail; perhaps the antispin devices had failed, and the rigging had become twisted. Swiftly, he rechecked the meters that showed the tension in the shroud-lines. Strange, on one side of the sail they were reading normally—but on the other, the pull was dropping slowly even as he watched.

In sudden understanding, Merton grabbed the periscope, switched to wide-angle vision, and started to scan the edge of the sail. Yes—there was the trouble, and it could have only one cause.

A huge, sharp-edged shadow had begun to slide across the gleaming silver of the sail. Darkness was falling upon *Diana*, as if a cloud had passed between her and the Sun. And in the dark, robbed of the rays that drove her, she would lose all thrust and drift helplessly through space.

But, of course, there were no clouds here, more than twenty thousand miles above Earth. If there was a shadow, it must be made by man.

Merton grinned as he swung the periscope toward the Sun, switching in the filters that would allow him to look full into its blazing face without being blinded.

"Maneuver 4a," he muttered to himself. "We'll see who can play best at *that* game."

It looked as if a giant planet was crossing the face of the Sun. A great black disc had bitten deep into its edge. Twenty miles astern, *Gossamer* was trying to arrange an artificial eclipse—specially for *Diana's* benefit.

The maneuver was a perfectly legitimate one; back in the days of ocean racing, skippers had often tried to rob each other of the wind. With any luck, you could leave your rival becalmed, with his sails collapsing around him—and be well ahead before he could undo the damage.

Merton had no intention of being caught so easily. There was plenty of time to take evasive action; things happened very slowly, when you were running a solar sailingboat. It would be at least twenty minutes before *Gossamer* could slide completely across the face of the Sun, and leave him in darkness.

Diana's tiny computer—the size of a matchbox, but the equivalent of a thousand human mathematicians—considered the problem for a full second and then flashed the answer. He'd have to open control panels three and four, until the sail had developed an extra twenty degrees of tilt; then the radiation pressure would blow him out of *Gossamer's* dangerous shadow, back into the full blast of the Sun. It was a pity to interfere with the auto-pilot, which had been carefully programed to give the fastest possible run—but that, after all, was why he was here. This was what made solar yachting a sport, rather than a battle between computers.

Out went control lines one to six, slowly undulating like sleepy snakes as they momentarily lost their tension. Two miles away, the triangular panels began to open lazily, spilling sunlight through the sail. Yet, for a long time, nothing seemed to happen. It was hard to grow accustomed to this slow motion world, where it took minutes for the effects of any action to become visible to the eye. Then Merton saw that the sail was indeed tipping toward the Sun—and that *Gossamer's* shadow was sliding harmlessly away, its cone of darkness lost in the deeper night of space.

Long before the shadow had vanished, and the disc of the Sun had cleared again, he reversed the tilt and brought *Diana* back on course. Her new momentum would carry her clear of the danger; no need to overdo it, and upset his calculations by sidestepping too far. That was another rule that was hard to learn. The very moment you had started something happening in space, it was already time to think about stopping it.

He reset the alarm, ready for the next natural or man-made emergency; perhaps *Gossamer*, or one of the other contestants, would try the

413

same trick again. Meanwhile, it was time to eat, though he did not feel particularly hungry. One used little physical energy in space, and it was easy to forget about food. Easy—and dangerous; for when an emergency arose, you might not have the reserves needed to deal with it.

He broke open the first of the meal packets, and inspected it without enthusiasm. The name on the label—SPACETASTIES—was enough to put him off. And he had grave doubts about the promise printed underneath. Guaranteed Crumbless. It had been said that crumbs were a greater danger to space vehicles than meteorites. They could drift into the most unlikely places, causing short circuits, blocking vital jets, and getting into instruments that were supposed to be hermetically sealed.

Still, the liverwurst went down pleasantly enough; so did the chocolate and the pineapple puree. The plastic coffee-bulb was warming on the electric heater when the outside world broke in on his solitude. The radio operator on the Commodore's launch routed a call to him.

"Dr. Merton? If you can spare the time, Jeremy Blair would like a few words with you." Blair was one of the more responsible news commenta-tors, and Merton had been on his program many times. He could refuse to be interviewed, of course, but he liked Blair, and at the moment he could certainly not claim to be too busy. "I'll take it," he answered.

"Hello, Dr. Merton," said the commentator immediately. "Glad you can spare a few minutes. And congratulations—you seem to be ahead of the field."

"Too early in the game to be sure of that," Merton answered cautiously.

"Tell me, Doctor—why did you decide to sail *Diana* yourself? Just because it's never been done before?"

"Well, isn't that a very good reason? But it wasn't the only one, of course." He paused, choosing his words carefully. "You know how critically the performance of a sun-yacht depends on its mass. A second man, with all his supplies, would mean another five hundred pounds. That could easily be the difference between winning and losing."

"And you're quite certain that you can handle *Diana* alone?"

"Reasonably sure, thanks to the automatic controls I've designed. My main job is to supervise and make decisions."

"But—two square miles of sail! It just doesn't seem possible for

414

one man to cope with all that!"

Merton laughed.

"Why not? Those two square miles produce a maximum pull of just ten pounds. I can exert more force with my little finger."

"Well, thank you, Doctor. And good luck."

As the commentator signed off, Merton felt a little ashamed of himself. For his answer had been only part of the truth; and he was sure that Blair was shrewd enough to know it.

There was just one reason why he was here, alone in space. For almost forty years he had worked with teams of hundreds or even thousands of men, helping to design the most complex vehicles that the world had ever seen. For the last twenty years he had led one of those teams and watched his creations go soaring to the stars. (But there were failures that he could never forget, even though the fault had not been his.) He was famous, with a successful career behind him. Yet he had never done anything by himself; always he had been one of an army.

This was his very last chance of individual achievement, and he would share it with no one. There would be no more solar yachting for at least five years, as the period of the quiet Sun ended and the cycle of bad weather began, with radiation storms bursting through the Solar System. When it was safe again for these frail, unshielded craft to venture aloft, he would be too old. If, indeed, he was not too old already. . . .

He dropped the empty food containers into the waste disposal, and turned once more to the periscope. At first, he could find only five of the other yachts; there was no sign of *Woomera*. It took him several minutes to locate her—a dim, star-eclipsing phantom, neatly caught in the shadow of the *Lebedev*. He could imagine the frantic efforts the Australasians were making to extricate themselves, and wondered how they had fallen into the trap. It suggested that *Lebedev* was unusually maneuverable; she would bear watching, though she was too far away to menace *Diana* at the moment.

Now the Earth had almost vanished. It had waned to a narrow, brilliant bow of light that was moving steadily toward the Sun. Dimly outlined within that burning bow was the night side of the planet, with the phosphorescent gleams of great cities showing here and there through gaps in the clouds. The disc of darkness had already blanked out a huge section of the Milky Way; in a few minutes, it would start to encroach upon the Sun.

The light was fading. A purple twilight hue—the glow of many sunsets, thousands of miles below—was falling across the sail, as *Diana* slipped silently into the shadow of Earth. The Sun plummeted below that invisible horizon. Within minutes, it was night.

Merton looked back along the orbit he had traced now a quarter of the way around the world. One by one he saw the brilliant stars of the other yachts wink out, as they joined him in the brief night. It would be an hour before the Sun emerged from that enormous black shield, and through all that time they would be completely helpless, coasting without power.

He switched on the external spotlight and started to search the now darkened sail with its beam. Already, the thousands of acres of film were beginning to wrinkle and become flaccid; the shroud-lines were slackening and must be wound in lest they become entangled. But all this was expected; everything was going as planned.

Forty miles astern, *Arachne* and *Santa Maria* were not so lucky. Merton learned of their troubles when the radio burst into life on the emergency circuit.

"Number Two, Number Six—this is Control. You are on a collision course. Your orbits will intersect in sixty-five minutes! Do you require assistance?"

There was a long pause while the two skippers digested this bad news. Merton wondered who was to blame; perhaps one yacht had been trying to shadow the other, and had not completed the maneuver before they were both caught in the darkness. Now there was nothing that either could do; they were slowly but inexorably converging together, unable to change course by a fraction of a degree.

Yet, sixty-five minutes! That would just bring them out into sunlight again, as they emerged from the shadow of the Earth. They still had a slim chance, if their sails could snatch enough power to avoid a crash. There must be some frantic calculations going on, aboard *Arachne* and *Santa Maria*.

Arachne answered first; her reply was just what Merton had expected.

"Number Six calling Control. We don't need assistance, thank you. We'll work this out for ourselves."

I wonder, thought Merton. But at least it will be interesting to watch. The first real drama of the race was approaching—exactly above the line

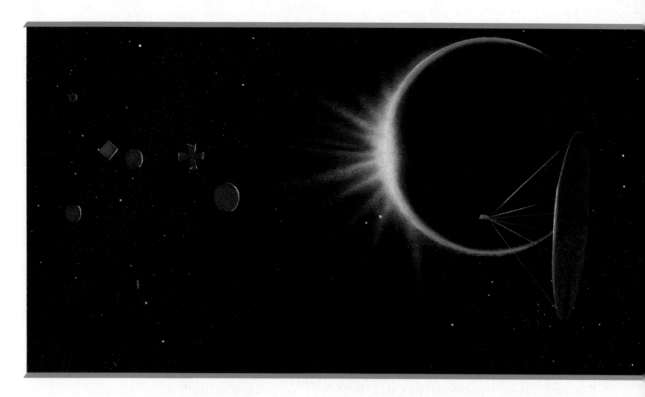

of midnight on the sleeping Earth.

For the next hour, Merton's own sail kept him too busy to worry about *Arachne* and *Santa Maria*. It was hard to keep a good watch on that fifty million square feet of dim plastic out there in the darkness, illuminated only by his narrow spotlight and the rays of the still distant Moon. From now on, for almost half his orbit round the Earth, he must keep the whole of this immense area edge-on to the Sun. During the next twelve or fourteen hours, the sail would be a useless encumbrance; for he would be heading into the Sun, and its rays could only drive him backward along his orbit. It was a

pity that he could not furl the sail completely, until he was ready to use it again. But no one had yet found a practical way of doing this. Far below, there was the first hint of dawn along the edge of the Earth. In ten minutes, the Sun would emerge from its eclipse; the coasting yachts would come to life again as the blast of radiation struck their sails. That would be the moment of crisis for *Arachne* and *Santa Maria*—and, indeed, for all of them.

Merton swung the periscope until he found the two dark shadows drifting against the stars. They were very close together—perhaps less than three miles apart. They might,

417

he decided, just be able to make it. . . .

Dawn flashed like an explosion along the rim of Earth, as the Sun rose out of the Pacific. The sail and shroud-lines glowed a brief crimson, then gold, then blazed with the pure white light of day. The needles of the dynamometers began to lift from their zeros—but only just. *Diana* was still almost completely weightless, for with the sail pointing toward the Sun, her acceleration was now only a few millionths of a gravity.

But *Arachne* and *Santa Maria* were crowding on all the sail they could manage, in their desperate attempt to keep apart. Now, while there was less than two miles between them, their glittering plastic clouds were unfurling and expanding with agonizing slowness, as they felt the first delicate push of the Sun's rays. Almost every TV screen on Earth would be mirroring this protracted drama; and even now, at this very last minute, it was impossible to tell what the outcome would be.

The two skippers were stubborn men. Either could have cut his sail, and fallen back to give the other a chance; but neither would do so. Too much prestige, too many millions, too many reputations, were at stake.

And so, silently and softly as snowflakes falling on a winter night, *Arachne* and *Santa Maria* collided.

The square kite crawled almost imperceptibly into the circular spider's web; the long ribbons of the shroud-lines twisted and tangled together with dreamlike slowness. Even aboard the *Diana*, busy with his own rigging, Merton could scarcely tear his eyes away from this silent, long drawn out disaster.

For more than ten minutes the billowing, shining clouds continued to merge into one inextricable mass. Then the crew capsules tore loose and went their separate ways, missing each other by hundreds of yards. With a flare of rockets, the safety launches hurried to pick them up.

That leaves five of us, thought Merton. He felt sorry for the skippers who had so thoroughly eliminated each other, only a few hours after the start of the race; but they were young men, and would have another chance.

Within minutes, the five had dropped to four. From the very beginning, Merton had had doubts about the slowly rotating *Sunbeam*. Now he saw them justified.

The Martian ship had failed to tack properly; her spin had given her too much stability. Her great ring of a

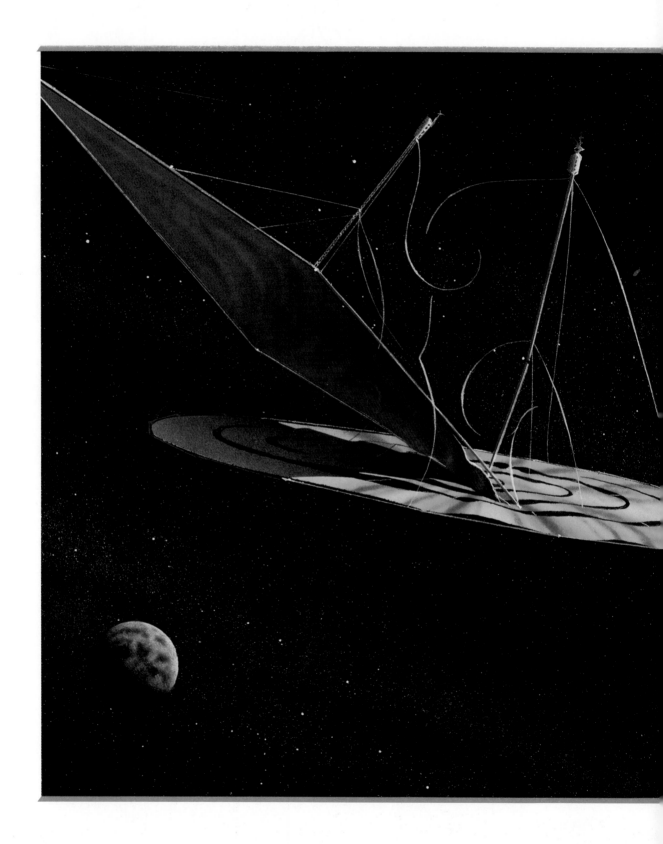

sail was turning to face the Sun, instead of being edge-on to it. She was being blown back along her course at almost her maximum acceleration.

That was about the most maddening thing that could happen to a skipper—worse even than a collision, for he could blame only himself. But no one would feel much sympathy for the frustrated colonials, as they dwindled slowly astern. They had made too many brash boasts before the race, and what had happened to them was poetic justice.

Yet it would not do to write off *Sunbeam* completely. With almost half a million miles still to go, she might still pull ahead. Indeed if there were a few more casualties, she might be the only one to complete the race. It had happened before.

However, the next twelve hours were uneventful, as the Earth waxed in the sky from new to full. There was little to do while the fleet drifted round the unpowered half of its orbit, but Merton did not find the time hanging heavily on his hands. He caught a few hours sleep, ate two meals, wrote up his log, and became involved in several more radio interviews. Sometimes, though rarely, he talked to the other skippers, exchanging greetings and friendly taunts. But most of the time he was content to float in weightless relaxation, beyond all the cares of Earth, happier than he had been for many years. He was—as far as any man could be in space— master of his own fate, sailing the ship upon which he had lavished so much skill, so much love, that she had become part of his very being.

The next casualty came when they were passing the line between Earth and Sun, and were just beginning the powered half of the orbit. Aboard *Diana*, Merton saw the great sail stiffen as it tilted to catch the rays that drove it. The acceleration began to climb up from the microgravities, though it would be hours yet before it would reach its maximum value.

It would never reach it for *Gossamer*. The moment when power came on again was always critical, and she failed to survive it.

Blair's radio commentary, which Merton had left running at low volume, alerted him with the news: "Hullo, *Gossamer* has the wriggles!" He hurried to the periscope, but at first could see nothing wrong with the great circular disc of *Gossamer's* sail. It was difficult to study it, as it was almost edge-on to him and so appeared as a thin ellipse; but presently he saw that it was twisting back and forth in slow, irresistible oscillations. Unless the crew could damp out these waves, by properly timed but gentle tugs on the shroud-lines, the sail would tear itself to pieces.

They did their best, and after twenty minutes it seemed that they had succeeded. Then, somewhere near the center of the sail, the plastic film began to rip. It was slowly driven outward by the radiation pressure, like smoke coiling upward from a fire. Within a quarter of an hour, nothing was left but the delicate tracery of the radial spars that had supported the great web. Once again there was a flare of rockets, as a launch moved in to retrieve the *Gossamer's* capsule and her dejected crew.

"Getting rather lonely up here, isn't it?" said a conversational voice over the ship-to-ship radio.

"Not for you, Dimitri," retorted Merton. "You've still got company back there at the end of the field. I'm the one who's lonely, up here in front." It was not an idle boast. By this time *Diana* was three hundred miles ahead of the next competitor, and his lead should increase still more rapidly in the hours to come.

Aboard *Lebedev*, Dimitri Markoff gave a good-natured chuckle. He did not sound, Merton thought, at all like a man who had resigned himself to defeat.

"Remember the legend of the tortoise and the hare," answered the Russian. "A lot can happen in the next quarter-million miles."

It happened much sooner than that, when they had completed their first orbit of Earth and were passing the starting line again—though thousands of miles higher, thanks to the extra energy the Sun's rays had given them. Merton had taken careful sights on the other yachts, and had fed the figures into the computer. The answer it gave for *Woomera* was so absurd that he immediately did a recheck.

There was no doubt of it—the Australasians were catching up at a fantastic rate. No solar yacht could possibly have such an acceleration, unless—

A swift look through the periscope gave the answer. *Woomera's* rigging, pared back to the very minimum of mass, had given way. It was her sail alone, still maintaining its shape, that was racing up behind him like a handkerchief blown before the wind. Two hours later it fluttered past, less than twenty miles away. But long before that, the Australasians had joined the growing crowd aboard the Commodore's launch.

So now it was a straight fight between *Diana* and *Lebedev*—for though the Martians had not given up, they were a thousand miles astern and no longer counted as a serious threat. For that matter, it was hard to see what *Lebedev* could do to overtake *Diana's* lead. But all the way round the second lap—through eclipse again, and the long, slow drift against the Sun, Merton felt a growing unease.

He knew the Russian pilots and designers. They had been trying to win this race for twenty years and after all, it was only fair that they should, for had not Pyotr Nikolayevich Lebedev been the first man to detect the pressure of sunlight, back at the very beginning of the twentieth century? But they had never succeeded.

And they would never stop trying. Dimitri was up to something—and it would be spectacular.

Aboard the official launch, a thousand miles behind the racing yachts, Commodore van Stratten looked at the radiogram with angry dismay. It had traveled more than a hundred million miles, from the chain of solar observatories swinging high above the blazing surface of the Sun, and it brought the worse possible news.

The Commodore—his title, of course, was purely honorary—back on Earth he was Professor of Astrophysics at Harvard—had been half expecting it. Never before had the race been arranged so late in the season; there had been many delays, they had gambled, and now it seemed they all might lose.

Deep beneath the surface of the Sun, enormous forces were gathering. At any moment, the energies of a million hydrogen bombs might burst forth in the awesome explosion known as a solar flare. Climbing at millions of miles an hour, an invisible fireball many times the size of Earth would leap from the Sun, and head out across space.

The cloud of electrified gas would probably miss the Earth completely. But if it did not, it would arrive in just over a day. Spaceships could protect themselves, with their shielding and their powerful magnetic screen. But the lightly built solar yachts, with their paper-thin walls, were defenseless against such a menace. The crews would have to be taken off, and the race abandoned.

John Merton still knew nothing of this as he brought *Diana* round the Earth for the second time. If all went well, this would be the last circuit, for both him and for the Russians. They had spiraled upward by thousands of miles, gaining energy from the Sun's rays. On this lap, they should escape from Earth completely—and head outward on the long run to the Moon. It was a straight race now. *Sunbeam's* crew had finally withdrawn, exhausted, after battling valiantly with their spinning sail for more than a hundred thousand miles.

Merton did not feel tired; he had eaten and slept well, and *Diana* was behaving herself admirably. The autopilot, tensioning the rigging like a busy little spider, kept the great sail trimmed to the Sun more accurately than any human skipper. Though by this time, the two square miles of plastic sheet must have been riddled by hundreds of micrometeorites, the pinhead-size punctures had produced no falling off to thrust.

He had only two worries. The first was shroud-line Number eight, which could no longer be adjusted properly. Without any warning, the reel had jammed; even after all these years of astronautical engineering, bearings sometimes seized up in vacuum. He could neither lengthen nor shorten the line, and would have to navigate as best he could with the others. Luckily, the most difficult maneuvers were over. From now on,

Diana would have the Sun behind her as she sailed straight down the solar wind. And as the old-time sailors often said, it was easy to handle a boat when the wind was blowing over your shoulder.

His other worry was *Lebedev*, still dogging his heels three hundred miles astern. The Russian yacht had shown remarkable maneuverability, thanks to the four great panels that could be tilted around the central sail. All her flip-overs as she rounded Earth had been carried out with superb precision; but to gain maneuverability she must have sacrificed speed. You could not have it both ways. In the long, straight haul ahead, Merton should be able to hold his own. Yet he could not be certain of victory until, three or four days from now, *Diana* went flashing past the far side of the Moon.

And then, in the fiftieth hour of the race, near the end of the second orbit around Earth, Markoff sprang his little surprise.

"Hello, John," he said casually, over the ship-to-ship circuit. "I'd like you to watch this. It should be interesting."

Merton drew himself across to the periscope and turned up the magnification to the limit. There in the field of view, a most improbable sight against the background of the stars, was the glittering Maltese cross of *Lebedev*, very small but very clear. And then, as he watched, the four arms of the cross slowly detached themselves from the central square and went drifting away, with all their spars and rigging, into space.

Markoff had jettisoned all unnecessary mass, now that he was coming up to escape velocity and need no longer plod patiently around the Earth, gaining momentum on each circuit. From now on, *Lebedev* would be almost unsteerable—but that did not matter. All the tricky navigation lay behind her. It was as if an old-time yachtsman had deliberately thrown away his rudder and heavy keel, knowing that the rest of the race would be straight downwind over a calm sea.

"Congratulations, Dimitri," Merton radioed. "It's a neat trick. But it's not good enough—you can't catch up now."

"I've not finished yet," the Russian answered. "There's an old winter's tale in my country, about a sleigh being chased by wolves. To save himself, the driver has to throw off the passengers one by one. Do you see the analogy?"

Merton did, all too well. On this final straight lap, Dimitri no longer

needed his co-pilot. *Lebedev* could really be stripped down for action.

"Alexis won't be very happy about this," Merton replied. "Besides, it's against the rules."

"Alexis isn't happy, but I'm the captain. He'll just have to wait around for ten minutes until the Commodore picks him up. And the regulations say nothing about the size of the crew—you should know that."

Merton did not answer. He was too busy doing some hurried calculations, based on what he knew of *Lebedev's* design. By the time he had finished, he knew that the race was still in doubt. *Lebedev* would be catching up with him at just about the time he hoped to pass the Moon.

But the outcome of the race was already being decided, ninety-two million miles away.

On Solar Observatory Three, far inside the orbit of Mercury, the automatic instruments recorded the whole history of the flare. A hundred million square miles of the Sun's surface suddenly exploded in such blue-white fury that, by comparison the rest of the disc paled to a dull glow. Out of that seething inferno, twisting and turning like a living creature in the magnetic fields of its own creation,

soared the electrified plasma of the great fire. Ahead of it, moving at the speed of light, went the warning flash of ultra-violet and X-rays. That would reach Earth in eight minutes, and was relatively harmless. Not so the charged atoms that were following behind at their leisurely four million miles an hour—and which, in just over a day, would engulf *Diana*, *Lebedev*, and their accompanying little fleet in a cloud of lethal radiation.

The Commodore left his decision to the last possible minute. Even when the jet of plasma had been tracked past the orbit of Venus, there was still a chance that it might miss the Earth. But when it was less than four hours away, and had already been picked up by the Moon-based radar network, he knew that there was no hope. All solar sailing was over for the next five or six years until the Sun was quiet again.

A great sigh of disappointment swept across the Solar System. *Diana* and *Lebedev* were halfway between Earth and Moon, running neck and neck—and now no one would ever know which was the better boat. The enthusiasts would argue the result for years; history would merely record: Race canceled owing to solar storm.

When John Merton received the

order, he felt a bitterness he had not known since childhood. Across the years, sharp and clear, came the memory of his tenth birthday. He had been promised an exact scale model of the famous spaceship *Morning Star*, and for weeks had been planning how he would assemble it, where he would hang it up in his bedroom. And then, at the last moment, his father had broken the news. "I'm sorry, John—it costs too much money. Maybe next year. . . ."

Half a century and a successful lifetime later, he was a heartbroken boy again.

For a moment, he thought of disobeying the Commodore. Suppose he sailed on, ignoring the warning? Even if the race were abandoned, he could make a crossing to the Moon that would stand in the record books for generations.

But that would be worse than stupidity. It would be suicide—and a very unpleasant form of suicide. He had seen men die of radiation poisoning, when the magnetic shielding of their ships had failed in deep space. No—nothing was worth that. . . .

He felt sorry for Dimitri Markoff as for himself; they both deserved to win, and now victory would go to neither. No man could argue with the Sun in one of its rages, even though he might ride upon its beams to the edge of space.

Only fifty miles astern now, the Commodore's launch was drawing alongside *Lebedev*, preparing to take off her skipper. There went the silver sail, as Dimitri—with feelings that he would share—cut the rigging. The tiny capsule would be taken back to Earth, perhaps to be used again—but a sail was spread for one voyage only.

He could press the jettison button now, and save his rescuers a few minutes of time. But he could not do so. He wanted to stay aboard to the very end, on the little boat that had been for so long a part of his dreams and his life. The great sail was spread now at right angles to the Sun, exerting its utmost thrust. Long ago it had torn him clear of Earth—and *Diana* was still gaining speed.

Then, out of nowhere, beyond all doubt of hesitation, he knew what must be done. For the last time, he sat down before the computer that had navigated him halfway to the Moon. When he had finished, he packed the log and his few personal belongings. Clumsily—for he was out of practice, and it was not an easy job to do by oneself—he climbed into the emergency survival suit.

He was just sealing the helmet when the Commodore's voice called over the radio. "We'll be alongside in five minutes, Captain. Please cut your sail so we won't foul it."

John Merton, first and last skipper of the sun-yacht *Diana*, hesitated for a moment. He looked for the last time round the tiny cabin, with its shining instruments and its neatly arranged controls, now all locked in their final positions. Then he said to the microphone: "I'm abandoning ship. Take your time to pick me up. *Diana* can look after herself."

There was no reply from the Commodore, and for that he was grateful. Professor van Stratten would have guessed what was happening—and would know that, in these final moments, he wished to be left alone.

He did not bother to exhaust the airlock, and the rush of escaping gas blew him gently out into space; the thrust he gave her then was his last gift to *Diana*. She dwindled away from him, sail glittering splendidly in the sunlight that would be hers for centuries to come. Two days from now she would flash past the Moon; but the Moon, like the Earth, could never catch her. Without his mass to slow her down, she would gain two thousand miles an hour in every day of sailing. In a month, she would be traveling faster than any ship that man had ever built.

As the Sun's rays weakened with

428

distance, so her acceleration would fall. But even at the orbit of Mars, she would be gaining a thousand miles an hour in every day. Long before then, she would be moving too swiftly for the Sun itself to hold her. Faster than any comet that had ever streaked in from the stars, she would be heading out into the abyss.

The glare of rockets, only a few miles away, caught Merton's eye. The launch was approaching to pick him up at thousands of times the acceleration that *Diana* could ever attain. But engines could burn for a few minutes only, before they exhausted their fuel—while *Diana* would still be gaining speed, driven outward by the Sun's eternal fires, for ages yet to come.

"Good-bye, little ship," said John Merton. "I wonder what eyes will see you next, how many thousand years from now?"

At last he felt at peace, as the blunt torpedo of the launch nosed up beside him. He would never win the race to the Moon; but his would be the first of all man's ships to set sail on the long journey to the stars.

Reader's Response

How did you feel about the decision John Merton made when he realized the race was over?

WRITING
ABOUT
READING

Writing a Futuristic News Story

The excitement of flight has attracted generations of people, including Leonardo da Vinci and Beryl Markham. You can capture some of this excitement by writing a news story about the dreamers, inventors, and explorers who made flight possible.

A good news story answers the questions *who, what, when, where, why,* and *how.* In a news story, the most important facts are presented first, and the least important facts are presented last.

Choose your favorite character from this unit, and write a news story about one major event in the character's life. Limit your story to five paragraphs. Plan to share your story with classmates.

Prewriting

Reread your favorite story or article in the unit. Make sure it contains at least one event that is newsworthy. Identify the event. Then review what happened from the viewpoint of a news reporter.

Imagine that you will interview a person who was part of the event. Prepare for your interview in the following ways.

◆ If possible, research the topic by reading about the event in another source.

◆ Prepare *who, what, when, where, why,* and *how* questions. Use the following questions as a model. They are for an interview with Daedalus.

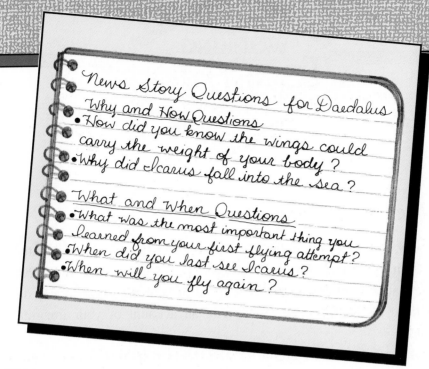

News Story Questions for Daedalus

Why and How Questions
- How did you know the wings could carry the weight of your body?
- Why did Icarus fall into the sea?

What and When Questions
- What was the most important thing you learned from your first flying attempt?
- When did you last see Icarus?
- When will you fly again?

Writing

Choose the most important event as a news story topic. Write your news story using facts you have gathered. These facts should answer your questions. Be sure that your news story tells the facts from the most important to the least important.

Revising

Read your story again. Did you answer most of the important questions in the beginning paragraph? Do your final paragraphs contain the least important details? Make sure that you used vivid action verbs.

Proofreading

Correct errors in spelling, capitalization, punctuation, and grammar. Type or print the story in columns. Be sure to include a headline at the top of your story.

Publishing

Make a class newspaper, *Flight Times*. Include editorials, comic strips, and advertisements for flight gear.

WORKING TOGETHER

Creating an Account of a Flight

Today, flying is routine, but in the past, every flight was an adventure. In this unit, you read stories about people's adventures in flight. Now imagine that you are embarking on a flight of your own in the early days of aviation. As a group, you will write an account of your imaginary adventure.

Make sure that each group member takes responsibility for one or more of these tasks:

◆ Contributing ideas

◆ Helping the group stay on the job

◆ Showing appreciation for others' ideas

Discuss what year your flight will take place, what kind of aircraft you will fly, and what the goal of your flight will be. For example, you might plan to be the first crew to fly over the South Pole.

Discuss what route you will take. Decide on obstacles you will face in your flight, such as weather and malfunctioning equipment. Figure out ways in which you, the flight crew, will overcome the problems and obstacles.

Once you have finished your planning, work together to write an account of your flight. To make your account more vivid, you might draw a map showing the route of your flight. You might also make a drawing of your aircraft.

When you have finished your account, share it with another group in your class. Discuss the obstacles that both groups face, and compare the ways in which you overcome those obstacles.

The Edge of the Cloud by K. M. Peyton *(World, 1969)*
A young bride accommodates her husband's devotion to
flying in the early days of aviation. The story combines
romance with aviation history.

Hot-Air Ballooning by Charles Coombs *(Morrow, 1981)*
The history of hot-air ballooning is covered in detail,
including people who have participated in it, kinds of
equipment needed, and various techniques used.

Dragonflight by Anne McCaffrey *(Ballantine, 1978)* The
planet Pern is protected from the deadly silver threads of
a wandering Red Star by the winged dragons and their
riders. The dragons and their riders are in decline, and it
is left to a Weyrwoman to go back in time to recruit
former Dragonriders to fight in the present.

Her Father's Daughter by Anne C. Ready *(Grosset, 1981)*
After her father is killed in an airplane crash, a girl con-
quers her fear of flying by learning to fly.

Enchantress from the Stars by Sylvia Engdahl *(Atheneum, 1970)* On the planet Andrecia, Elana becomes
involved in a struggle to save the Younglings from the
invading Imperial forces.

WHISPERS
FROM THE
PAST

Perhaps nothing is so lost that it can never be found.

What motivates people to dig into the past?

WOODEN MUMMY CASE
OF HAMETTAWY,
Egyptian, 1090–945 B.C.

THE DOG OF POMPEII

BY LOUIS UNTERMEYER

*Archaeologists can give us some clues about what it
was like to live in Pompeii almost two thousand years ago.
But some things can only be imagined.*

Tito and his dog Bimbo lived (if you could call it living) under the wall where it joined the inner gate. They really didn't live there; they just slept there. They lived anywhere. Pompeii was one of the liveliest of old Latin towns, but although Tito was never an unhappy boy, he was not exactly a merry one. The streets were always lively with swinging chariots and bright red trappings; the open-air theaters rocked with laughing crowds; sham-battles and athletic sports were free for the asking in the great stadium. Once a year the Caesar visited the pleasure-city and the fire-works lasted for days; the sacrifices in the Forum were better than a show. But Tito saw none of these things. He was blind—had been blind from birth. He was known to every one in the poorer quarters. But no one could say how old he was, no one remembered his parents, no one could tell where he came from. Bimbo was another mystery. As long as people could remember seeing Tito—about twelve or thirteen years—they had seen Bimbo. Bimbo had never left his side. He was not only dog, but nurse, pillow, play-mate, mother and father to Tito.

Did I say Bimbo never left his master? (Perhaps I had better say comrade, for if anyone was the master, it was

437

Bimbo.) I was wrong. Bimbo did trust Tito alone exactly three times a day. It was a fixed routine, a custom understood between boy and dog since the beginning of their friendship, and the way it worked was this: Early in the morning, shortly after dawn, while Tito was dreaming, Bimbo would disappear. When Tito woke, Bimbo would be sitting quietly at his side, his ears cocked, his stump of a tail tapping the ground, and a fresh-baked bread—more like a large round roll—at his feet. Tito would stretch himself; Bimbo would yawn; then they would breakfast. At noon, no matter where they happened to be, Bimbo would put his paw on Tito's knee and the two of them would return to the inner gate. Tito would curl up in the corner (almost like a dog) and go to sleep, while Bimbo, looking quite important (almost like a boy) would disappear again. In half an hour he'd be back with their lunch. Sometimes it would be a piece of fruit or a scrap of meat; often it was nothing but a dry crust. But sometimes there would be one of those flat rich cakes, sprinkled with raisins and sugar, that Tito liked so much. At supper-time the same thing happened, although there was a little less of everything, for things were hard to snatch in the evening with the streets full of people. Besides, Bimbo didn't approve of too much food before going to sleep. A heavy supper made boys too restless and dogs too stodgy—and it was the business of

a dog to sleep lightly with one ear open and muscles ready for action.

But, whether there was much or little, hot or cold, fresh or dry, food was always there. Tito never asked where it came from and Bimbo never told him. There was plenty of rainwater in the hollows of soft stones; the old egg-woman at the corner sometimes gave him a cupful of strong goat's milk; in the grape-season the fat wine-maker let him have drippings of the mild juice. So there was no danger of going hungry or thirsty. There was plenty of everything in Pompeii, if you knew where to find it—and if you had a dog like Bimbo.

As I said before, Tito was not the merriest boy in Pompeii. He could not romp with the other youngsters and play Hare-and-Hounds and I-Spy and Follow-Your-Master and Ball-against-the-Building and Jack-Stones and Kings-and-Robbers with them. But that did not make him sorry for himself. If he could not see the sights that delighted the lads of Pompeii he could hear and smell things they never noticed. He could really see more with his ears and nose than they could with their eyes. When he and Bimbo went out walking he knew just where they were going and exactly what was happening.

"Ah," he'd sniff and say, as they passed a handsome villa, "Glaucus Pansa is giving a grand dinner tonight. They're going to have three kinds of bread, and roast pigling, and stuffed goose, and a great stew—I think bear-stew—and a fig-pie." And Bimbo would note that this would be a good place to visit tomorrow.

Or, "H'm," Tito would murmur, half through his lips, half through his nostrils. "The wife of Marcus Lucretius is expecting her mother. She's shaking out every piece of goods in the house; she's going to use the best clothes—the ones she's been keeping in pine-needles and camphor—and there's an extra girl in the kitchen. Come, Bimbo, let's get out of the dust!"

Or, as they passed a small but elegant dwelling opposite the public-baths, "Too bad! The tragic poet is ill again. It must be a bad fever this time, for they're trying smoke-fumes instead of medicine. Whew! I'm glad I'm not a tragic poet!"

Or, as they neared the Forum, "Mm-m! What good things they have in the Macellum today!" (It really was a sort of butcher-grocer-market-place, but Tito didn't know any better. He called it the Macellum.) "Dates from Africa, and salt oysters from sea-caves, and cuttlefish, and new honey, and sweet onions, and—ugh—water-buffalo steaks. Come, let's see what's what in the Forum." And Bimbo, just as curious as his comrade, hurried on. Being a dog, he trusted his ears and nose (like Tito) more than his eyes. And so the two of them entered the center of Pompeii.

The Forum was the part of the town to which everybody came at least once during each day. It was the Central Square and everything happened here. There were no private houses; all was public—the chief temples, the gold and red bazaars, the silk-shops, the town-hall, the booths belonging to the weavers and jewel-merchants, the wealthy woolen market, the shrine of the household gods. Everything glittered here. The buildings looked as if they were new—which, in a sense, they were. The earthquake of twelve years ago had brought down all the old structures and, since the citizens of Pompeii were ambitious to rival Naples and even Rome, they had seized the opportunity to rebuild the whole town. And they had done it all within a dozen years. There was scarcely a building that was older than Tito.

Tito had heard a great deal about the earthquake, though being about a year old at the time, he could scarcely remember it. This particular quake had been a light one—as earthquakes go. The weaker houses had been shaken down, parts of the out-worn wall had been wrecked; but there was little loss of life, and the brilliant new Pompeii had taken the place of the old. No one knew what caused these earthquakes. Records showed they had happened in the neighborhood since the beginning of time. Sailors said that it was to teach the lazy city folk a lesson and make them appreciate those who risked the dangers of the sea to bring them luxuries and protect their town from invaders. The priests said that the gods took this way of showing their anger to those who refused to worship properly and who failed to bring enough sacrifices to the altars and (though they didn't say it in so many words) presents to the priests. The tradesmen said that the foreign merchants had corrupted the ground and it was no longer safe to traffic in imported goods that came from strange places and carried a curse with them. Everyone had a different explanation—and everyone's explanation was louder and sillier than his neighbors'.

They were talking about it this afternoon as Tito and Bimbo came out of the side-street into the public square. The Forum was the favorite promenade for rich and poor. What with the priests arguing with the politicians, servants doing the day's shopping, tradesmen crying their wares, women displaying the latest fashions from Greece and Egypt, children playing hide-and-seek among the marble columns, knots of soldiers, sailors, peasants from the provinces—to say nothing of those who merely came to lounge and look on—the square was crowded to its last inch. His ears even more than his nose guided Tito to the place where the talk was the loudest. It was in front of the Shrine of the Household Gods that, naturally enough, the householders were arguing.

"I tell you," rumbled a voice which Tito recognized as bathmaster Rufus, "there won't be another earthquake in my lifetime or yours. There may be a tremble or two, but earthquakes, like lightnings, never strike twice in the same place."

"Do they not?" asked a thin voice Tito had never heard. It had a high, sharp ring to it and Tito knew it as the accent of a stranger. "How about the two towns of Sicily that have been ruined three times within fifteen years by the eruptions of Mount Etna? And were they not warned? And does that column of smoke above Vesuvius mean nothing?"

"That?" Tito could hear the grunt with which one question answered another.

"That's always there. We use it for our weather-guide. When the smoke stands up straight we know we'll have fair weather; when it flattens out it's sure to be foggy; when it drifts to the east—"

"Yes, yes," cut in the edged voice. "I've heard about your mountain barometer. But the column of smoke seems hundreds of feet higher than usual and it's thickening and spreading like a shadowy tree. They say in Naples—"

"Oh, Naples!" Tito knew this voice by the little squeak that went with it. It was Attilio, the cameo-cutter. "*They* talk while we suffer. Little help we got from them last time. Naples commits the crimes and Pompeii pays the price. It's become a proverb with us. Let them mind their own business."

"Yes," grumbled Rufus, "and others, too."

"Very well, my confident friends," responded the thin voice which now sounded curiously flat. "We also have a proverb—and it is this: Those who will not listen to men must be taught by the gods. I will say no more. But I leave a last warning. Remember the holy ones. Look to your temples. And when the smoke-tree above Vesuvius grows to the shape of an umbrella-pine, look to your lives."

Tito could hear the air whistle as the speaker drew his toga about him and the quick shuffle of feet told him the stranger had gone.

"Now what," said the cameo-cutter, "did he mean by that?"

"I wonder," grunted Rufus, "I wonder."

Tito wondered, too, and Bimbo, his head at a thoughtful angle, looked as if he had been doing a heavy piece of pondering. By nightfall the argument had been forgotten. If the smoke had increased no one saw it in the dark. Besides, it was Caesar's birthday and the town was in a holiday mood. Tito and Bimbo were among the merry-makers, dodging the charioteers who shouted at them. A dozen times they almost upset baskets of sweets and jars of Vesuvian wine, said to be as fiery as the streams inside the volcano, and a dozen times they were cursed and cuffed. But Tito never missed his footing. He was thankful for his keen ears and quick instinct—most thankful of all for Bimbo.

They visited the uncovered theatre and, though Tito could not see the faces of the actors, he could follow the play better than most of the audience, for their attention wandered—they were distracted by the scenery, the costumes, the by-play, even by themselves—while Tito's whole attention was centered in what he heard. Then to the city-walls, where the people of Pompeii watched a mock naval-battle in which the city was attacked by the sea and saved after thousands of flaming arrows had been exchanged and countless colored torches had been burned. Though the thrill of flaring ships and lighted skies was lost to Tito, the shouts and cheers excited him as much as any and he cried out with the loudest of them.

The next morning there were *two* of the beloved raisin and sugar cakes for his breakfast. Bimbo was unusually active and thumped his bit of a tail until Tito was afraid he would wear it out. The boy could not imagine whether Bimbo was urging him to some sort of game or trying to tell something. After a while, he ceased to notice Bimbo. He felt drowsy. Last night's late hours had tired him. Besides, there was a heavy mist in the air—no, a thick fog rather than a mist—a fog that got into his throat and scraped it and made him cough. He walked as far as the marine gate to get a breath of the sea. But the blanket of haze had spread all over the bay and even the salt air seemed smoky.

He went to bed before dusk and slept. But he did not sleep well. He had too many dreams—dreams of ships lurching in the Forum, of losing his way in a screaming crowd, of armies marching across his chest, of being pulled over every rough pavement of Pompeii.

He woke early. Or, rather, he was pulled awake. Bimbo was doing the pulling. The dog had dragged Tito to his feet and was urging the boy along. Somewhere. Where, Tito did not know. His feet stumbled uncertainly; he was still half asleep. For a while he noticed nothing except the fact that it was hard to breathe. The air was hot. And heavy. So heavy that he could taste it. The air, it seemed, had turned to powder, a warm powder that stung his nostrils and burned his sightless eyes.

Then he began to hear sounds. Peculiar sounds. Like animals under the earth. Hissings and groanings and muffled cries that a dying creature might make dislodging the stones of his underground cave. There was no doubt of it now. The noises came from underneath. He not only heard them—he could feel them. The earth twitched; the twitching changed into an uneven shrugging of the soil. Then, as Bimbo half-pulled, half-coaxed him across, the ground jerked

away from his feet and he was thrown against a stone-fountain.

The water—hot water—splashing his face revived him. He got to his feet, Bimbo steadying him, helping him on again. The noises grew louder; they came closer. The cries were even more animal-like than before, but now they came from human throats. A few people, quicker of foot and more hurried by fear, began to rush by. A family or two—then a section—then, it seemed, an army broken out of bounds. Tito, bewildered though he was, could recognize Rufus as he bellowed past him, like a water-buffalo gone mad. Time was lost in a nightmare.

It was then the crashing began. First a sharp crackling, like a monstrous snapping of twigs; then a roar like the fall of a whole forest of trees; then an explosion that tore earth and sky. The heavens, though Tito could not see them, were shot through with continual flickerings of fire. Lightnings above were answered by thunders beneath. A house fell. Then another. By a miracle the two companions had escaped the dangerous side-streets and were in a more open space. It was the Forum. They rested here awhile—how long he did not know.

Tito had no idea of the time of day. He could *feel* it was black—an unnatural blackness. Something inside—perhaps the lack of breakfast and lunch—told him it was past noon. But it didn't matter. Nothing seemed to matter. He was getting drowsy, too drowsy to walk. But walk he must. He knew it. And Bimbo knew it; the sharp tugs told him so. Nor was it a moment too soon. The sacred ground of the Forum was safe no longer. It was beginning to rock, then to pitch, then to split. As they stumbled out of the square, the earth wriggled like a caught snake and all the columns of the temple of Jupiter came down. It was the end of the world—or so it seemed.

To walk was not enough now. They must run. Tito was too frightened to know what to do or where to go. He had lost all sense of direction. He started to go back to the inner gate; but Bimbo, straining his back to the last inch, almost pulled his clothes from him. What did the creature want? Had the dog gone mad?

Then, suddenly, he understood. Bimbo was telling him the way out—urging him there. The sea-gate, of course. The sea-gate—and then the sea. Far from the falling buildings, heaving ground. He turned, Bimbo guiding him across open pits and dangerous pools of bubbling mud, away from buildings that had caught fire and were dropping their burning beams. Tito could no longer tell whether the noises were made by the shrieking sky or the agonized people. He and Bimbo ran on—the only silent beings in a howling world.

New dangers threatened. All Pompeii seemed to be thronging toward the marine gate and, squeezing among the crowds, there was the chance of being trampled to death. But the chance had to be taken. It was growing harder and harder to breathe. What air there was choked him. It was all dust now—dust and pebbles, pebbles as large as beans. They fell on his head, his hands—pumice stones from the black heart of Vesuvius. The mountain was turning itself inside out. Tito remembered a phrase that the stranger had said in the Forum two days ago: "Those who will not listen to men must be taught by the gods." The people of Pompeii had refused to heed the warnings; they were being taught now—if it was not too late.

Suddenly it seemed too late for Tito. The red hot ashes blistered his skin, the stinging vapors tore his throat. He could not go on. He staggered toward a small tree at the side of the road and fell. In a moment Bimbo was beside him. He coaxed. But there was no answer. He licked Tito's hands, his feet, his face. The boy did not stir. Then Bimbo did the last thing he could—the last thing he wanted to do. He bit his comrade, bit him deep in the arm. With a cry of pain, Tito jumped to his feet, Bimbo after him. Tito was in despair, but Bimbo was determined. He drove the boy on, snapping at his heels, worrying his way through the crowd; barking, baring his teeth, heedless of kicks or falling stones. Sick with hunger, half-dead with fear and sulphur-fumes, Tito pounded on, pursued by Bimbo. How

long he never knew. At last he staggered through the marine-gate and felt soft sand under him. Then Tito fainted . . .

Someone was dashing sea-water over him. Someone was carrying him toward a boat.

"Bimbo," he called. And then louder, "Bimbo!" But Bimbo had disappeared.

Voices jarred against each other. "Hurry—hurry!" "To the boats!" "Can't you see the child's frightened and starving!"

"He keeps calling for someone!" "Poor boy, he's out of his mind." "Here, child—take this!"

They tucked him in among them. The oar-locks creaked; the oars splashed; the boat rode over toppling waves. Tito was safe. But he wept continually.

"Bimbo!" he wailed. "Bimbo! Bimbo!"

He could not be comforted.

Eighteen hundred years passed. Scientists were restoring the ancient city; excavators were working their way through the stones and trash that had buried the entire town. Much had already been brought to light—statues, bronze instruments, bright mosaics, household articles; even delicate paintings had been preserved by the fall of ashes that had taken over two thousand lives. Columns were dug up and the Forum was beginning to emerge.

It was at a place where the ruins lay deepest that the Director paused.

"Come here," he called to his assistant. "I think we've discovered the remains of a building in good shape. Here are four huge mill-stones that were most likely turned by slaves or mules—and here is a whole wall standing with shelves inside it. Why! It must have been a bakery. And here's a curious thing. What do you think I found under this heap where the ashes were thickest? The skeleton of a dog!"

"Amazing!" gasped his assistant.

"You'd think a dog would have had sense enough to run away at the time. And what is that flat thing he's holding between his teeth? It can't be a stone."

"No. It must have come from this bakery. You know it looks to me like some sort of cake hardened with the years. And, bless me, if those little black pebbles aren't raisins. A raisin-cake almost two thousand years old! I wonder what made him want it at such a moment?"

"I wonder," murmured the assistant.

Reader's Response

What do you admire about the author's ability to make up a story about something that happened so long ago?

THE DOG OF POMPEII

Checking Your Comprehension

1. What was the ancient city of Pompeii like?
2. Describe the relationship between Tito and Bimbo.
3. How did Tito feel about his disability?
4. What theories did Pompeiians have about the earthquakes that struck their town?
5. Based on the details in the story, how do you think Pompeii's attitude toward outsiders helped bring about their downfall?
6. How was Tito saved?
7. Why did Bimbo leave Tito? What makes you think so?

Writing to Learn

THINK AND OBSERVE *Bimbo* is the Italian word for "baby." When Tito's dog was a puppy, this name might have been appropriate. What would you name him if he were your dog? Make a chart like the one below and for each quality list examples from the story. Try to add at least two more qualities with examples.

Bimbo's Qualities		
Loyalty	Intelligence	Courage
Examples: Almost never left Tito	Examples:	Examples:

WRITE Give Bimbo a new name based on the qualities you noted. Explain why you think the new name is appropriate.

447

A Strategy for Thinking:

Making a Pro-and-Con Chart

Do you remember the last argument you had with someone? You presented opinions on one side of the issue while the other person presented opinions on the other side. Could you understand the other point of view?

Most of the time, both sides of an argument can be supported. You may not always agree with someone else's side of an argument, but it is very important to be able to understand and evaluate their point of view. If you understand other viewpoints, you will understand an issue better. You may even wind up changing your own views about an issue.

Learning the Strategy

How can you learn to evaluate both sides of an issue? One way is to make a pro-and-con chart. *Pros* are arguments for a given issue and *cons* are arguments against a given issue. To make a pro-and-con chart, you must first ask a question about the material you are reading. Then make a chart with the pros listed on one side and the cons listed on the other. The pros and cons will help you evaluate your opinion about the issue. For example, read the following passage from "The Dog of Pompeii."

> "I tell you," rumbled a voice which Tito recognized as bathmaster Rufus, "there won't be another earthquake in my lifetime or yours. There may be a tremble or two, but earthquakes, like lightning, never strike twice in the same place."

"Do they not?" asked a thin voice Tito had never heard. "How about the two towns of Sicily that have been ruined three times within fifteen years by the eruptions of Mount Etna? . . .and does that column of smoke above Vesuvius mean nothing?"

"That? . . .That's always there. We use it for our weather guide."

Now ask a question that can be addressed using arguments from the story. The pros and cons are listed in the chart below.

SHOULD TITO AND THE RESIDENTS OF POMPEII HAVE LEFT POMPEII?	
Pros:	Cons:
◆ Earthquakes do, in fact, happen many times in one place. ◆ Residents of Pompeii should heed the warning of the smoke above Vesuvius.	◆ Some say that earthquakes never occur in the same place twice. ◆ The smoke above Vesuvius is always there.

Using the Strategy

Go back and reread "The Dog of Pompeii." As you read, add to the pro-and-con chart above. Look for statements for and against the issue of whether Tito and the residents of Pompeii should have left the city.

Applying the Strategy to the Next Selection

The next selection, "Lost and Found: Pompeii," is a factual account of the eruption of Mount Vesuvius. As you read, list the pros and cons of whether the Pompeians should have left their city.

◀◆▶ The writing connection can be found on page 515.

LOST AND FOUND: POMPEII

by Ron and Nancy Goor

~~~~~~

Can you picture the sights and sounds of Pompeii on the day Mt. Vesuvius erupted? Can you imagine the horrified panic? Archaeologists can, because the incredible forces that destroyed the city have also preserved it.

The following report provides the only eyewitness record to the eruption of Vesuvius in A.D. 79. In this letter to the historian Tacitus, Pliny the Younger describes the catastrophe and what happened to his uncle, Pliny the Elder, a renowned natural historian and Admiral of the Roman fleet stationed at Misenum.

"My uncle was stationed at Misenum, in active command of the fleet. On 24 August, in the early afternoon, my mother drew his attention to a cloud of unusual size and appearance . . . like a pine . . . for it rose to a great height on a sort of trunk and then split off into branches. My uncle ordered a boat to be made ready. As he was leaving the house he was handed a message from Rectina. . . . She implored him to rescue her from her fate. He gave orders for the warships to be launched and went on board with the intention of bringing help to many more people besides Rectina. Ashes were already falling, hotter and thicker as the ships drew near, followed by bits of pumice and blackened stones, charred and cracked by the flames: then suddenly they were in shallow water, and the shore was blocked by the debris from the mountain. . . . [The] wind was full in my uncle's favour, and he was able to bring his ship in.

"Meanwhile on Mount Vesuvius broad sheets of fire and leaping flames blazed at several points. My uncle tried to allay the fears of his companions by repeatedly declaring that these were nothing but bonfires left by peasants or empty houses on fire. . . . Then he went to rest. . . . By this time the courtyard giving access to his room was full of ashes mixed with pumice-stones, and if he had stayed in the room any longer he would never have got out. He was wakened and joined the rest of the household who had sat up all night. They debated whether to stay indoors or take their chance in the open, for the buildings were now shaking with violent shocks, and seemed to be swaying to and fro as if they were torn from their foundations. Outside there was the danger of falling pumice-stones, even though these were light and porous. . . . [A]fter comparing the risks, they chose the latter."

◄◆►
Should the Pompeians have left? Add this information to your pro-and-con chart.

Excerpt adapted from *Pompeii: Exploring a Roman Ghost Town* by Ron and Nancy Goor, published by Thomas Y. Crowell/Harper & Row. Reprinted by permission of Harper & Row, Publishers, Inc.

Later that day Pliny the Elder was overcome by poisonous fumes. He was one of the thousands of victims claimed by Mount Vesuvius. In another letter to Tacitus, Pliny the Younger describes his own flight at dawn the morning of his uncle's death.

"[D]arkness fell, not the dark of a moonless or cloudy night, but as if the lamp had been put out in a closed room. You could hear the shrieks of women, the wailing of infants, and the shouting of men. Many besought the aid of the gods, but still more imagined that there were no gods left. . . . At last the darkness thinned. . . . We were terrified to see everything changed, buried deep in ashes like snowdrifts." ◈◈

Add information from this passage to your pro-and-con chart.

〜〜〜〜〜

WHERE DID ALL THE PEOPLE GO?

This is a ghost town called Pompeii. The buildings have no roofs. The walls are missing or damaged. Staircases lead nowhere. The city is silent. Why does Pompeii look like a war-torn city? Look above the buildings and trees. A mountain looms over the city—a mountain called Mt. Vesuvius. This is no ordinary mountain. Mt. Vesuvius is a volcano. On August 24, A.D. 79, Mt. Vesuvius transformed Pompeii from a lively, crowded city into a ghost town.

〜〜〜〜〜

A THRIVING ROMAN TOWN

Nineteen hundred years ago Pompeii was a small, bustling Roman city. It was primarily a commercial and agricultural town. It was probably similar to many small towns throughout the vast Roman Empire.

In A.D. 79 Pompeii was a prosperous town of ten to twenty thousand people. It was ideally situated as a center of trade. It lay on the only route between the fertile valleys of the region known as Campania and the sea. Pompeii had two good ports: one on the Bay of Naples (which is part of the Mediterranean Sea) and the other one on the Sarno River. Pompeii traded with other small Roman towns nearby, as well as with distant empires such as Egypt and Spain.

A wealth of natural resources also contributed to Pompeii's prosperity. The sea provided Pompeians with one of their favorite foods—fish—and one of their most popular products—garum, a spicy sauce made from fish entrails. Its fertile volcanic soil and mild climate helped make Pompeii a successful agricultural center. Pompeians raised grain, grapes, olives, sheep, and flowers. They made and sold bread, wine, olive oil, wool, perfume, and garlands of flowers.

In A.D. 79 Pompeians planted vineyards and grazed their sheep on the slopes of Mt. Vesuvius. They did not know Mt. Vesuvius was an active volcano. It had not erupted in so long that its sides were green with vegetation.

EARTHQUAKE OF A.D. 62

The first signs that Mt. Vesuvius was waking up came in A.D. 62. Pressure building beneath the volcano caused a violent earthquake in southern Italy. Damage in Pompeii was extensive. Roofs caved in. Columns crumbled to the earth. Statues crashed to the ground. A major water reservoir cracked open and flooded the streets of Pompeii. The energetic Pompeians immediately began rebuilding the city. Most homes were repaired and redecorated in the first few years. Seventeen years after the earthquake many temples and other public buildings were still being rebuilt.

MT. VESUVIUS BLOWS ITS STACK

Use information from this passage in your chart.

In late August of A.D. 79 the earth began to rumble and shake. Streams and well water disappeared as if dried up by some great heat. The sea heaved and churned. Animals became restless. Mt. Vesuvius was about to blow its stack.

At about one o'clock on the afternoon of August 24, A.D. 79, Pompeians were eating lunch or preparing to rest. Suddenly a deafening sound was heard. The top of Mt. Vesuvius blasted off. Expanding gases from deep inside the volcano hurled volcanic ash and red-hot stones thousands of feet into the air. Fountains of fire, smoke, and molten lava gushed out of the mouth of the volcano. Violent earthquakes shook the ground for miles around. Volcanic dust covered the sky and completely blotted out the sun. The day became darker than the blackest night. The sea roared and rose up in great waves.

Volcanic matter shot out of Mt. Vesuvius, forming a giant mushroom-shaped cloud that rose twelve miles into the sky. The cloud spread over Pompeii and the Sarno plain and released a rain of ash and lava stone. Volcanic debris accumulated at the rate of six inches an hour. It piled on top of roofs until they crashed under its weight. It fell until the city was covered under a blanket twelve feet thick. The harbor became so filled with volcanic deposits that no ships could sail.

POMPEII DIES AT 6:30 A.M., AUGUST 25

Eleven hours after the first explosion, the force of the eruption weakened. The twelve-mile-high column of debris above the volcano collapsed, sending a glowing avalanche of ash, stone, and superheated gases roaring down the west side of the volcano.

During the night and the next morning the column collapsed five more times—each time causing another fiery surge to roar down the volcano at speeds of 60 to 180 miles per hour, and temperatures above 212°F. Three of these surges came close to Pompeii, but did not reach the walls. At about 6:30 A.M. on August 25 the fourth surge blasted through Pompeii at hurricane speeds. It blew off roofs and knocked people over. The hot, ash-filled air clogged their lungs and snuffed out their lives. The poisonous gases that rose out of the depths of the volcano seeped into their rooms and asphyxiated them. And still the ash kept falling. When it finally stopped, only the tips of roofs that had not caved in could be seen.

This ruin is what remains of a bakery; it is one of the buildings that was covered in volcanic ash on the day Mount Vesuvius erupted.

DEATH

The people of Pompeii were terrified. Some grabbed the nearest donkeys and headed for the city gates. Some ran to the sea. Some escaped. Many did not.

Some Pompeians decided it was too dangerous to leave their homes. Eighteen members of the House of Diomedes ran to the cellar. They clung to each other as they waited for the ash to stop falling. Poisonous gases seeped into their hideaway, and they all died.

A muleteer huddled by the gymnasium wall. He covered his face to keep out volcanic dust and ash.

Use information from this passage in your chart.

This Pompeian wall painting survived the destruction. It depicts a Roman ceremony that may have been taking place at the time of the eruption.

A guard dog chained up in the House of Vesonius Primus struggled frantically to free himself. But the ash kept falling, and soon he was completely buried under many feet of ash and stone.

~~~~~~~~~

BURIED AND SOON FORGOTTEN

In the first few days after the eruption some people tried to dig through the ash to get to their houses. Looters stole sculptures, jewelry, and other objects of value. But it was dangerous to dig into the buried city. Pockets of poisonous gases still lay trapped under the lava. Soon no one returned to Pompeii. Grass grew over the site. People called the area Civitas, which means "ancient city." It was not long before they forgot that the thriving city of Pompeii had ever existed.

~~~~~~~~~

HOW WAS POMPEII DISCOVERED?

Years passed. Centuries passed. For more than 1500 years Pompeii lay buried and forgotten. In 1594 Pompeii was *almost* discovered by accident. Workmen digging an underground channel to bring water from the Sarno River to a rich man's villa came across bits and pieces of ruined buildings. They even found an inscription with the words *decurio Pompeiis*. This was an important clue, but not even the architect in charge, Domenico Fontana, connected the words with the lost city of Pompeii. Pompeii remained buried and undiscovered for another 154 years.

~~~~~~~~~

HERCULANEUM IS DISCOVERED

In 1709 the Austrian Prince d'Elbeuf had a well dug on his property in the town of Resina. By accident the prince's workmen dug into the ancient theater of Herculaneum, a nearby city that was buried by the same eruption that destroyed Pompeii. Prince d'Elbeuf made a world-shattering discovery—he rediscovered Herculaneum. But the prince was not interested in his find for its historic value. He was interested

457

only in the treasures he could collect to decorate his villa. By tunneling into the theater and looting it, the prince's workers destroyed the best-preserved theater of ancient times.

However, excavation at Herculaneum was soon abandoned. The mud-lava that covered this seaside resort had hardened into stone too difficult to excavate.

~~~~~~~~~

DIGGING OUT POMPEII

The excitement inspired by the discoveries at Herculaneum encouraged scholars to look for other ruins nearby that might reveal treasures of their own. In 1748 a Spanish engineering officer, Roque de Alcubierre, dug through the dirt and hardened ash covering Pompeii and reached the Temple of Fortuna Augusta. Pompeii was officially rediscovered and excavations began in earnest. In 1763 an inscription including the words *Res publica Pompeianorum* was uncovered near the city wall. This evidence confirmed that Civitas was indeed the long-lost Pompeii.

This wall painting, called "Flora," was found in a villa near Pompeii.

The first excavators were careless. They dug through thirty feet of earth and hardened ash with no care for what lay underneath. They destroyed many objects that gave clues about the Roman way of life. These early excavators had no interest in Pompeii for what it told about the past. They wanted only to take paintings, sculptures, mosaics, and other beautiful objects for private collections.

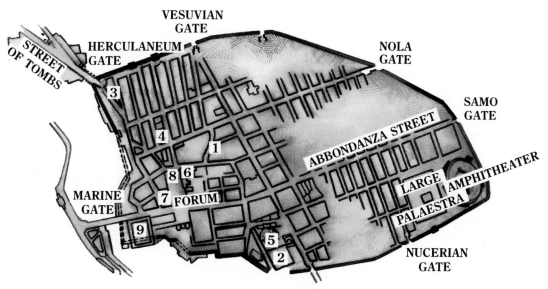

1. Bakery of Modestus
2. Gladiator's Barracks
3. House of the Surgeon
4. House of the Tragic Poet
5. Large Theater
6. Macellum
7. Temple of Apollo
8. Temple of Jupiter
9. Temple of Venus

Map of Pompeii

Fortunately, in the 1860s the archaeologist Giuseppi Fiorelli instituted a scientific method for excavating Pompeii. He divided the city into regions. Every block and every doorway had a number. Digging was done methodically from the surface of the earth downward—slowly and carefully. Every object was numbered and catalogued. Paintings were left where they were found. In this map of Pompeii you can see the way Fiorelli divided the city into blocks and regions. Notice how much of Pompeii is still buried after more than two hundred years of excavation. Beneath this crust of lava, Pompeii still has many secrets to tell. Secrets and clues that will increase our understanding of Roman life remain to be discovered.

~~~~~~~~~~

WHY ARE POMPEII AND HERCULANEUM SO IMPORTANT?

The rediscovery of Pompeii and Herculaneum ignited the imagination and interest of people the world over. In fact, discoveries in Pompeii, Herculaneum, and other small Roman towns and villas at the

459

base of Mt. Vesuvius continue to make headline news. Why?

Roman heritage is our heritage. The Romans came into contact with many different peoples. They incorporated the best aspects of many civilizations into their own culture, which they spread throughout the world they conquered. We are the inheritors of this culture. Roman law is the basis of Western law. We read stories based on Roman myths. We construct buildings patterned after Roman temples.

Pompeii provides a window into our past. Over the years, buildings deteriorate or are destroyed. Objects decay and turn to dust. New objects replace the old. The past is slowly erased and forgotten. Not so in Pompeii. The ash that destroyed Pompeii also preserved it exactly as it was on August 24, A.D. 79.

〜〜〜〜〜

BRINGING POMPEII TO LIFE

Should the Pompeians have left their city earlier? Use your pro-and-con chart to review the arguments. Then draw your own conclusion.

When Mt. Vesuvius buried Pompeii and the small towns nestled around its base, it preserved a wealth of clues about Roman life. Cooking utensils, furniture, tools, jewelry, games, food, casts of bodies, plant roots, wooden doors and gates, and paintings and graffiti covering walls of buildings and tombs are but some of the millions of clues. Archaeologists study these clues to learn what a Roman town of the first century A.D. was like.

♦ LIBRARY LINK ♦

For some fascinating details describing everyday life in the ancient city of Pompeii, you'll want to read the entire book Pompeii: Exploring a Roman Ghost Town *by Ron and Nancy Goor.*

Reader's Response

In this article, the authors powerfully described the destruction of Pompeii. Which details or events seemed most vivid to you?

LOST AND FOUND:
POMPEII

Checking Your Comprehension

1. Who provided history with the only eyewitness record of the eruption of Vesuvius in A.D. 79?
2. What were some of the reasons for Pompeii's prosperity?
3. Did the people of Pompeii suspect that Mt. Vesuvius might one day erupt and destroy the city? What makes you think they did or did not?
4. What were four signs that indicated Mt. Vesuvius was going to erupt in A.D. 79?
5. What happened to Pompeii after the blast?
6. Compare the first excavations with those carried out by Fiorelli.
7. Why are finds such as the ones at Pompeii and Herculaneum important to people who live in the twentieth century?

Writing to Learn

THINK AND IMAGINE Before the final destruction of Pompeii, Mt. Vesuvius sent audible and visible signs of a possible eruption. What were some of these signs? Copy and add to the list below.

Strange Events
1. streams dried up
2. animals restless

WRITE Pretend you were in Pompeii in the days just before the eruption. Write a journal entry recording what is going on and how you as a person of those times interpret the events.

READING FICTION

Vocabulary:

Etymologies

Did you know that the word *volcano* comes from *Vulcan*—the name of the Roman god of fire? The ancient Romans did not have our scientific understanding of the causes of volcanic eruptions. They believed eruptions such as the one that buried Pompeii were caused by Vulcan, their angry and destructive god of fire.

Like the word *volcano*, English words come from many different languages and often have interesting stories behind them. You can learn these stories by studying the etymologies of words. A word's *etymology* tells its origin, history, and evolution. In other words, it tells you how the meaning of a word has changed over time.

Sometimes the current meaning of a word may be far from the original one. Look at the etymology of the word *promenade*, for example. *Promenade* can be traced to the Latin prefix *pro-*, meaning "forth," and the Latin word *minari*, which means "to threaten animals." Later, the Romans used the word *prominare* to mean "to drive animals." The French borrowed the Latin word and changed its meaning in the process. The French word became *promener* and the meaning changed to "to take a walk." Then, the English language borrowed the word from the French as *promenade*, meaning "a leisurely walk" or "a public place for such a walk."

Most words in our language today have their own history. Like the word *promenade*, the spelling and meaning of many words have changed over time. However, it is still usually possible to trace the words we use from their current meanings back to their origins.

Studying etymology can help you to understand the meanings of words you may not know. This is because words with common roots often have similar meanings. For example, *car* and *chariot* both come from the Latin word *carrus,* meaning "two-wheeled vehicle." The meanings of the English words, of course, both have to do with wheeled vehicles as well.

You don't have to search through ancient texts to find the etymologies of words; you can simply use a dictionary. Most dictionaries show the etymology in brackets after the pronunciation or at the end of the entry. The dictionary entry below gives a detailed etymology of the word *stadium.*

> **sta•di•um** (stā´ dē əm) [Middle English, from Latin, from Greek *stadion,* a fixed measure of length, from *span,* to draw or pull] **n.** a place for outdoor games, meetings, etc., with rising rows of seats around an open field.

The etymology shows that *stadium* comes from a Greek word meaning a measure of length. (It was the standard measure used for racetracks.) The Greek word in turn came from an earlier Greek word, *span,* meaning "to pull or draw." Before *stadium* found its way into English, it passed through both Latin and Middle English.

Think about *that* the next time you go to a ball game.

Using What You Have Learned

Read the list of words below. For words you don't know, write down what you think they might mean based on their roots. For words you do know, explain how the roots help you understand the meaning.

     1. harmonica   **3.** monotone   **5.** melodramatic
     2. prehistoric   **4.** shepherd   **6.** seaworthy

As You Read

In "Digging for China," you will encounter the word *trench*. See if you can guess the original meaning of the word; then look up the etymology in a dictionary to see how close you came.

DIGGING FOR CHINA

BY PATRICIA BEATTY

If historical artifacts could talk, just imagine the stories they might tell. Consider the case of a simple jade bead. . . .

Dust! Wind and dust! The constant springtime dustiness in California made thirteen-year-old Wong Chun Li sigh and put down the hoe he'd been using to weed the Wong Sing's gardens. It wasn't only the dust that irritated him, but even so early in this Chinese New Year, the Year of the Snake, the unrelenting sun pressing hot upon him was more than he could bear. His black shoes, white stockings, and loose-fitting dark blue trousers were coated with dust, and his cotton jacket, a match to his trousers, was blackened with sweat. Wong Chun Li slipped cautiously away from the rows of carrots, onions, and garlic plants and sauntered to the shed in the center of the garden. He'd rest where the boss couldn't catch sight of him and order him back to work.

Taking off his wide-brimmed conical hat, his hoe poised on his shoulder, he crept around to the shady side of the building, facing Riverside's Chinatown. At the water barrel, he drank from the tin dipper, then he leaned against the shed, thinking and frowning. His eyes fell on Mount Rubidoux, the huge brown rock that towered over the field and this American city that remained so strange to him. How vastly different from his village in South China was this town of pallid-faced "ghost" people! Where were the tea fields, the fish-filled, swift-flowing rivers bustling with ships? Here the river ran mostly underground. Where were the heavy rains that kept the earth moist for two crops of rice a year? Where were the misty waterfalls and cloud-wreathed mountains and the green hillside terraces? In his native village of Gomm Benn, every farmer raised a pig

or two, ducks and geese, and doves. When he'd traveled about Riverside with an uncle to sell vegetables, he'd observed only dogs and cats—not one pig.

When Wong Chun Li, the oldest son of his family, had been sent to join his uncles and cousins and earn money to send home, he'd expected this American town to be more like China. Yes, oranges were grown here as in Guandong Province, but there the resemblance ended. Riverside was not one bit like the great cities of Hangchow and Canton, where silk cloth was made, and every street had small shops devoted to selling special products such as ivory, silk, leather, furniture, and precious jade.

Jade! Wong Chun Li touched the green bead on the string around his neck, the bead his grandfather had found near Gomm Benn and given to him. The bead was very old, according to the scholar of Gomm Benn, and the word carved on it meant "good fortune." The scholar had scratched Wong Chun Li's name in Chinese characters on its back.

As he lifted his second dipperful of water, the ladle was suddenly knocked from his hand. A fist, accompanied by a resounding shout, crashed into the side of his head, sending his black queue swaying wildly. One quick glance showed him the blue eyes, pale freckly face, and red hair of the same boy who'd attacked him last week near Chinatown and given him a nosebleed. Leaping back and dropping his hoe, Wong Chun Li gave the American boy a kick to his side that doubled him over. But the redhead quickly recovered. As Wong Chun Li ducked to avoid the next blow, the freckled hand caught the string with the jade bead, jerking it loose and sending it sailing across the field. Just then the boys heard the angry shouting of Wong Sing coming at a run, waving his hoe, and the smirking redhead took to his heels.

Wong Chun Li didn't dare to talk back to his elders so he did not reply to the man's angry words. His mind was filled with one thought only, "That bead was my good luck! I need it; I hope I can get it back."

As soon as his field work was done, Wong Chun Li searched

long and hard for his bead. Alas, it was surely lost. Its color was the same green as the weeds growing in the garbage heap of Chinatown— it was so impossible to see that it seemed invisible.

Dust! Dust and wind! A santana[1] storm from the Mojave[2] desert made the air in Riverside yellow and biting, and caused the tall palms to sway restlessly. Martha Stirling held a handkerchief over her nose as she walked to school that bleak February morning. She hated the acrid winds that seemed to make everyone so grouchy. Mr. Sloan, the math teacher, would definitely be a bear this morning. He usually was a bear, anyway, storm or no storm. He doled out good grades as if they came out of his savings account at the bank—except to Peter Chang, the teacher's pet. Today he gave Martha a C+, when Martha felt she deserved a B. As usual, Peter got the only A in the class.

Peter Chang was also in Martha's social studies class, but here Martha challenged Peter, matching him A for A. Now as Martha entered Ms. Whelan's classroom, she saw that the social studies teacher had a visitor. The visitor was young, like Ms. Whelan, not too tall, and had her dark hair cut short. But that's where the resemblance to Ms. Whelan stopped—she sure was dressed differently! She was clad in a pale green jacket, blue jeans, brown work shoes, and a bright green baseball cap that said "Boston Celtics" on it. No, she definitely was not a teacher!

Ms. Whelan introduced her enthusiastically, "This is my friend Liz McCarthy from Boston, where I used to live. She's come here as a graduate student at a local college and will be talking to you this morning."

The newcomer smiled and said, "I've come here to invite you girls and boys to work on an archaeological dig with me and a lot of other Riversiders."

Martha stiffened. A dig? Was she asking them to dig with a shovel, a garden chore she hated?

As if she had read Martha's mind, Liz McCarthy said, "You won't be digging with shovels! I'm studying to be an archaeologist, and I've

[1]santana (san tan′ ə): a hot, dry wind from the Santa Ana Mountains.
[2]Mojave (mō hä′ vē)

come with my professor to help dig up the area that used to be your old Chinatown. It will soon be paved over for a parking lot, so we have to hurry with the project!"

"Where is it?" asked Peter Chang.

"On Brockton Avenue."

Martha frowned. She lived on Brockton and there wasn't any Chinatown on that street. Then she remembered all the people she'd seen digging down in the hollow not far from her old grammar school and she realized that they hadn't been dressed like construction workers with hard hats.

Ms. McCarthy continued, "I'm asking at middle schools to see if any of you will volunteer to come this Saturday and help us. You won't get paid, and you'll work hard, but it could be exciting. Figure it as one way to dig for China."

Up went Peter Chang's hand, making Ms. Whelan grin. Teacher's pet again, huh? Up shot Martha's hand, too. That game wouldn't work here.

"Peter Chang and Martha Stirling," announced Ms. Whelan. "Liz, these students will be your volunteers. You said you only wanted two from here."

"Good! We'll see you two at eight o'clock at Brockton Avenue. We'll supply what you'll need."

At supper Martha told her parents about the "dig" and asked, "Where did the Chinatown go that used to be down in the hollow? What happened to it?"

Her father answered, "I don't remember it at all. It had already disappeared when I was your age, but your great-grandfather knew it well. He said parts of it burned down, and then the people just sort of disappeared."

"Oh! Why'd they come here in the first place, Dad?"

Mrs. Stirling replied to this, "To help lay the rails for the railroads. When the railroads were finished, the Chinese continued to come here to grow and sell vegetables and work in Riverside's orange groves and packing plants."

Martha's father added, "Your Great-Grandpa Reynolds can tell

468

you some stories about old Chinatown when he comes to dinner Saturday night. He's often told me how he used to buy lichee nuts and ginger candy down there."

Martha nodded. Although Great-Grandpa Reynolds was over ninety, he certainly didn't act that old, and Martha knew he'd have a story to tell.

That next Saturday morning at eight, Martha arrived at the hollow on Brockton where the "dig" was. The site covered several acres, and it was swarming with people—men, women, high-school kids, and kids her own age. To Martha's disgust, "early-bird" Peter Chang was already there, crouched down on the ground inside a shallow trench, peering at its sides.

As Martha scowled at him, Liz McCarthy greeted her and presented her with a trowel, a bucket, and a brush. "Hi, I'm glad to see you brought your lunch. Your friend, the boy from your class, is over there in trench B, section C. The trenches are marked by letters on poles and divided by string lines. Go over and join him."

Reluctantly, Martha went to the site Liz McCarthy had indicated. "You work on that side of this trench and I'll work on this one," she growled at Peter.

"That suits me," muttered Peter, and Martha suddenly realized that Peter didn't much like her either.

Liz McCarthy came to stand at the edge of the two-foot deep trench and watched Martha crawl down inside it. Bending over, she instructed Martha, "Work carefully. Look in the sides of the trench for pieces of bone or glass or broken pottery. When you see something, trowel it loose and brush off as much dirt as you can without breaking anything. Take everything out and put it gently into your bucket, and, when your bucket's full, take it to the tall man over there. That's Professor Clarke. He'll take what you've found and classify it and mark it on the map and he'll sieve the dirt left over for tiny artifacts. See you later."

Martha set to work, troweling. The first thing she found was a piece of animal bone, and the next item she unearthed was a tiny lavender bottle. Pretty dull stuff! But maybe she'd find a gold piece;

she knew Riversiders used that kind of money when Great-Grandpa was a boy. Wouldn't that be a find, though?

By mid-afternoon Martha had taken out twenty buckets of chinaware, glass fragments, and animal and fish bones to be classified and sieved. She watched the professor and Liz McCarthy and other of Clarke's students mark and map her finds as "pig bones," "turtle shell fragments," "medicine vials," and "shards" of dishes, all found a foot-and-a-half below the trench top.

When Liz McCarthy came by late in the afternoon, Peter Chang hailed her to ask, "Why's everything I find eighteen inches down from the top when the Chinatown that used to be here isn't more than a hundred years old?"

The woman sat down beside the trench and nodded, then said, "That's because over the years the level of the ground rises, thanks to dust and sand blown over it and plants and garbage decaying in it. Some really old sites in Europe were many feet underground. That's why archaeologists dig so much. You know, your great-grandchildren won't be walking on the ground you walk on today."

Martha said, "I thought digging was only done in places like Egypt or Greece—I didn't think it was done here."

Liz McCarthy shook her head. "It isn't only old kings' tombs and monuments that archaeologists excavate. We dig in lots of places now. Not long ago I worked on a street dig near my home in Boston. When subways are dug and roads are built, archaeologists come with trowels, brushes, cameras, and maps and work right alongside the earth-moving machines. We salvage whatever we can to see how our ancestors lived—broken dishes, animal bones, jewelry, human skeletons." She got up. "Okay, good luck, you two!"

Near five o'clock, Martha complained aloud, "My back hurts. This isn't exciting."

"My legs ache," Peter Chang answered, speaking to her for the first time all afternoon, "and you're right—it isn't exciting. It sure is hard work."

Martha nodded, thought for a moment, then asked, "Do you have to work this hard to get all those A's in math?"

"Yeah, I do, but even hard work wouldn't get me in the school chorus, like you. When I auditioned, they said I couldn't carry a tune in a shopping bag, but you sure can sing."

Well, well, a compliment! Martha had been selected in her first audition for the chorus. At least Peter recognized talent when he heard it! she thought proudly. Martha twisted around to ask, "Isn't there anything down here but old bones and glass and busted dishes?"

"I guess not, Martha. That's all I found, too. I suppose it's what the old Chinese here threw away, so we can't expect much. Some of the other people are digging where the old houses used to be, and they've found important things that Professor Clarke has had photographed. Maybe we're digging in the old-time garbage dump."

Martha nodded. She'd also seen the camera positioned vertically over some of the trenches where old houses used to be—but there were no cameras in their dull section. No photographer had come to them, and they had been digging all day.

Suddenly a voice called out, "Quitting time! Turn in your buckets."

Peter shrugged as he checked the contents of his bucket, "I only have a quarter of a bucket of dirt and old bones and dishes." He peered into Martha's bucket. "Since that's all you have, too, let's put them together, so that we'll get sieved faster."

"Okay, Peter, that sounds good."

As they left the trench, Martha told herself that Peter Chang wasn't as bad as she'd thought. That was nice what he'd said about her singing. A few minutes later they stood together waiting as Professor Clarke sieved their bucket.

Suddenly, while they sighed with weariness and aching muscles, Professor Clarke cried out, "Here's an old jade bead! Who's bucket is this?"

Martha and Peter looked at each other, "It's *both* of ours," said Martha.

"That's right," agreed Peter.

"Well, you two kids have made the best find of the day. It's a beauty. It's valuable—and not just because it's very old. This artifact will go into a museum display. Congratulations! I'm proud of you. Which one of you found it?"

Martha said, "I didn't."

"I didn't," echoed Peter.

"Then it just came up with the dirt in the bucket. That happens all the time with very small pieces," Professor Clarke concluded.

Together Martha and Peter looked at the small green bead lying in the mesh of the sieve. The front of the bead was carved, and when the professor turned it over, they saw Chinese characters scratched on the back of it.

Martha asked, "What does the carving on front mean, or is it just a design?"

"It means 'good fortune'," Peter Chang quickly responded, and to the professor added, "I know that Chinese character."

"Then what does the scratching on the back mean?" asked Martha, turning the piece over again.

"I don't know that one, but just about everybody who's Chinese knows 'good fortune' and 'happiness' and 'long life,' I guess," Peter answered, a note of pride in his voice.

Professor Clarke clapped Peter on the back, "Well, it's good to know that much, and we'll find someone who knows Chinese characters proficiently to tell us about the writing on the back later on. Tell me, do you know what Chinese year this is—1985, I mean?"

"The year of the Ox," said Peter. "My mother told me it was."

By now Ms. McCarthy had joined them to examine the bead. She shook each of them by the hand and asked, "Will you be back tomorrow? We're in a hurry, so we dig on Sundays, too. I think it's obvious that you're going to be lucky diggers."

Looking at each other, Martha and Peter grinned and nodded.

"See you tomorrow, Pete," said Martha as she walked south on Brockton.

"Yeah, see you then, Mart," Peter waved as he walked away toward 14th Street.

That night when Martha's great-grandfather came to Saturday night supper, Martha excitedly told her family about the "dig," the bottles and bones and broken china—and finally, the jade bead.

After everyone had inquired about the details surrounding the find, Martha asked her great-grandfather, "Didn't you used to visit Chinatown a lot while it still existed?"

"You bet I did, Martha!" The old man chuckled. "As a kid, I made a pest of myself there before I got to know and like the Chinese and the taste of lichee nuts. A lot of people didn't like the Chinese because they worked really hard for low wages and took jobs nobody else would take. I used to go down to Chinatown around 1905 and fight a Chinese boy my age until one afternoon he taught me a lesson. Later on he and I got to be pretty good friends. He worked hard and eventually became head boss of the vegetable growers. He went home to China a rich man—over fifty years ago. He had some good luck here, all right! Many others died here or drifted away to other cities. Our Chinatown just died out. There weren't many families down there—just men—and never many kids."

Martha asked, "What was the name of the Chinese boy you used to fight with?"

"Wong something or another. I forget the rest of it. They were all named Wong because they all came from the same village in China and were sort of related to one another. I often think of my Chinese-American pal."

Martha grinned at the old man from whom she'd inherited her freckles, blue eyes, and red hair, "I think I'm making a new friend—Peter Chang. He's really smart, but I used to think he was stuck up. Now I think he's only sort of shy. He's going to be digging with me tomorrow."

Reader's Response

Would you enjoy the opportunity to be part of an archaeological dig similar to the one Peter and Martha joined?

DIGGING FOR CHINA

 ## Checking Your Comprehension

1. Compare Wong Chun Li's native Gomm Benn to his new town, Riverside.
2. Why did Wong Chun Li come to Riverside?
3. Why was the green jade bead important to Wong?
4. Did Martha's feelings toward Peter change from the beginning to the end of the story? What clues led you to your answer?
5. Who was the red-haired boy who attacked Wong Chun Li?
6. What did you think of the way in which the author linked the past to the present?

 ## Writing to Learn

THINK AND INFER Imagine that you are either Martha or Peter. Copy and complete the journal entry below.

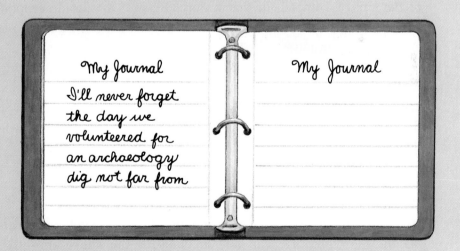

My Journal

I'll never forget the day we volunteered for an archaeology dig not far from

My Journal

WRITE Use the journal entry you wrote to write a letter about what you learned during the dig. If you wrote Martha's journal entry, for example, pretend you are Martha and write about Peter.

475

Comprehension:

Cause and Effect

"**H**appy is he who can learn the causes of things," the great Roman poet Virgil once wrote. While knowing the causes of things may not *always* make you happy, understanding cause and effect will certainly make you a better learner. It will help you to discover the relationships between events, and to uncover the deeper significance of those events. Understanding cause and effect will help you decide *why* things happen; sometimes it might even help you to determine *what will* happen in the future.

Virgil wrote the line above just a few years after the destruction of the city of Pompeii. In that historical event, a volcanic eruption was the *cause* of the city's destruction. The destruction of the city was an *effect* of the eruption.

Sometimes an author will state cause-and-effect relationships explicitly, using clue words such as *caused, because, therefore, since, so,* and *as a result* to indicate that one event was the cause of another. In the following sentence from "Pompeii: Lost and Found," the word "caused" is the clue:

Pressure building beneath the volcano caused a violent earthquake in southern Italy.

Sometimes synonyms for the word *cause,* such as *create, originate,* or *produce,* can act as clues to the cause-and-effect relationship. In the following sentence, the word *transformed* tells you that Mt. Vesuvius *caused* the change in Pompeii.

On August 24, A.D. 79, Mt. Vesuvius transformed Pompeii from a lively, crowded city into a ghost town.

Authors do not always state the relationship between a cause and an effect directly. When they do not, ask yourself these questions:

What happened?
Why did it happen?

There are no word clues to help you find cause and effect in the following sentences from "Pompeii: Lost and Found." But the questions above will help you find them.

The people of Pompeii were terrified. Some grabbed the nearest donkeys and headed for the city gate.

What happened? People tried to flee the city. Why did they try to flee? They were terrified. The *cause* was the people's terror. The *effect* was that they tried to flee.

Multiple Causes and Effects

Sometimes one effect can have many causes. The following passage from "Pompeii: Lost and Found" identifies four causes of Pompeii's prosperity:

In A.D. 79 Pompeii was a prosperous town of ten to twenty thousand people. It was ideally situated as a center of trade. It lay on the only route between the fertile valleys of the region known as Campania and the sea. Pompeii had two good ports: one on the Bay of Naples (which is part of the Mediterranean Sea) and the other on the Sarno River. Pompeii traded with other small Roman towns nearby, as well as with distant empires such as Egypt.

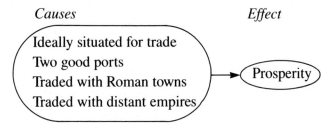

Causes   *Effect*

Ideally situated for trade
Two good ports
Traded with Roman towns
Traded with distant empires → Prosperity

477

Just as many causes may lead to one effect, one cause may lead to many effects. This passage from "Pompeii: Lost and Found" cites six effects that resulted from the eruption of Mt. Vesuvius:

Suddenly a deafening sound was heard. The top of Mt. Vesuvius blasted off. Expanding gases from deep inside the volcano hurled volcanic ash and red-hot stones thousands of feet into the air. Fountains of fire, smoke, and molten lava gushed out of the mouth of the volcano. Violent earthquakes shook the ground for miles around. Volcanic dust covered the sky and completely blotted out the sun. The day became darker than the blackest night. The sea roared and rose up in great waves.

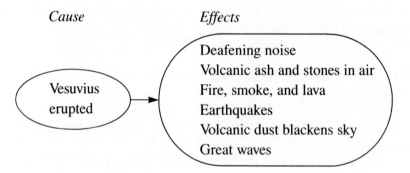

Cause

Effects

Vesuvius erupted

Deafening noise
Volcanic ash and stones in air
Fire, smoke, and lava
Earthquakes
Volcanic dust blackens sky
Great waves

Sometimes a single event can be the *effect* of one cause, and then be the *cause* of another occurrence, forming what amounts to a cause-and-effect chain. There is such a chain in the following sentences:

Pressure building beneath the volcano caused a violent earthquake in southern Italy. Damage in Pompeii was extensive.

Pressure under the volcano caused an earthquake, which in turn caused extensive damage.

Tracing Causes and Effects

The following passage from "Pompeii: Lost and Found" explains why the eruption led to so many deaths.

At about 6:30 A.M. on August 25 the fourth surge blasted through Pompeii at hurricane speeds. It blew off roofs and knocked people over. The hot ash-filled air clogged their lungs and snuffed out their lives. The poisonous gases that rose out of the depths of the volcano seeped into their rooms and asphyxiated them.

We can diagram the cause and effect relationships this way:

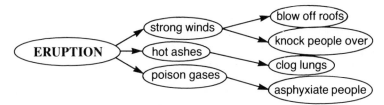

Using What You Have Learned

Read the following passage from "Pompeii: Lost and Found." Then answer the questions below it.

The first excavators were careless. They dug through thirty feet of earth and hardened ash with no care for what lay underneath. They destroyed many objects that gave clues about the Roman way of life. These early excavators had no interest in Pompeii for what it told about the past. They wanted only to take paintings, sculptures, mosaics, and other beautiful objects for private collections.

1. Why did the early excavators dig at Pompeii?
2. Why were they careless?
3. What was the result of their carelessness?
4. Why did they take the paintings, sculptures, and mosaics?

As You Read

The next selection you will read, "The Mysterious Mayas," is about the ruins of another great civilization. As you read, think about what may have caused the death of the Mayan Empire.

As they hacked their way through the jungles of Central America, two nineteenth-century archaeologists discovered something too remarkable to be believed.

THE MYSTERIOUS MAYAS

by James Norman

For weeks two exhausted men, a young American and his English companion, with their Indian guides and bearers, battled through a dark rain forest that seemed to have been uninhabited since the day of creation.

The jungle, like a green sea, had swallowed them. Eyes inflamed, suffering from the fetid heat and the swarms of mosquitoes buzzing about their heads, the two young men began to wonder why they had ever come on such an insane journey. Everything was strange and nerve-racking. Odors of decay rose from the surrounding swamps. Their ears were assaulted by the weird howl of invisible monkeys and the distant call of hunting jaguars. The eerie shapes of mahogany and logwood trees, and the dripping tangle of vines blocked their passage. Even at midday the overhead foliage was so

481

dense the men felt as though they were struggling through a murky night.

One of the young men paused on the trail to wipe sweat from his insect-bitten brow. He was short and strongly built, characteristics which were sharply in contrast to his graceful movements and sensitive long hands.

"It can't be that there is a lost city in this dismal hole," he said in a voice that had a decidedly clipped British accent. "Really, John, I've lost hope. Perhaps we should turn back."

His companion, taller, slimmer, fair in complexion, and memorable because of his exceptionally long nose, smiled grimly. "I'm somewhat skeptical, too," he replied. "I still have some hope, but not much expectation."

The year was 1839. The two young men, John Lloyd Stephens of New York and Frederick Catherwood of London, were on the first leg of one of the most remarkable travel adventures in history. They were in quest of a lost civilization. On the basis of shreds of information that most people of their time considered completely false, they had journeyed thousands of miles to the mysterious jungles of Honduras in search of a city no one else believed existed.

Although their trek was fraught with doubts and narrow escapes from death, they found their "lost city." Reaching the Copán River and passing

Detail of a Maya column, Copán, Honduras

through a tiny jungle settlement inhabited by mestizos[1] and Christianized Indians, they came at last to an ancient, handbuilt stone wall in the forest. Hacking each step of the trail open with machetes, they found a flight of steps leading up to a terrace utterly choked with tangled tropical growths. One of the Indians began cutting away at the vines, revealing to Stephens' startled gaze a tall, carved stone figure.

Both Stephens and Catherwood were completely awed. The sculpture

482

[1]mestizos (me stē′ sōs): persons of mixed Spanish and Native American ancestry

was magnificent beyond description. As the party slashed on through the dense lianas,[2] a second, a third, then a dozen more of the intricately carved figures were uncovered. In addition, there were glimpses of walls, stairways, pyramids, and temples reaching up through the matted treetops toward the sunlight.

The silent, unoccupied city was quite large. But more important than size were the remarkable architecture and elaborate sculptured walls that suggested a civilization more advanced than the Egypt of the Pharaohs. The elation felt by Stephens and Catherwood would be hard to describe, however, because in their day no one believed the Americas had ever been inhabited by civilized people capable of creating wonderful cities.

During the next few days of feverishly exploring the ruins, Stephens sometimes paused in wonder, asking, "Who built this city? What kind of men and women strolled across its broad plazas and among its handsome buildings? Where did they come from? How did they vanish?"

Both Stephens and Catherwood had visited the splendid ancient cities of Greece and Egypt. There, at least, at the foot of the Acropolis or along the glistening Nile, people could be found who had vague memories of the glorious past. Athens still had its Greeks; Cairo and Alexandria, their Egyptians. But here in the Central American jungle no descendants of the unknown race of builders lingered around the ruins. In the squalid tropical village near the ruins, no one among the Indians or mestizos had any idea who had built the city. Most of the villagers, in fact, were so uninterested that few of them had ever gone to see the site.

When the marvels of Copán, this lost city, were unveiled to the young adventurers, Stephens and Catherwood began to collect trophies that would mean something to the archaeologists of their day. Stephens began taking measurements of the buildings and monuments as well as writing detailed descriptive notes about them. Catherwood, an accomplished artist, began making meticulous sketches of the carvings and hieroglyphics on the temples.

━━━━━━━━

The adventurous travels of Stephens and Catherwood to Copán marked the birth of archaeology in the New World. Stephens and Catherwood inspired dozens of people, tireless adventurers and scholars, searching for clue after clue to the mystery of the vanished Mayan empire.

Less than a dozen years before Texas and California joined the United States, serious historians and most educated

[2]lianas (lē ä' nəs): climbing plants or vines

people in Europe and America had no idea that several great Indian civilizations had existed right at the doorstep of the United States. Leading scholars ridiculed any suggestion that there had been advanced civilizations in the Americas before the arrival of Columbus.

One noted historian of the early nineteenth century, Doctor William Robertson, wrote in his *History of America* that it was a positive fact there had been no ancient people on the American continent who had made any considerable progress in civilization, and none who were skilled in any of the arts.

Dr. Robertson was an eminent authority. One did not argue with him any more than one would dare argue with Albert Einstein. Thus, during the period of Thomas Jefferson and Andrew Jackson, it was understandable why people knew so little about the Indian heritage of the New World.

When John Lloyd Stephens and Frederick Catherwood finally emerged from the jungles with the reports of what they had found, it was like a bomb exploding. The world of scholarship was shaken to its foundations. Historians saw their carefully built theories of history—as they imagined it—quickly crumble. Some historians stubbornly refused to admit, in spite of the proofs Stephens and Catherwood presented,

that there had been ancient civilizations in the Americas. Others developed wild and fanciful theories to account for the lost cities. Some claimed the cities had been built by Phoenician colonists or by Egyptians. Many argued that Mexico and Central America had once been joined to the fabled lost continent of Mu, or that the Mayan cities had been built by people from the mysterious island of Atlantis.

One of the most popular theories of that time was that the Indians of Mexico and Central America were remnants of the wandering Lost Tribes of Israel. It was argued that the Lost Tribes might have built the Mayan cities, and that the civilization in the Americas had vanished thousands of years before Columbus' famous voyage.

A few clearheaded people, including John L. Stephens, rejected this theory. They believed someone else had built the hidden cities. But who?

The Mayan Empire

"Who were the mysterious people," Stephens asked, "who built these amazing cities of silent stone?" He then asked, "How old are the cities?"

It was a challenge that sent daring adventurers hacking their way with razor-sharp machetes through the mosquito-infested jungles. It sent researchers grubbing through libraries and old documents. In fewer than one hundred years these people dug up a mountain of puzzling clues and came up with brilliant guesses and deductions.

Instead of being members of the Lost Tribes of Israel or settlers from Plato's imaginary Atlantis, the early settlers in the New World were Mongolians. Sparked by an ancient population explosion, the need for more hunting grounds, and certain climatic conditions, they came across Siberia, then across what is now the Bering Strait to Alaska. At that time the strait area may have been a natural land bridge connecting the two continents. These copper-skinned, black-haired, sturdy travelers came in steady migratory waves. They pushed slowly down the Yukon and Mackenzie river valleys, spreading over North America, then southward to Mexico and South America.

These first inhabitants began arriving as early as thirty thousand years ago. In certain caves found as far apart as New Mexico and Peru, skeletal remains and primitive hunting gear have shown that a modern-type human being, hardly different in appearance from the Indians of the United States or Guatemala, lived and hunted on this continent for at least fifteen thousand years.

Such early pioneers were nomads. They lived dangerously, hunting down mammoths, bison, and smaller game

Part of a mural in a Maya temple at Bonampak, Mexico

with crude weapons. They supplemented their meat diet with wild roots, berries, and fruit. Then, at some remote time a kind of miracle occurred. Somewhere in Central or South America the right combination of conditions came about—sun, soil, rainfall, certain seeds, and the imaginative human mind. The result was the discovery of how to cultivate Indian maize, or corn, the great food staple of the Americas.

The domestication of corn made the inhabitants independent of hunting and gathering. They could settle down, and one thing led to another. They were soon able to tame other food-bearing plants: tomatoes, avocados, beans, melons, squash, and potatoes—crops that the Old World knew nothing about. From such simple beginnings people moved on to experiment with other gifts of progress: living in villages, sharing community projects, and, eventually, creating cities.

Among the nomads who entered Mexico were the ancestors of the Mayas. Experts are still not certain who they might have been or where they lived. Some believe they might have been the Olmecs, a shadowy people who lived in the jungles along the rim of the Gulf of Mexico. The Olmecs were skilled artisans, wonderful sculptors and pottery makers, and they had come far enough along the road to civilization to have notions of astronomy and a calendar.

Olmec stone mask

Whether they sprang from the Olmecs or from among people farther south, shortly after the time of Christ they began erecting handsome ceremonial cities on the American continent. Long before the 1530s, the distant Mayas had become one of the great civilizations of the world. Mayan priests knew a great deal more about astronomy and mathematics than did Henry VIII's best advisers. Mayan architects could build a castle with a great deal more art and science than the English king's best architects.

The Mayan empire, as it might be called, covered a vast area: the present Mexican states and territories of Yucatán, Quintana Roo, Campeche, Tabasco, and Chiapas; the Department of Petén and the nearby highlands in Guatemala; also, the western section of the Republic of Honduras and all of Belize. In all, it consisted of a region the size of our six New England states plus New York, New Jersey, and a part of Pennsylvania.

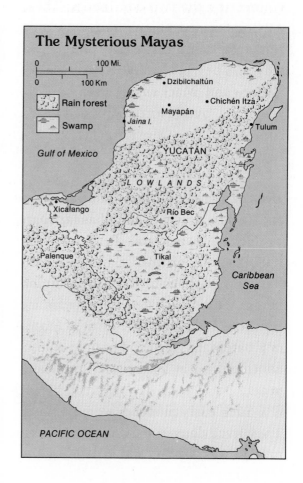

The Mysterious Mayas

0   100 Mi.

0   100 Km

Rain forest

Swamp

Gulf of Mexico

• Dzibilchaltún

• Chichén Itzá

Mayapán

Jaina I.

• Tulum

YUCATÁN

L O W L A N D S

• Xicalango

• Río Bec

Palenque

• Tikal

Caribbean Sea

PACIFIC OCEAN

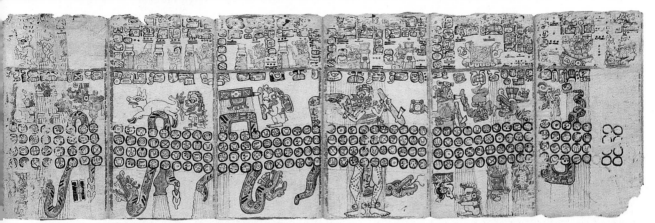

The Mayans used a form of hieroglyphics to convey information about the calendar, astronomy, and religious ceremonies. This is one of three remaining books made of paper from fig tree bark.

It was not easy country to live in. With the exception of Angkor in Cambodia, no major civilization has ever flowered in such an unfavorable climate. Much of the region is covered with dense tropical rain forests. The forests average 125 to 150 feet in height. There are great areas of humid swamps and lowlands covered with brush so thick one can scarcely cut a trail through it. The rainfall is torrential. In one place the average rainfall is 16.4 feet per year—feet, not inches! The heat throughout much of the year is enervating and tropical diseases are rampant. Yet, somehow, the Mayas created stunning cities and maintained an empire for centuries in the heart of this inhospitable region.

The Mayan empire lasted roughly over three thousand years. Experts divide its history into three periods of development: preclassic, classic, and postclassic.

The preclassic epoch, beginning about 1500 B.C., was the formative stage of the Mayan civilization. The people had begun to build religious centers, which later served as the foundation for their ceremonial cities. They made excellent pottery, wove cotton fabrics, and carved ably in stone. About 355 B.C., it is believed, they began to develop their calendar, which would become one of the most accurate in history. By the close of this early period they had devised the beginning of their enigmatic form of hieroglyphic writing. They were trading with other tribes as far away as central Mexico.

The Mayan classic period, often called the "Old Empire," was the golden age of the people. It dates from about A.D. 300 to around A.D. 900. Its focus was the center of the Mayan country—Chiapas, Guatemala, and Honduras. Here in the magnificent stone and stucco cities, now known as Palenque,

Tikal was a great ceremonial center where the Mayas built large plazas, pyramids, temples, and palaces.

Yaxchilán,[3] Piedras, Negras, Petén, Tikal, and Copán, Mayan architects, sculptors, and painters created marvelous works. Priests skillfully mapped the movements of the stars and devised one of the most complex religions known.

The Old Empire ended when, for some unexplainable reason, the entire people of the central region abandoned their cities, almost as though at a signal. They seemed at the peak of their vigor and cultural accomplishments, yet everything stopped. Tools were put down, farmers left their fields, priests stopped burning fragrant incense in the temples. It was as if all the people had gotten up from their tables, with din-

[3] Yaxchilán (Yäks chē län´)

ner unfinished, to go out on errands, and had never come back.

After the disappearance of the Old Empire there followed a transitional period, lasting a few hundred years, during which a pure Mayan culture flourished on the Peninsula of Yucatán.

The postclassic or New Empire epoch of Mayan history was also centered in Yucatán. During this period the Mayas were no longer alone. Invaders from central Mexico dominated the region and helped build Chichén Itzá, one of the most breathtaking cities in the entire region.

The Mayas were among the world's greatest builders. Alone in the Central American jungle, without knowing about the temples of India, Egypt, and Greece, they erected citadels and ceremonial cities of comparable importance and beauty. They covered them with paintings and intricately carved sculpture that has seldom been matched anywhere. Two thousand years ago they knew subtle engineering tricks, such as how to thicken a column or the center of a broad stairway to eliminate the illusion of sag.

Intellectually the Mayas were to the New World what the Greeks were to the Old World—the initiators and guardians of very advanced attainments in the arts and some sciences. In their mathematics they made advances that went beyond concepts developed in ancient Greece and Rome—concepts that were only later matched by Hindu and Arabian mathematicians.

All this is merely a thumbnail sketch of the absorbing civilization that existed in the Americas while people living in what are now England and Germany went about dressed in animal skins and clubbed each other with crude weapons. Today we know where the Mayas came from, how they built their temples. We know what they ate, who their gods were, and what they believed. But less than one hundred years ago even the name *Maya* was unknown or forgotten.

When Columbus made his harrowing westward voyage, only a few remnants of the enormous and brilliant Mayan people still occupied a few cities in Yucatán. The heirs of that important civilization had long since abandoned most of their cities.

By the time Cortés and his followers had established themselves in the New World beginning in 1521, an immense silence had crept over the deserted Mayan cities. Within a century's time the jungle had become lord of the lost cities, while jaguars prowled secretively through the deserted corridors of empty palaces and monkeys howled down their derision.

489

THE MOON AND THE YEAR

FROM THE MAYA

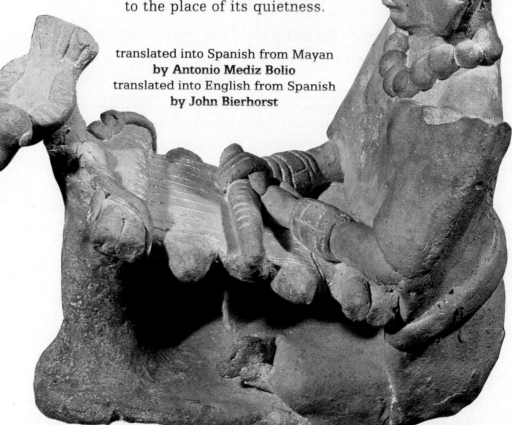

The moon and the year
travel and pass away:
also the day, also the wind.
Also the flesh passes away
to the place of its quietness.

translated into Spanish from Mayan
by Antonio Mediz Bolio
translated into English from Spanish
by John Bierhorst

Reader's Response

Did you share the excitement that the archaeologists felt
when they made their discovery? Why or why not?

THE MYSTERIOUS
MAYAS

Checking Your Comprehension

1. What quest brought Stephens and Catherwood to the jungles of Honduras?
2. What is the author's attitude, or point of view, regarding the Mayan empire? How can you tell?
3. Explain how the cultivation of corn was the turning point of civilization in North America.
4. Where were the original settlers of North America from? How did they first come here?
5. What difficulties did the Mayas face because of their environment?
6. Why do you think the Mayan civilization disappeared so suddenly?

Writing to Learn

THINK AND QUESTION   Decide what are the most important points in the article, then copy and complete the chart below by writing four additional test questions for your class.

Questions on "The Mysterious Mayas":
1. What inspired Stephens and Catherwood to seek the lost civilization?
2.
3.
4.
5.

WRITE   Review your list of questions. Choose the one you think is most interesting and write your own answer to that question.

THE CAVE NEAR TIKAL

by Luz Nuncio

What happened to the great Mayan civilization? Finding the answer to that question is just a matter of knowing where the clues are and of finding them before it's too late!

It might have been the strain and hurry of the plane trips that day, first from Mexico City to Guatemala City, and then on to Tikal in the lowlands of northern Guatemala. Or it might have been the heat and humidity of the Tikal rain forest in August. Or maybe it was just happiness. Fourteen-year-old Elena Torres thought about the reasons she might be feeling so lightheaded this evening. She was sitting on a low wooden bench outside Don Miguel's thatched house in Tikal, watching darkness take over the rain forest. Little by little, the cries of parrots and howler monkeys were giving way to the haunting noises of the night creatures, hidden overhead and all around the dense vegetation.

It was probably just happiness, Elena thought. At long last she was here, in Tikal, Guatemala! Here the ancient Maya had flourished a thousand years ago and then mysteriously vanished, leaving their glorious city to be swallowed up by the rain forest. For Elena, student of archaeology and most especially of the ancient Maya, to be here was happiness enough. But to be here to discover something that nobody knew about the ancient Maya, to solve the mystery, maybe, of what had made them leave this place—*that* was enough to make anyone lightheaded. As the night settled in the rain forest, Elena thought back to the day when she and her parents first learned of the cave near Tikal with its beautiful, strange inscriptions that nobody could read. Although it had only been a week ago, it seemed like hundreds of years,

as far away in time as this rain forest was in distance from her home in the rush and commotion of Mexico City. . . .

"I have wonderful news, Elenita!" Luisa Torres came into the living room to find her daughter absorbed in the sports section of the newspaper.

"What is it, mother?" asked Elena, looking up surprised. Although her mother usually came home with interesting news from her job as an archaeologist at the National Museum of Anthropology, she seldom came home in the middle of the day, and she seldom sounded as excited and happy as she was sounding now.

"Dr. Portales called me this morning from Tikal," explained Mrs. Torres. "He told me that a huge cave with ancient Maya glyphs painted all over its walls was discovered there just last week. It seems a young Maya boy found it while he was looking for his dog in the rain forest."

"Dr. Portales went into the cave yesterday, thinking that the glyphs were probably like the ones he's deciphered on the ruins at Tikal National Park. But it turns out they're not like anything he knows, and he thinks maybe your father and you and I should go down there to see if we can help figure them out. I told him—"

"Oh, mother, that sounds wonderful!" shouted Elena happily.

"Well, that's what I told him!" Mrs. Torres exclaimed, laughing, "Now the only question is your father. I'll have to call him to see if he can leave his project in Chichén Itzá and join us down there."

493

Elena's father was also an archaeologist at the National Museum of Anthropology in Mexico City. Like his wife, Roberto Torres was a specialist in deciphering the glyphs, or picture writing, of the highly developed Indian civilizations that had flourished throughout Mexico and Central America as many as two thousand years before the Spanish conquest. It was not difficult for Mrs. Torres and Elena to persuade him to fly down to Tikal.

"It'll be good to be in Tikal again," said Mr. Torres. "I've always loved the feeling the rain forest there gives me, like it's full of secrets, some of which we'll never know . . . you'll see what I mean when we get there, Elenita. . . ."

Suddenly Elena sat up straight on the wooden bench, her lightheadedness gone. Somewhere nearby, in the darkness of the rain forest all around her, a creature was moving. Was it a jaguar, or a boa constrictor, or some fierce crocodile that would creep stealthily out of the still, hot gloom and attack her? She looked back at the thatched house just a few feet behind her. Everyone was in there, accounted for— her parents and Dr. Portales were laughing and chatting with their hosts, Don Miguel and Doña Tila Uuc. Would there be time to call them for help when the creature attacked, she wondered?

"Balam, get over here!" shouted a voice right behind Elena, causing her to stifle a scream. Don Miguel, a slight, agile Maya peasant in his late fifties, had come silently out of the house with a lantern in his hand. At the sound of his voice, a skinny, brown-spotted mutt trotted meekly out of the darkness. Elena sighed with relief.

"That dog is always wandering off!" complained Don Miguel to Elena.

"I thought it was a jaguar or something coming out of the rain forest," said Elena sheepishly.

"What, Balam?" asked Don Miguel, surprised. "Well, *Balam* means 'jaguar' in our language, but the only reason we call him that is because my grandson thought he would grow up to be big and scary. But he just grew up, that's all, poor little Balam!"

At that moment, Elena's parents and Dr. Portales stepped to the doorway of the house. Dr. Portales had been Mr. and Mrs. Torres's archaeology professor when they were students at the excavation project in Tikal. He was a short, stout, distinguished-looking man with graying hair and beard. It was very rarely that Dr. Portales looked as serious and preoccupied as he did now. Usually, he was a cheerful, amiable man, in love with his work and as excited and awed by it as any beginning archaeology student.

"How nice of you to come out to join us," said Don Miguel to Dr. Portales and Elena's parents. "The little one and I were just talking about the ferocious jaguars in the rain forest." Don Miguel winked at Elena.

"I wish the jaguars were all we had to worry about," said Dr. Portales sadly.

"For me, the most frightening, most destructive beast of all walks on two legs and calls himself civilized. He comes into beautiful, wild places like this to vandalize and loot and, maybe, even to kill."

"That's why I tell you we have no time to lose," continued Dr. Portales, turning again to Elena's parents. His tone was urgent. "Looters have found out about the cave, and they've already done some terrible damage to the walls and columns in there. Even the most expert reader of Maya script could not read around the holes and scratches they've made to cut out whatever they can sell to foreign galleries and museums."

"I feel sad to say it, but I thought that would happen," sighed Mrs. Torres. "I remember when we were first here, working on the project to clear the rain forest away from Tikal," added Mr. Torres. "I was scarcely older than Elena. One night I made the mistake of going by a part of the site that we hadn't started working on yet. There was so much to do, we couldn't watch every part of the site, even though we knew that all around us, hidden by the rain forest, there were precious artifacts. I surprised a gang of men who were sawing apart an ancient stone monument. Luckily, they got scared when they saw me and ran away. But things could have turned out much worse—these looters have a big business going and they're not happy when you get in their way."

"Yes, that's so," said Dr. Portales, shaking his head. "But it's our business to not even let them have a way, or if you want to be cynical, to at least learn as much as we can from the ruins and now from these cave walls and columns before they get to them."

"Please don't worry, my friends," said Don Miguel consolingly. "Tomorrow morning, very early, I will take you to the cave and show you the pictures."

Dr. Portales relaxed and put his arm around Don Miguel's shoulders. "Yes," he said, smiling, "tomorrow morning we'll get going. Right now we should all get some sleep."

"Actually, before we go to sleep," said Don Miguel, "I have something to show you that was given to me at the market the other day." Don Miguel went inside the house and came back out with a tattered, three-year-old issue of an American sports magazine. He turned to an article full of photographs of baseball players.

"I was hoping you could look at it and tell me what it says sometime. I've been looking at it for days now, and I think I know what the pictures are about, but I would be most grateful if you could tell me what the words say."

"I can help you, Don Miguel," said Elena. "I've been studying English at school and I can read it pretty well."

"And she also knows a little bit about baseball," teased Mr. Torres.

"Yes," said Elena shyly. In fact, she knew a great deal about baseball. The summer she was twelve, her parents had worked on a dig of Maya ruins in Belize. Every day, Elena would help them in the morning, and head back to the hotel in the afternoon to watch a North American team, the Chicago Cubs, on television. Little by little, Elena had figured out the game and developed a passionate interest in playing and watching it.

"Ah, then, it is not only a pleasure, but good fortune as well to have you here," said Don Miguel happily to Elena.

An hour later, everything was still at Don Miguel's house. As she fell asleep, Elena listened to the rain forest, dark and secret and alive with the rustle of its night creatures. Balam was not one of them— he was curled up peacefully in a corner of the room. But out there real jaguars might be lurking, thought Elena—and other beasts, too.

The following day, the Torres family, Dr. Portales, and Don Miguel set out shortly after dawn. The day was hotter than usual in the already steamy rain forest, and everybody except Don Miguel kept tripping on the muddy trail over huge fallen trees and climbing vines.

As they advanced, Elena tried to conjure up an image of the time when the first archaeologists made their way through the wild green press of trees and vines to uncover the ruins at Tikal. They had come at a time when nobody, including the descendants of the ancient Maya themselves, had been willing to place much importance on the stone structures that were barely visible under the moss and fallen trees of the rainforest. Now, everybody recognized the importance of these ruins. "Maybe too many people recognize it now," Elena thought worriedly, remembering the looters.

"Just a little more, we're almost there," called Don Miguel, as the group laboriously followed his trail. Then, just when Elena thought she needed to stop again to rest, the spry old gentleman cried out, "Here it is!"

The visitors looked up in astonishment. Suddenly, the rain forest had given way to the huge black entrance of a cave, perhaps sixty feet high and forty feet wide. The white stalactites hanging down in irregular lengths made the entrance seem like the enormous jaws of some monstrous, ancient Maya deity. For a moment, the visitors stood still and marveled at this magnificent work of nature. No wonder the Maya had come here to confide the record of their lives! The cave entrance seemed to be an opening into a hallowed, timeless place, a place where secrets could be kept forever.

Before they entered the cave, Dr. Portales reached into his knapsack and pulled out flashlights for himself and the Torres family. Don Miguel had brought his own flashlight, which had been a gift from Dr. Portales. The flashlights of the group

barely pierced the dark, steep slope beyond the cave entrance. Their path took them though narrow, sharply winding tunnels and along slender ledges in the limestone walls of cave chambers unfathomably deep.

"Careful!" shouted Don Miguel. The group came to a standstill, clinging to the niches and ridges in the cavern wall. A few moments later, they heard the loud, echoing splash of a large rock falling into the water in the black depths of the cave. A piece of the ledge ahead of Don Miguel had fallen away.

"There is enough space left on the ledge for us to go ahead," said Don Miguel softly and slowly. "We will just have to move even more carefully. We're very close now . . . just watch for the ledge to grow smaller, then right where it ends, there will be a crack in the wall leading into the room with the pictures, . . . just feel the wall for the crack, . . . let your hands be your eyes."

Suddenly, Elena noticed that she could no longer see the outline of Don Miguel's body ahead of her. Her heart began to pound as she felt along the wall to find him.

"I am here, little one," she heard from the other side of the wall. "Give me your hand and I'll pull you through."

Elena inched along the ledge until she felt the long, jagged edge of the crack in the wall. The strong grip of Don Miguel's hand pulled her off what was now just a strip of ledge and into a chamber of glistening white columns and walls.

The room became brighter as the rest of the members of the group entered the chamber and turned their flashlights on its walls.

497

"How beautiful!" exclaimed Mrs. Torres, as she played the beam of her flashlight along delicately painted columns of glyphs.

"Wait, there's a date there." Mr. Torres bent closer towards the glyph at the beginning of one of the columns. "It's 3 Ahau 3 Mol in the Maya calendar—"

Elena checked the Maya calendar tables her mother had brought. "That's June 30, A.D. 741!" she exclaimed.

"Elenita is indeed her parent's daughter!" laughed Dr. Portales. "Yes, the paintings and glyphs here span about three decades—from A.D. 733 to 762, a time when the civilization at Tikal was at its highest point. Over here, we have drawings of Maya ballplayers with their full uniform on. As you can see, they are very similar to the style and content of drawings that we've found at Tikal and elsewhere in what used to be Maya territory."

"I like these the best of all," announced Don Miguel after looking closely at the pictures of Maya ballplayers wearing the conventional torso armor, jaguar skin, and kneepads.

"They *are* beautifully done," agreed Mrs. Torres, "but I wonder what the glyphs next to them can mean. Please, all of you, shine your lights on the walls while I photograph them. These glyphs could be very important . . . they could tell us what happened to the Maya who lived at Tikal."

Elena could scarcely contain her excitement as her mother photographed the neat drawings and columns of symbols. If they could read these glyphs, and if the glyphs were indeed about specific events in Maya history, they might be able to solve the riddle of the collapse of Tikal little more than a century after scribes had painted in this cave. This was perhaps the greatest mystery surrounding the civilization at Tikal—how it had vanished so suddenly and completely. Two hundred years after these glyphs had been drawn, squatters were occupying the already crumbling temples and palaces at Tikal and looting the graves of the rulers buried in them. One hundred years later, Tikal had been completely deserted, and the rain forest had grown over it for nearly a thousand years.

"I think I've got it all now," said Mrs. Torres, packing her camera gear and the Maya calendar tables back in her knapsack. "We really should head back now."

As slowly and carefully as they had come into the chamber, the group made their way out. The feeling of anticipation among them was even greater now that they had the photographs of the glyphs. Soon they would be able to study them closely, and later they would return to the cave to see if they could excavate pottery or artifacts from the chamber floor.

Inch by inch, the group retraced their steps behind Don Miguel. They were past the narrow ledge and slipping on the wet clay floor of a small tunnel when they heard a low, distant rumble that seemed to come from the depths of the cave.

"It's an earthquake!" shouted Don Miguel as the rumble became louder and the ground beneath them started to shake even more violently.

They had barely gotten beyond the white fringe of stalactites at the cave entrance when they heard a loud crash behind them. Then came utter silence. The tremor had stopped.

"Mother, are you all right?" cried Elena.

"I'm fine, Elena," answered her mother, "just a little bruised." Then, after a moment, Mrs. Torres continued tearfully, "But I lost my knapsack in the cave. I had to let go of it when I tried to protect myself from the rocks."

"We can go back and find it another day," said Elena comfortingly, but Dr. Portales placed a gentle hand on her shoulder.

"I'm afraid not, Elenita. Look behind you."

What Elena saw when she turned around made her eyes also fill with tears. A huge row of stalactites had fallen across the cave entrance, completely blocking the path beyond the slope. The jaws of the monstrous Maya deity that had permitted access into the cave to scribe, looter, and archaeologist alike had snapped shut forever.

For a few minutes, the group rested in mournful silence outside the cave. Then they started their trek back through the hushed rain forest.

Elena did not look back at the cave. As she walked through the difficult trail back to Don Miguel's house, she thought about the glyphs and drawings she had seen in the cave, and tried to remember what they looked like so that she could draw them as soon as possible.

Elena thought of the looters, too. Perhaps that was the way it was meant to be. Perhaps nature was reclaiming the cave, hiding its contents once again, as it had done for more than one thousand years, to keep them from the unscrupulous people who wanted to profit from them. And perhaps the price that archaeologists had to pay of never knowing what was in the cave near Tikal was really a small price, since they could at least rest assured that the glyphs and drawings of the ancient Maya would remain undisturbed. The musicians on the walls would play their unknown song, the ballplayers would continue their mysterious, ritualistic game, with no witnesses—benevolent or otherwise—ever again.

That evening, Don Miguel, Doña Tila and the Torres family were all invited to dinner at Dr. Portales's house. On the way there, they drove past Tikal National Park and stopped to gaze at the ruins of the palaces, temples, and ballcourts the ancient Maya had somehow built and decorated in the hostile rain forest around them. For the moment, until another discovery came along, and until looters could be kept from it, this was all that people could know about the ancient civilization at Tikal. It was a great deal, but there was a great deal more hidden—enough to make Elena a little lightheaded just at the thought of it.

 Reader's Response

What do you think you will remember about this selection a year from now?

THE CAVE NEAR TIKAL

Checking Your Comprehension

1. What is Tikal? Where is it located?
2. Why did the Torres family come to Tikal?
3. Why were Elena and the others excited by what they found in the caves of Tikal?
4. What are some of the dangers that archaeologists face in their work?
5. How did the earthquake seal the secret of the glyphs forever?
6. Was Elena happy or sad about what happened to the cave at Tikal? Explain. What thought process did you go through to arrive at your answer?
7. From the details of the story, what do we know about the ancient Mayas?

Writing to Learn

THINK AND DISCOVER The characters in this story had great expectations for solving the mysteries of the lost Mayan Empire. On your paper, copy the chart below showing their expectations and complete the chart by listing next to each expectation what actually happened.

What was expected:	What actually happened:
1. deciphering glyphs for a lost civilization	1.
2. finding significant archaeological artifacts	2.
3. enjoying a successful exploration	3.

WRITE Write a short narrative about something you once expected to happen. List your expectations. Then tell what actually happened.

Study Skill:

Graphic Aids

Although archaeologists have learned a great deal about Mayan civilization, there are still many questions to be answered. The archaeologists of the future will have no such problems learning about our way of life because we've compiled vast amounts of information about ourselves. This information is organized and presented in a variety of ways.

Graphs

Graphs are useful for making comparisons because they show the similarities and differences between items. A *pie graph*, such as the one in Figure 1, is useful for showing percentages; it can show how much of a whole is taken up by each of its parts.

Figure 1: THE FIVE LARGEST AMERICAN COUNTRIES

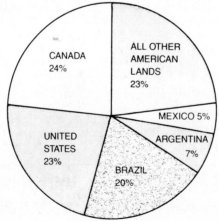

Percentages total more than 100% because of rounding.

You can see that about two thirds of the total land area of North, South, and Central America is taken up by Canada, the United States, and Brazil. Mexico and Argentina total about 12 percent, and the remaining 23 percent is divided among smaller countries.

A *bar graph* is best for comparing amounts. The bar graph in Figure 2 shows at a glance that the United States is the most populous American country.

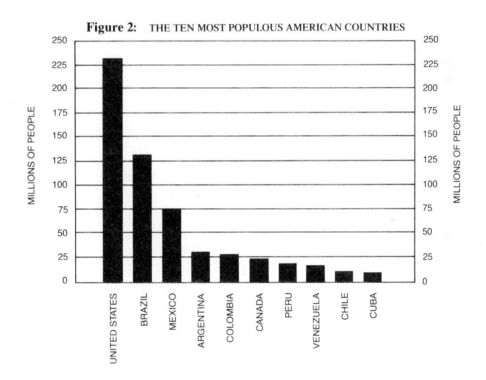

Figure 2:   THE TEN MOST POPULOUS AMERICAN COUNTRIES

To show how something changes over time, a *line graph* is best. By looking at the line graph in Figure 3, you can follow the growth of population in Anglo-America and Latin America from the year 1650 to the present. You can even make some predictions about future growth, based on the slant of the lines.

503

Figure 3: POPULATION GROWTH OF ANGLO-AMERICA AND LATIN AMERICA: 1650–2000

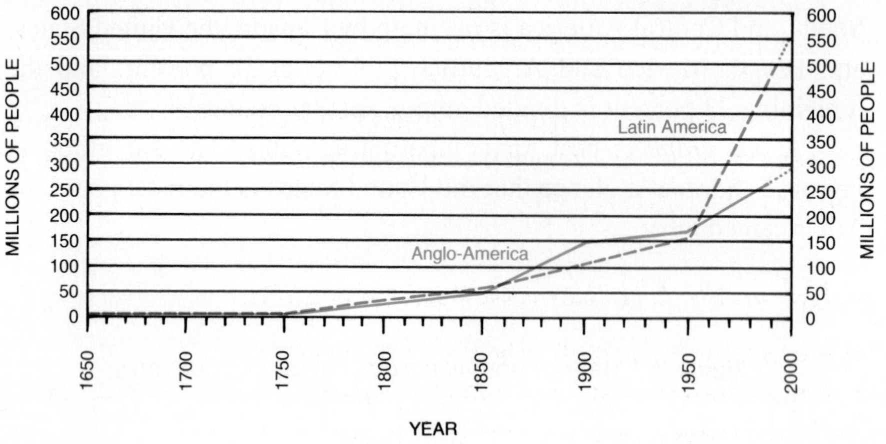

Tables

Graphs are fine for showing comparisons, but when you are concerned with actual numbers, *tables* are better. By combining the information that was presented in the graphs, the table in Figure 4 gives you a picture of how crowded the countries are.

Figure 4: THE TEN LARGEST AMERICAN COUNTRIES:
AREA, POPULATION, AND POPULATION DENSITY

Country	Area (in sq mi)	Population	Population density (per sq mi)
Argentina	1,068,301	29,100,000	25
Bolivia	424,164	5,900,000	13
Brazil	3,286,487	131,300,000	38
Canada	3,831,033	24,900,000	6
Chile	292,135	11,500,000	38
Columbia	439,737	27,700,000	62
Mexico	761,604	75,700,000	96
Peru	496,224	19,200,000	36
United States	3,678,896	234,200,000	62
Venezuela	352,144	18,000,000	40

The last column shows population density—the average number of people who live in a certain land area (in this case, a square mile). To arrive at this figure, the population is divided by the area of the country. Argentina, for example, has an average of twenty-five people per square mile. The greater the population density, the more people there are in an area of land.

Key Points About Tables and Graphs

1. Pie graphs are useful for showing percentages.
2. Bar graphs are used for comparing amounts.
3. Line graphs can show how things change over time.
4. Tables list facts and numbers in columns for easy comparisons.

Using What You Have Learned

Use the graphic aids in this lesson to answer the following questions.

1. Which two countries take up almost half of the land of the Americas?
2. Which country has a population three times that of Canada?
3. Which figure would you use to find out how much the population of Latin America increased from 1900 to 1950?
4. Which country is the least crowded? Which is the most crowded?

As You Read

When you are reading nonfiction, think about how tables and graphs clarify information for you.

The Tomb of

King Tutankhamen
by Robin Cook

*After more than ten years of searching in the desert, How-
ard Carter discovers what might be the greatest archaeological find of the century—the tomb of a fabled Egyptian king.*

Because the ancient Egyptians were buried with many of their household goods and personal possessions, the excavation of their tombs has told us much about how they lived. For any archaeologist, the most exciting find is the tomb of a king, or pharaoh. Since these men had great wealth, there is always the hope that their tombs will turn up splendid treasures. All too often, however, the tombs have been found empty—stripped by looters hundreds of years before.

Howard Carter, an English archaeologist, had spent about ten years searching for the tomb of King Tutankhamen. Now he had found it. But would there be anything of value beyond the sealed door?

NOVEMBER 26, 1922

The excitement was infectious. Even the Sahara sun knifing through the cloudless sky could not diminish the suspense. The fellahin quickened their pace as they brought basket after basket of limestone chips from the entrance to Tutankhamen's tomb. They had reached a second door thirty feet down a corridor from the first. It too had been sealed for three thousand years. What lay beyond? Would the tomb be empty like all the others robbed in antiquity? No one knew.

Sarwat Raman, the beturbaned foreman, climbed the sixteen steps to ground level with a layer of dust clinging to his features like flour. Clutching his galabia, he strode across to the tent marquee, which provided the only bit of shade in the remorselessly sunny valley.

"Beg to inform your Excellency that the entrance corridor has been cleared of rubble," said Raman, bowing slightly. "The second door is now fully exposed."

Howard Carter looked up from his lemonade, squinting from under the black homburg he insisted on wearing despite the shimmering heat. "Very good, Raman. We will inspect the door as soon as the dust settles."

"I will await your honorable instructions." Raman turned and retreated.

"You are a cool one, Howard," said Lord Carnarvon, christened George Edward Stanhope Molyneux Herbert. "How can you sit here and finish your lemonade without knowing what is behind that door?" Carnarvon smiled and winked at his daughter, Lady Evelyn Herbert. "Now I can understand why Belzoni employed a battering ram when he found Seti I's tomb."

"My methods are diametrically opposed to those of Belzoni," said Carter defensively. "And Belzoni's methods were appropriately rewarded with an empty tomb, save for the sarcophagus." Carter's gaze moved involuntarily toward the nearby opening of Seti I's tomb. "Carnarvon, I'm not really certain what we've found here. I don't think we should allow ourselves to get too excited. I'm not even sure it's a tomb. The design is not typical for an eighteenth-dynasty pharaoh. It could be just a cache of Tutankhamen's belongings brought from Akhetaten. Besides, tomb robbers have preceded us, not once but twice. My only hope is that it was robbed in antiquity and someone thought it important enough to reseal the doors. So I truly have no idea what we are going to find."

Maintaining his English aplomb, Carter allowed his eyes to roam about the desolate Valley of the Kings. But his stomach was in knots. He had never been so excited in all of his forty-nine years. In the previous six barren seasons of excavation, he had found nothing. Two hundred thousand tons of gravel and sand had been moved and sifted, for absolutely nothing. Now the suddenness of the find after only five days of excavating was overwhelming. Swirling his lemonade, he tried not to think or hope. They waited. The whole world waited.

he larger dust particles settled in a fine layer on the sloping corridor floor. The group made an effort not to stir the air as they entered. Carter was first, followed by Carnarvon, then his daughter, and finally A. R. Callender, Carter's assistant. Raman waited at the entrance after giving Carter a crowbar. Callender carried a large flashlight and candles.

"As I said, we are not the first to broach this tomb," said Carter, nervously pointing to the upper-left-hand corner. "The door was entered and then resealed in that small area." Then he traced a larger circular area in the middle. "And again in this much larger area here. It is very strange." Lord Carnarvon bent over to look at the royal necropolis seal, a jackal with nine bound prisoners.

"Along the base of the door are examples of the original Tutankhamen seal," continued Carter. The beam of the flashlight reflected the fine dust still suspended in the air, before illuminating the ancient seals in the plaster.

"Now, then," said Carter as coolly as if he were suggesting afternoon tea, "let's see what is behind this door." But his stomach contorted into a tight mass, aggravating his ulcer, and his hands were damp, not so much from the heat as from the unexpressed tension. His body quivered as he lifted the crowbar and made a few preliminary cuts into the ancient plaster. The bits and pieces rained down about his feet. The exertion gave expression to his pent-up emotions, and each lunge was more vigorous than the last. Suddenly the crowbar broke through the plaster, causing Carter to stumble up against the door. Warm air issued from the tiny hole, and Carter fumbled with the matches, lighting a candle and holding a flame to the opening. It was a crude test for the presence of oxygen. The candle continued to burn.

No one dared to speak as Carter gave the candle to Callender and continued working with the crowbar. Carefully he enlarged the hole, making certain that the plaster and stone blocking fell into the corridor and not into the room beyond. Taking the candle again, Carter thrust it through the hole. It burned contentedly. He then put his head to the hole, his eyes straining in the darkness.

In a moment time stood still. As Carter's eyes adjusted, three thousand years disappeared as in a minute. Out of the blackness emerged a golden head of Amnut, ivory teeth bared. Other gilded beasts loomed, the flickering candlelight throwing their exotic silhouettes on the wall.

"Can you see anything?" asked Carnarvon excitedly.

"Yes, wonderful things," answered Carter finally, his voice for the first time betraying emotion. Then he replaced the candle with his flashlight, and those behind him could see the chamber filled with unbelievable objects. The golden heads were part of three funerary beds. Moving the light to the left, Carter gazed at a jumble of gilded and inlaid chariots heaped in the corner. Tracing back to the right, he began to ponder the curiously chaotic state of the room. Instead of the prescribed stately order, objects appeared to have been thrown about without thought. Immediately to the right were two life-size statues of Tutankhamen, each with a kilt of gold, wearing gold sandals, and armed with mace and staff.

Between the two statues was another sealed door.

Carter left the opening so the others could have a better look. Like Belzoni, he was tempted to crash down the wall and dive into the room. Instead, he calmly announced that the rest of the day would be devoted to photographing the sealed door. They would not attempt to enter what was obviously an antechamber until morning.

NOVEMBER 27, 1922

It took more than three hours for Carter to dismantle the ancient blocking of the door to the antechamber. Raman and

510

a few other fellahin helped during this stage. Callender had laid in temporary electric wires, so the tunnel was brightly lit. Lord Carnarvon and Lady Evelyn entered the corridor when the job was almost complete. The last baskets of plaster and stone were hauled away. The moment of entry had arrived. No one spoke. Outside, at the mouth of the tomb, hundreds of reporters from newspapers around the world tensely waited for their first view.

Howard Carter and Lord Carnarvon at the entrance to the burial chamber

For a brief second Carter hesitated. As a scientist he was interested in the minutest detail inside the tomb; as a human being he was embarrassed by his intrusion into the sacred realm of the dead; and as an explorer he was experiencing the exhilaration of discovery. But, British to the core, he merely straightened his bow tie and stepped over the threshold, keeping his eye on the objects below.

Without a sound he pointed at a beautiful lotiform cup of translucent alabaster on the threshold, so Carnarvon could avoid it. Carter then made his way over to the sealed door between the two life-size statues of Tutankhamen. Carefully he began to examine the seals. His heart sank as he realized that this door had also been opened by the ancient tomb robbers and then resealed.

Carnarvon stepped into the antechamber, his mind reeling with the beauty of the objects so carelessly scattered around him. He turned to take his daughter's hand as she prepared to enter, and in the process noticed a rolled papyrus leaning against the wall to the right of the alabaster cup. To the left was a garland of dead flowers, as if Tutankhamen's funeral had been only yesterday, and beside it a blackened oil lamp. Lady Evelyn entered, holding her father's hand, followed by Callender. Raman leaned into the antechamber but did not enter for lack of space.

"Unfortunately, the burial chamber has been entered and resealed," said Carter, pointing toward the door in front of him. Carefully Carnarvon, Lady Evelyn, and Callender moved over to the archaeologist, their eyes following his finger. Raman stepped into the antechamber.

"Curiously, though," continued Carter, "it has been entered only once, instead of twice, like the doors into the antechamber. So there is hope that the thieves did not reach the mummy." Carter turned, seeing Raman for the first time. "Raman, I did not give you permission to enter the antechamber."

"I beg your Excellency's pardon. I thought that I could be of assistance."

"Indeed. You can be of assistance by making sure no one enters this chamber without my personal approval."

"Of course, your Excellency." Raman silently slipped from the room.

"Howard," said Carnarvon, "Raman is undoubtedly as enchanted as we with the find. Perhaps you could be a little more generous."

"The workers will all be allowed to view this room, but I will designate the time," said Carter. "Now, as I was saying, the reason I feel hopeful about the mummy is that I think the tomb robbers were surprised in the middle of their sacrilege. There is something mysterious about the way these priceless objects are haphazardly thrown about. It appears as if someone spent a little time rearranging things after the thieves, but not enough to put everything back in its original state. Why?"

Carnarvon shrugged.

"Look at that beautiful cup on the threshold," continued

Carter. "Why wasn't that replaced? And that gilded shrine with its door ajar. Obviously a statue was stolen, but why wasn't the door even closed?" Carter stepped back to the door. "And this ordinary oil lamp. Why was it left within the tomb? I tell you, we'd better record the positioning of each object in this room very carefully. These clues are trying to tell us something. It is very strange indeed."

Sensing Carter's tension, Carnarvon tried to look about the tomb through his friend's trained eyes. Indeed, leaving an oil lamp within the tomb was surprising, and so was the disarray of the objects. But Carnarvon was so overwhelmed by the beauty of the pieces he could think of nothing else. Gazing at the translucent alabaster cup abandoned so casually on the threshold, he yearned to pick it up and hold it in his hands. It was so enticingly beautiful. Suddenly he noticed a subtle change in its orientation with regard to the garland of dried flowers and the oil lamp. He was about to say something when Carter's excited voice rang out in the chamber.

"There's another room. Everyone take a look." Carter was squatting down, shining his flashlight beneath one of the

Howard Carter examines the sarcophagus of Tutankhamen.

funerary beds. Carnarvon, Lady Evelyn, and Callender hurried over to him. There, glittering in the circle of light from the torch, another chamber took form, filled with gold and jeweled treasure. As in the anteroom, the precious objects had been chaotically scattered, but for the moment the Egyptologists were too awed by their find to question what had happened three thousand years in the past.

Later, when they would be ready to explore the mystery, Carnarvon was already fatally ill with blood poisoning. At 2 A.M. on April 5, 1923, less than twenty weeks after the opening of Tutankhamen's tomb and during an unexplainable five-minute power failure throughout Cairo, Lord Carnarvon died. His illness reputedly was started by the bite of an insect, but questions were raised.

Within months four other people associated with the opening of the tomb died under mysterious circumstances. One man disappeared from the deck of his own yacht lying at anchor in the placid Nile. *The New York Times* was moved to write about the deaths: "It is a deep mystery, which it is all too easy to dismiss by skepticism." A fear began to infiltrate the scientific community. There were just too many coincidences.

Reader's Response

What exploration or discovery would you like to play a role in?

The Tomb of King Tutankhamen

Checking Your Comprehension

1. How did the archaeologists feel as they prepared to open the door to Tutankhamen's tomb?
2. What puzzled Carter about the state of the tomb?
3. How were Carter's methods different from those used by Belzoni?
4. Why do you think Carter hoped that the tomb had been robbed in antiquity and then resealed?
5. Explain why you think Carter did not allow Raman to enter the antechamber.
6. What do you think might be the answer to the mystery that puzzled Carter? What led you to this conclusion?
7. Find two examples of facts the author uses to tell the story. Then find two examples in the selection where the author uses his own opinion of what might have occurred.

Writing to Learn

THINK AND EVALUATE Copy the pro-and-con chart below. On the left, list all the reasons you can think of why archaelogists should explore ancient tombs. On the right, list all the reasons you can think of why they should not.

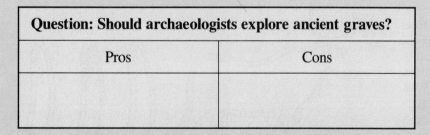

Question: Should archaeologists explore ancient graves?	
Pros	Cons

WRITE Use one of your lists to compose a letter to the editor of an archaeology magazine. Express your own opinion about whether archaeologists should or should not explore ancient tombs. Explain why you feel as you do.

Decoding the Rosetta Stone

▲ The Rosetta Stone is in the British Museum.

▲ These hieroglyphics represent the name of the ruler Ramses III. The circle at the top represents the sun god Ra, and the shepherd's staff at the right stands for "ruler."

Although ancient Egyptians lived thousands of years ago, they are still ranked among the world's greatest builders and inventors. Their pyramids were constructed by hoisting stones weighing two and a half tons—without the use of machines. Egyptians preserved the bodies of their dead so well that the remains have lasted for thousands of years. Even now, scientists don't completely understand how the Egyptians accomplished these feats.

The Egyptians also did a lot of writing. They covered buildings and walls with stories and information about their lives. Perhaps you have seen some of their writing, called hieroglyphics, in museums. Hieroglyphics look like strange and beautiful pictures

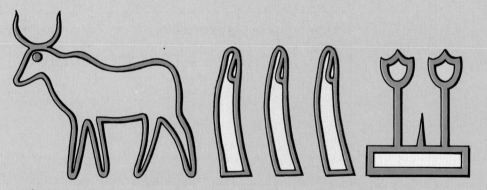

▲
To represent 32,000 cattle, the Egyptians drew three fingers and two lotus plants next to the image of an ox.

516

combined with letter-like symbols. Now we are able to read hieroglyphics, but for hundreds of years no one could decipher them.

Scholars had tried for a long time to understand what the pictures and symbols meant, but there were no clues to their meaning. Some scholars finally concluded that hieroglyphics represented a code known only to ancient Egyptian priests and would never be understood.

Then one day, in 1799, a French soldier working on the foundations of a fortress in the city of Rosetta in Egypt found a black stone tablet. It was covered with hieroglyphics and with another ancient Egyptian language. But this stone also contained a section written in ancient Greek that seemed to correspond to the hieroglyphics, and ancient Greek was something people could read.

After years of painstaking work, Jean Francois Champollion was able to match the Greek words with the Egyptian words. The mystery of hieroglyphics was solved. Champollion produced a text describing the language of hieroglyphics. With it, archaeologists who uncover Egyptian writings are able to read the messages on them and to give us a better understanding of ancient Egyptian society.

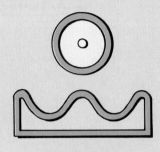

▲ These hieroglyphics represent the sun, hill country, and a mouth.

▶ The Egyptians used hieroglyphics to represent their ideas regarding life and death.

517

In the year 4022, archaeologist Howard Carson discovers and interprets the remains of a mysterious ancient culture—ours!

THE TREASURES OF
TOMB
26

written and illustrated by
David Macaulay

In the year 4020, a great mystery surrounded the continent of North America. Its civilization had disappeared thousands of years before under the weight of heavy pollution and third- and fourth-class mail. There were signs that a complex civilization with skilled artisans had once thrived, but little was actually known of how these fascinating people lived. Little, that is, until Howard Carson's amazing discovery.

Before his forty-second birthday, Howard Carson had accomplished nothing of interest. Of obscure parentage, he spent his first four decades untroubled by public attention. In fact, it was not until the autumn of his life that Carson achieved the unprecedented mediocrity that was to make him, by the time of his death, unique among amateurs.

During his early forties, while rapidly consuming the remnants of a trust fund, Carson's interests were divided between his collection of antique space shuttles and a number of questionable, albeit visionary, experiments relating to increased camel-hump productivity. He must also have had some interest in history, because we know that he possessed at this time a fairly up-to-date translation of the writings of the ancient scholar Hoving and a rather dog-eared facsimile of the *Michelin Fragments*, and that he was a subscriber to the *National Geographic Magazine*.

In 4022 pressure brought on by the anticipated failure of yet another of his experiments led the desperate Carson to seek a change. He entered the 116th Cross-Continental North American Catastrophe Memorial Marathon. Little did he know when he set sail for East Usa what lay in store. Less than a month later, and already well behind the rest of the pack, Carson found himself crossing the great rubble heaps along the perimeter of a deserted excavation site.

The ground below his feet suddenly gave way. He was precipitated headlong downward. When the dust had settled and he had recovered his spectacles, he found himself at the bottom of an ancient shaft, facing the entrance of a long-forgotten tomb. The shaft, probably dug by tomb robbers shortly after the tomb was sealed, had been covered initially by the natural vegetation of the surface. More recently, the whole area had been buried under vast quantities of soil from the adjacent excavation.

Unimpressed and rather annoyed at this inconvenience, Carson's first thought was to call out for assistance, but, before he could utter a sound, light from the shaft caught the area around the handle on the tomb door. Upon closer inspection, he discovered that the sacred seal which was traditionally placed on the door following the burial rites was still in place. Staff artists' reconstructions of similar, but always defiled, tombs that had appeared in his most recent *National Geographic* flooded his mind. Thunderstruck, he realized he was on the threshold of history. His entire body trembled as he contemplated the possible significance of his find. The mysterious burial customs of the late twentieth-century North Americans were finally (and as it turned out, magnificently) to be revealed.

Less than a month later, aided by his companion, Harriet Burton, who "enjoyed sketching," and a dedicated group of volunteers, Carson began the first of seven years' work on the excavation of the Motel of the Mysteries complex, and most specifically on the removal and recording of the treasures from Tomb 26.

While Carson paced back and forth in a supervisory manner, Harriet numbered each of the items surrounding the entrance as well as those on the great door. Descriptions of the most significant discoveries are to be found in her diary:

Number 21, "the gleaming Sacred Seal, which had first caught Howard's attention, was placed on the door by the officials after the burial to protect the tomb and its inhabitant for eternity."

Number 28, "the Sacred Eye, which was believed to ward off evil spirits."

Number 18, "the partially exposed Plant That Would Not Die. One of these exquisite plants, which had apparently been grown in separate pieces and then joined together, was placed on each side of the entrance."

Numbers 19 and 20, "containers in which the sacrificial meal was offered to the gods of eternal life."

Once the exterior of the tomb had been recorded in detail, preparations for entering it were begun. With a steady hand, Carson, who had presumably picked up a few tricks in his time, jimmied the lock. With his helpers peering nervously from a safe distance, he cautiously pried open the door. The creaking of the ancient hinges, in Miss Burton's own words, "cut through the silence like the scream of a ghostly fleeing spirit." Suddenly, to Carson's astonishment, the door stopped dead. A frantic but successful search for the obstruction revealed a beautifully crafted chain about two thirds up the inside of the door, linking it with the sturdy frame. Clearly this stood as the final barrier between the present and the past. Once the workers had sawed through the chain, they withdrew, and Carson continued to open the great door.

At first, everything was dark. Carson lit a match. Still everything was dark. Carson lit two matches. Still, everything was dark. Attempting to avoid a rather protracted delay, Harriet eased the large spotlight toward the entrance with her foot. As the blanket of darkness was stripped away from the treasures within the tomb, Carson's mouth fell open. Everywhere was the glint of plastic. Impatiently, the others waited for a response. "Can you see anything, Howard?" they asked in unison.

"Yes," he replied . . .

"WONDERFUL THINGS!"

The cataloging of each item in the tomb and the excavation of the surrounding area took many years and was accompanied by sensational press coverage. When the Treasures were finally moved to a major museum for exhibition, thousands of people lined up— each hoping for at least a glimpse of these marvels from the past.

═══ THE TREASURES ═══

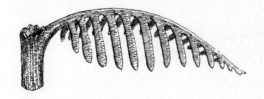

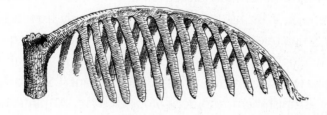

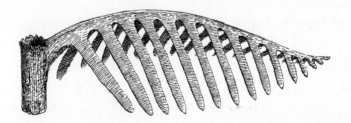

Three Fragments from the Plant That Would Not Die

This plant, developed by the ancients specifically for eternal life, was grown in separate pieces through a now lost biological process. The proportion and size of each plant could then be perfectly matched to its ultimate location. Many such plants were found throughout the complex.

The Sacred Seal

Constructed of *plasticus eternicus*, this particular treasure has proportions of classic beauty. It was placed upon the handle of the great outer door by the necropolis officials following the closing of the tomb.

The Great Altar

This magnificent structure, toward which everything in the outer chamber was directed, represents the essence of religious communication as practiced by the ancient North Americans. Although it was capable of communication with a large number of gods, the altar seems to have been intended primarily for communion with the gods MOVIEA and MOVIEB. Judging by the impact marks on the top and sides of the upper altar, some aspect of this communication was dependent upon pounding the surface. Communication with the altar was symbolically continued into eternal life by placing the communicator box in the hand of the deceased. Below the exquisite glass face of the upper altar are a number of sealed spaces for offerings.

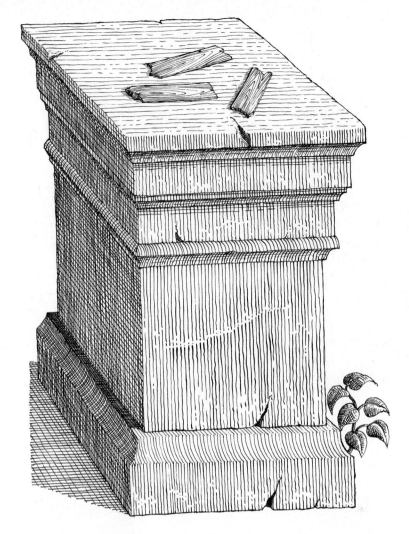

Fragments of *Plasticus Petrificus*

Called simply "Formica" by the ancients (MICA being the god of craftsmanship), these three priceless fragments from the front of the Great Altar represent an unequaled degree of aesthetic sophistication and almost superhuman technical skill. The richness of the coloring and the intricacy of the linear engraving can only be approximated today by using the finest woods.

The Bell System

This highly complex percussion instrument was found near the statue of WATT. Markings similar to those on the face of the upper altar imply a symbolic connection to the gods. The Bell System was played by holding one half of the instrument in each hand and banging them together in some pre-established rhythmic pattern. The impact would cause a small bell inside the larger of the two pieces to ring. Both halves were connected by a beautifully crafted coil which would miraculously reform itself into the identical number of loops after each playing.

The Internal Component Enclosure

This exquisitely fashioned container, a twentieth-century adaptation of the ancient Canopic[1] jar, stood on a specially designed table in the outer chamber. The exterior surface of the container was fashioned out of *plasticus petrificus*, while the interior was lined with a priceless translucent substance. Since no trace of an internal organ was found in the ICE its function as a Canopic jar is considered to have been merely symbolic.

---

[1] Canopic (kə nō′ pik): A jar in which the ancient Egyptians preserved the internal organs of a deceased person, usually for burial with a mummy.

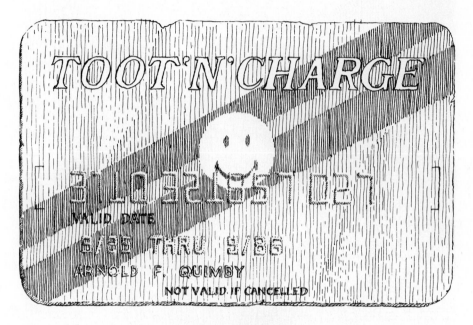

Small Relief

This extremely fine piece of workmanship served as a portable shrine which was to be carried through life and into eternal life. Its delicate inscriptions were intended to identify an individual's religious preference along with the burial site to which the body should be delivered when necessary. Matching inscriptions were found on the main doors of the great sanctuary. Because the ancients were unable to predict the exact time of death, each of the shrines had to last for an entire year.

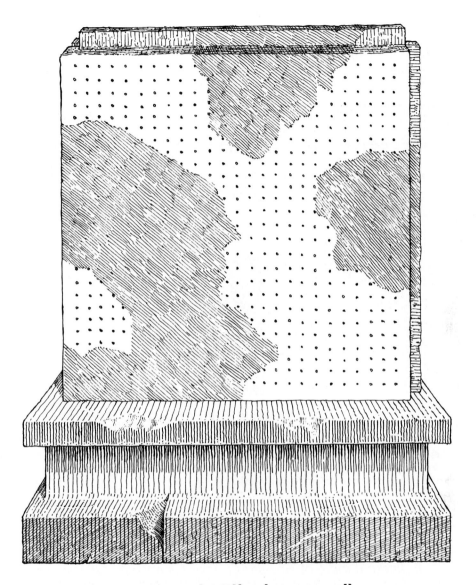

A Mosaic Tile (restored)

Unlike their predecessors, the ancient North Americans covered the ceilings of their buildings, rather than the floors, with intricate mosaics. Each tile was decorated with a series of parallel perforations, and then a color was added by applying the occasional and always subtle watermark.

Epilogue

In the years to come, hundreds of people would travel to the Motel of the Mysteries to view the vast complex of tombs—complete with ceremonial pool.

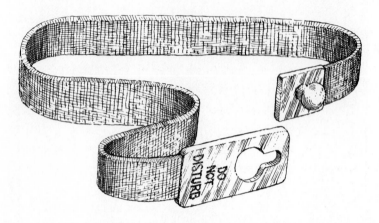

SACRED SEAL BELT

This attractive all-leather belt is made especially for THE MUSEUM SHOP by a famous Italian belt maker. The beautiful two-piece buckle is based on the Sacred Seal and the handle from the outer door. Great care has been taken to accurately reproduce the inscription and the proportions of the original. Both pieces are available in either silver or 24-karat gold.

♦ LIBRARY LINK ♦

To find out more of Howard Carter's hilarious interpretations of twentieth-century life, look for Motel of the Mysteries *by David Macaulay.*

Reader's Response

What do you think are the most telling things that your culture will leave for the future?

THE TREASURES OF
TOMB 26

Checking Your Comprehension

1. According to the story, what became of the civilization of North America?
2. What kind of person was Howard Carson?
3. What was the turning point in Carson's life?
4. What was the ancient burial site that Carson uncovered?
5. Discuss what conclusions Carson might have made if he had discovered a car, a baseball stadium, or a school building. How did you decide what his conclusions might be?
6. What do you think was the author's purpose in writing this story?

Writing to Learn

THINK AND ANALYZE Think of an item that could be misinterpreted in the future. Sketch the item and label it as a future archaeologist might, as in the example below.

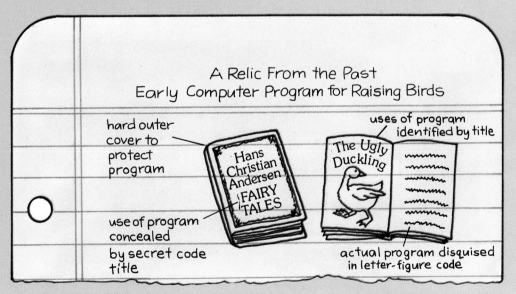

A Relic From the Past
Early Computer Program for Raising Birds

hard outer cover to protect program

use of program concealed by secret code title

Hans Christian Andersen FAIRY TALES

uses of program identified by title

The Ugly Duckling

actual program disquised in letter-figure code

WRITE Prepare a report as written by an archaeologist of the future about the item you chose.

531

THE POETS SPEAK OF TIME

From a mysterious wrecked statue, to a small blue bead, to an ancient mummy—these poems appeal to our fascination with antiquity.

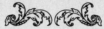

OZYMANDIAS

I met a traveller from an antique land
Who said: "Two vast and trunkless legs of stone
Stand in the desert. Near them, on the sand,
Half sunk, a shattered visage lies, whose frown,
And wrinkled lip, and sneer of cold command,
Tell that its sculptor well those passions read
Which yet survive, stamped on these lifeless things,
The hand that mocked them, and the heart that fed:
And on the pedestal these words appear:
My name is Ozymandias, King of Kings:
Look on my works, ye Mighty, and despair!
Nothing beside remains. Round the decay
Of that colossal wreck, boundless and bare
The lone and level sands stretch far away."

PERCY BYSSHE SHELLEY

ONE
SMALL
BLUE BEAD

One small blue bead . . .
A turquoise bead
No larger than
An apple seed . . .

You might not notice
A thing so small.
You might walk by
And not see it at all
Though it shines as blue
As a piece of the sky
And bright as the flash
Of an eagle's eye.

When men still lived in cliffs and caves
And great beasts roamed the land,
There was a boy who held this bead
Clutched tightly in his hand.
Now it lies forgotten
In the desert sand.

How long has it been there?
Who can say?
Maybe ten thousand years
And one long day,
For this is a wide and lonely land
Where hardly a footstep disturbs the sand
And very few people happen to pass
A certain clump of tall dry grass
That hides this bit of blue.
But someone will find it.
Will that someone be you?

Here's a map to follow.
It's drawn to show
Where men went wandering
Ages ago.
And if it leads you to the bead
There in the sand,
Before you stoop beside it
Or take it in your hand
Look off into the desert sky,
Watch the eagles floating high,
Listen to the wind . . . and try
To let time blow away, away
Back to a dim and ancient day . . .

BYRD BAYLOR SCHWEITZER

MANHOLE COVERS

The beauty of manhole covers—what of that?
Like medals struck by a great savage khan,
Like Mayan calendar stones, unliftable, indecipherable,
Not like old electrum, chased and scored,
Mottoed and sculptured to a turn,
But notched and whelked and pocked and smashed
With the great company names:
Gentle Bethlehem, smiling United States.
This rustproof artifact of my street,
Long after roads are melted away, will lie
Sidewise in the graves of the iron-old world,
Bitten at the edges,
Strong with its cryptic American,
Its dated beauty.

KARL SHAPIRO

MUMMY

So small a thing
This mummy lies,
Closed in death
Red-lidded eyes,
While, underneath
The swaddled clothes,
Brown arms, brown legs
Lie tight enclosed.
What miracle
If he could tell
Of other years
He knew so well;
What wonderment
To speak to me
The riddle of
His history.

MYRA COHN LIVINGSTON

GRANUAILE

As the sunlight in its glory
Ever shines on fair Clew Bay
And Croagh Patrick old and hoary
Rises o'er the ruins grey
As the streamlets in the meadows
In their pride come dancing down
Nestled close among the mountains
Stands pleasant Newport Town.

Just a mile from where the turrets
Of the ancient town uprise
And the frowning peak of Nephin
Soars in grandeur to the skies
Lie a massive heap of ruins
In their loneliness sublime
Though scattered and dismantled now
By tyranny and time.

'Twas a proud and stately castle
In the years of long ago
When the dauntless Grace O'Malley
Ruled a queen in fair Mayo.
And from Bernham's lofty summit
To the waves of Galway Bay
And from Castlebar to Ballintra
Her unconquered flag held sway.

She had strongholds on her headlands
And brave galleys on the sea
And no warlike chief or viking
E'er had bolder heart than she.
She unfurled her country's banner
High o'er battlement and mast
And 'gainst all the might of England
Kept it flying 'til the last.

The armies of Elizabeth
Invaded her on land
Her warships followed on her track
And watched by many a stand
But she swept her foes before her
On the land and on the sea
And the flag of Grace O'Malley
Waved defiant, proud and free.

ANONYMOUS

READING FICTION

Literature:
Theme

What do you think makes an author want to write a story? Sometimes authors write because they have ideas that they want to get across to their readers. These ideas—the points the author wants to make—are called the *theme*. If an author has been able to express ideas through the theme of a story, then we can share in those ideas— and perhaps even learn something about ourselves, too.

The following passage expresses the major theme of "The Diary of Anne Frank."

> I know it's terrible, trying to have any faith. When people are doing such horrible things. But you know what I sometimes think? I think the world may be going through a phase, the way I was with Mother. It'll pass, maybe not for hundreds of years, but some day. . . . I still believe, in spite of everything, that people are really good at heart.

The theme of this play, as shown in the passage above, is that people can behave decently toward each other in spite of horrible circumstances—that people are basically good at heart.

Implied Themes

Authors do not always state their themes directly. When they do not, you can infer them from what the characters do, say, and think, and from what happens to them. Sometimes you can infer the theme of the story by asking yourself questions like these:

What does the main character want most?
What problems stand in the way of reaching this goal?
What is the result or outcome?

You can discover the theme of "The Dog of Pompeii" by asking these questions about Bimbo:

QUESTION	ANSWER
What does Bimbo want?	Bimbo wants to take care of Tito.
What problems stand in Bimbo's way?	Bimbo is only a dog trying to take care of a boy, his attempts at communication are not always understood, and the erupting volcano puts Tito in grave danger.
What is the result or outcome?	Bimbo does save Tito, but in the process loses his own life.

Stating the Theme

The answers to the questions about Bimbo tell you that the theme has something to do with friendship. It might be stated like this: A true friend is willing to confront all kinds of difficult obstacles in order to help another friend.

Be sure not to confuse the theme with the specific events in a story. The theme is an *idea* that can best be stated in sentence form. A theme goes beyond specific characters and events to give us some insight into general truths.

Read and Enjoy

The story you are about to read, "In the Center of the Eye," contains ideas about friendship and discovery, among other topics. As you read, see if you can figure out the author's theme.

Archaeologists of the future may be making their excavations on other planets, such as the planet Balthor.

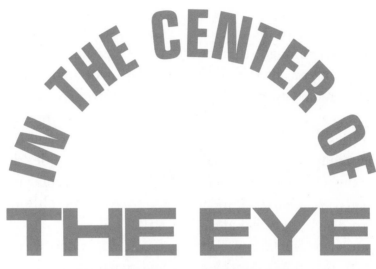

IN THE CENTER OF THE EYE

BY H. M. HOOVER

Fifteen-year-old Lian is flying her aircar back to the Mount Balthor observatory, where she and her parents work as astrophysicists, when she is caught in a storm and forced to make a crash landing. She is rescued the next morning by Dr. Jeffrey Farr, an archaeologist who is on the planet Balthor to study the ruins of an ancient civilization. Dr. Farr and his colleague, Dr. Scott, offer to put Lian up at their camp until her parents, who are busy studying a supernova, can come for her.

The site of the ancient ruins is a series of wooded mounds that form the pattern of a huge green eye. Working along with Dr. Farr and Dr. Scott in the ancient ruins are two types of intelligent creatures from other planets— crablike animals known as tolats, *and lavender creatures called* amalfi. *Then there are local creatures, the* lumpies, *heavyset gray animals with six legs and seal-like faces.*

Lian suspects that the lumpies have some sort of telepathic powers, and she is very curious about them. One after-noon she is resting on a hill, listening to a song that someone seems to be singing in her mind, when three lum-pies pass by. Not quite knowing why, Lian begins to follow them.

The lumpies led her to the far side of the hill, down through a thicket, and beside an oblong meadow bare of trees. They seemed in no hurry, almost aimless.

Orange berries grew at the mead-ow's edge. They stopped to pick and eat them. Their fingers were very deft. When they moved on, it was to wander downhill into a heavily wooded area.

Vines flourished over a low cliff. The three left the path and approached the cliff, pushed aside some vines, and disappeared behind them. Lian stopped and waited, watching to see where they would re-emerge. But they did not, and when some minutes passed, she decided they had grown tired of being followed and had given her the slip. And very neatly, too.

She imagined this trio of chubby gray creatures tiptoeing away into the woods and smiled at the image. She walked up the slope to investigate, but slowly, just in case they were hiding back there, watching her. She did not want to irritate or startle them. Even gentle animals bit when provoked.

"Hello?" she called and patted the vines.

There was no response. Birds sang among the trees.

She pulled some vines aside and saw a cavelike hollow space behind them. The lumpies were not there. She slipped inside and let the vines fall shut. Gravel scrunched beneath her boots. It was a pleasant hiding place. The sunlit leaves made an opaque wall of jade that shadowed green on green. The cliff nar-rowed down to nothing to her right. She turned left and followed the tun-nel-like curve of the outcropping. Around the second bend she saw an opening in the cliff wall and stopped still.

It was a doorway, perfectly round and machine tooled, as if designed for a huge vault. A few yards away, almost buried in soil and leaves, lay the mas-sive door that had once fit that frame. Lian stood there, taking in the meaning of it all, then reached over and knocked on the cliff wall. It rang not as stone but as a foamed metal, part of the ruin. Lumpies went through that doorway; she could see their finger marks all over it.

Her first impulse was to run back to the dig and tell Dr. Farr. But tell him what—"I found an open door"? That sounded rather silly even to consider. Besides, they probably knew about it.

He said they had sonar-tested and measured the whole site. Probably it was only a wall remaining from a ruin and not exciting at all. Still, there were no human tracks. She went up to have a look, thinking, That's how the lumpies gave me the slip.

The door led into a ruin, but not the ruin she expected. It opened on a wide, dim corridor that stretched away into darkness. Its floor was covered with mud and leaves. Lumpie tracks were everywhere, and the vaulted walls were hand-marked as high as they could reach. One glance and Lian knew she had made an important find.

"I wonder where it goes," she whispered to herself. "To the center of the eye?" It would be interesting to learn what was under that green hill, learn it by herself without having to explain about the singing to people who might not believe her.

The lumpies must have come in here; it couldn't be too dangerous or they wouldn't go in and out. And it must be here that they had learned to sing. She checked to see that nothing lurked on either side of the doorway and then entered. It was very still inside. There was a cellar smell of dampness and age.

"Hello?" she called. There was no echo. These walls were as sound-absorptive as the corridors of a starship. "Lumpies? Are you in there?"

If they were, they weren't answering.

Lian set off down the hall, walking almost on tiptoe. Between every other support beam was a closed door, like an oddly shaped hatch. She did not want to touch them for fear one would fall on her, as the outer door had fallen off. After about three minutes she turned and looked back. It seemed a long way to the entrance. Suppose there was something alive in here. Suppose the roof was ready to collapse. Her footsteps slowed.

Suddenly they loomed up out of the shadows, their eyes shining gray with reflected light from the distant door. She gave a yelp of fright and ran. They did not chase her. Afterward she was not sure why she stopped running, except that she knew they meant no harm and had only been waiting for her. She turned back to join them.

They led her through dark hallways and down dim corridors, past shadowy things vaguely seen, and none of it recognizable. Only a faint glow from the ceiling overhead kept her from feeling trapped in a labyrinth. As they went deeper into the ruins, passageways stood open, dark and mysterious. Twice she saw what could have been wall murals, but it was too dark to be sure.

The passageway ended. In the dim light she could see no door or

branching hall. Her guides stopped as if confused, and exchanged finger signs, then sat on their haunches and looked at one another.

"What is it?" said Lian. "Is this what you wanted to show me?" They smiled their clown smiles, then turned to look at the wall again. She felt a flicker of irritation and disappointment and at the same time she understood a remark Dr. Scott had made earlier that day about wishing the lumpies would stop playing the fool.

But that was unfair of her, she decided. They had already given her the knowledge of the existence of this place. What more did she expect? Or want? Ruins were of no real interest to her.

But she did expect more, even if she wasn't sure what. She stepped around the lumpies and approached the wall. Directly past them the floor began to slant, ramplike. One did not usually find walls built across ramps, but one often found security gates at the top of ramps. If that was what this was, then her exploration in here was ended. With no power source to move it, the gate would never open.

But its existence would be of interest to the archaeologists. She ran her hands along the rough texture of the wall and found a seam and then a frame that reached from the floor to as high as she could stretch. She checked the wall on the other side of the ramp, and

as she felt for the matching seam, her fingers struck against a switch plate.

It was too dark to see what it looked like. There were holes in it, a radial design, perhaps a plug of some sort. She looked back at the lumpies, wondering if they knew it was a security gate—or if they knew what lay behind it. One lumpie got up slowly and came over to join her. At close range it smelled of grass and berries and a mustard-like scent of its own. It stood erect, peered nearsightedly at the thing her touch had found, then reached past her and fit its fingertips into the holes.

"Very good!" she said, and then was interrupted by the hum of a motor. A faint crack of light appeared along the floor and grew slowly higher. "This can't be!" Lian informed the trio, who gazed at the light in wide-eyed simpleness, the one beside her with its hand still on the switch. "What's in there?" She reached up and pulled that supple hand away from the switch plate. The gate continued to rise. She began to back away, just in case. It was probably an old power cell still functioning by freakish circumstances . . . but just in case there was anything alive . . .

There was not.

The Counter looked out upon a small and rather monstrous alien and three of its responsibilities. It hummed the greeting signal.

Lian saw a great amphitheater, the center of it occupied by what looked like a massive and very elaborate computer. Glassed booths lined the circular walls. Opaque green glass covered the dome. Looking up at the light patches caused by disarrayed soil and vines, she recognized the trail of her footsteps up and down that dome and the spot where she had rested. A shiver went over her. From here that roof looked very thin.

The air rushing past them to escape down the dark hallway felt warm and dry. It smelled of machinery and dust and some aged sweetness. Hidden speakers whispered a song of eight notes, paused, then repeated at slightly louder volume, paused, then repeated again, like an alarm signal, or a coda.

Dust in the recording device crackled in amplifiers. Dust covered the endless expanse of blue floor. Dusty cameras like huge eyes peered at them from either side of the gateway. They were being greeted and recorded by some still-functioning relic from the past.

The lumpie beside her inhaled deeply, as if it had been holding its breath, and moved closer to her. It looked so worried she impulsively put her arm around its shoulders and found it was a solid creature and as nice to touch as a very expensive leather glove. She hugged, then patted it reassuringly.

"It's all right," she said. "It's all machinery. Nothing will harm us if we're careful."

Something brushed against her right hand, then twined through her fingers. She glanced down to find herself holding hands with the other lumpie, who was also holding hands with the third.

"I'm sure we all feel safer now," she said, and laughed at the thought of the picture they must make. "It would be nicer, of course, if we could talk it over. But since we can't, I will talk and you can all smile. It will be just like home."

The lumpies looked at her.

"The first thing we must do if we're going inside is make sure we can get back out. That means we must secure this door." She freed herself from their huddling and looked about for something with which to wedge the track. Some distance down the hall lay a pile of rubble. From it she selected a sturdy strip of metal and tugged it back across the floor to the ramp. It was too heavy to lift. The lumpies watched her, wide-eyed.

"Thank you all," she said as she shoved the wedge into place at an angle against the gate track. "I couldn't have done it without you." She hand-measured to make sure there was enough room for her to squeeze through that space if the gate slid down upon the wedge. Then she gauged the girth of the largest of her companions and hoped for the best.

"Come," she invited them. "Let's go see who lived here."

She walked down the ramp, out onto the floor of the dome, and stood there for a moment, hands on hips, surveying the area. It looked alien, but not as alien as it would have to most people. Lian had spent a good part of her life in enclosures very much like this where humans were dwarfed by space, tile, and glass barrenness and elaborate machinery. All that was lacking here was the giant telescope, angled skyward.

The click of her boot heels on the floor was firm and sure of itself. Camera eyes followed her as she made a slow circle of the place, peering into the glass booths at the dials and terminal boards.

"It seems to be a central control room," she called to her three followers, who had advanced as far as the ramp's end and stood watching. "Some of the dials and gauges are still registering. Perhaps this was the power plant for the city . . . but why so intricate for a city so small?"

Every so often along the curved wall there was a switch panel like the one at the ramp gate. On impulse she placed her hands palm to palm and tried to approximate a lumpie finger ar-rangement, then touched the plate. Her fingers were too broadly tipped and would not fit. But a lumpie hand would. She gave them a speculative glance, then went over and held out her hand to the one who had opened the door. "I need you," she said. "Don't give me a soulful look. I just want to know something. It won't hurt you."

Very reluctantly the lumpie took her hand and accompanied her to the nearest booth, where she fit its hand to the switch plate. Two yards to the right a glass panel slid open. Even though she had suspected it, she found it hard to believe.

"It's yours?" she whispered. "You lived here . . ." She stared, perplexed, at this wide-eyed creature, who returned the stare. "What have you done with it? What have you done to yourselves? You're not simple-minded! You're not animals . . . you are . . ." She released its hand, and the creature galloped across the floor to rejoin its companions at the end of the ramp. From that point they continued to watch her.

But what were they? Masters—or servants of a superior race? None had been in here in—how long? Or maybe the configuration of this switch that fit a lumpie touch was only circumstance and she had not only jumped but made a quantum leap to conclusions.

In the background the speakers still

repeated those eight notes, and absent-mindedly she whistled them. The speaker shut off in mid-note. "I will talk and you can all smile. It will be just like home!" She whirled around. It was a computer's voice, not a replay of a recording of her own speech, but the unit's eerie mimicry without understanding. "I will talk and you can all smile," it repeated. She walked over for a closer look.

"Go ahead and talk," she said, but the computer did not.

The central unit was sheathed in anodized gold and for most of its length was covered by a domed transparent housing. Its design was more elegant than the newest of tolat computers, yet Lian suspected this unit had been functioning since long before the first tolat computer existed. There was a distinct wheeze as its air-intake ducts came on, but what appeared to be a spectrograph was analyzing the chemical components of something. The ratios looked familiar, and she wondered if it was analyzing her breath.

She wondered, too, if it contained a translator. If the race which had built it came from another planet, as Dr. Farr had said they might . . . Turning to face a camera eye, she held up the appropriate number of fingers and began to count. "One, two, three, four—" and then stopped. This was a silly waste of time. If the computer could translate, she would need a year to program it verbally. The tolats would figure it out and translate the language on their own units.

She decided she had better head back to the dig to report before Dr. Farr decided she was lost again. Besides, this was all a little too much to take in and comprehend at one time. She yawned, a wide yawn, half from fatigue and half from nerves. The snake's head of a camera focused on her mouth and lurched sideways as she politely covered the yawn with her hand.

"I'm an omnivorous mammal, sentient, and in an adolescent stage," she said, "if you really care." Then, noticing her sleeve was dirty, she began to brush it off as she circled the computer for a total view of it before leaving. At the far end was an oddly shaped opening, wide and black as a cave mouth, into the computer's interior. Without slowing her pace, she detoured closer to look inside.

It sucked her in as a black hole pulls in the mass of a star orbiting too near. Only half of her scream escaped.

The Counter could not remember such an intractable specimen. Even though its appendages were held immobile, it persisted in ordering them

to act, wasting valuable time. It was difficult to do a proper analysis.

The specimen's first reaction was fear, an emotion familiar to the Counter from past experience with the people. Its next emotion was anger. That was new and very interesting. This thing totally resented being analyzed, considered it in some abstract way a violation of its entire unit, and at the same time, helpless though it was, it counted on release and planned retribution to the violator.

The Counter paused to consider this factor. It found it illogical but perhaps useful for the unit's ultimate survival.

The unit was partially encased in synthetic fibers, acidic long-chain monomers. Its natural covering was far more complex. The Counter took cell samples and noted the puncture of this covering to obtain a liquid sample of the interior was met with new anger by the specimen.

The Counter's low power source was rapidly being drained by the specimen's struggles. The Counter administered a relaxant charge; the mind responded with more or less rational thought images. Could the Counter have smiled, it would have, for it found this mind's current overwhelming urge was to find a way to communicate with the Counter.

The Counter did a thorough search of the memory banks of the alien mind, recorded the data for later analysis, paid particular interest to its data on astrophysics, noted the unit's prolonged sense of isolation from its own kind, and its seemingly resultant affection for other living creatures.

Before releasing the specimen, the Counter assimilated its language codes. It was possible the specimen could be taught a basic understanding of the people's language . . . if the Counter could get the people to speak again. The specimen could not be reprogrammed to adequately absorb and convert radiant impulses; its existing equipment transmitted but only partially received. The Counter regretted this; it would have greatly simplified communication.

Once it could have transposed, translated, and speaker-communicated with this alien in a matter of hours. Now, in this aged and diminished state, with not even a fraction of its normal power, that seemed beyond the cells' capacity. Still, if given time to think it over, perhaps, like its people, the Counter could talk again.

One moment she was wrapped in blackness, dreaming; the next she was out and standing some distance from the computer. The three lumpies were beside her, patting her hands and peering over her, as if to make sure she was unharmed. She let them pat as she tried to remember what had happened, why she had dreamed all those things forgotten years ago. That computer thought . . . talked . . . ? Was it a medical unit fifty generations advanced? Or more . . .

The largest lumpie made a moaning noise and touched her left arm. She glanced down and saw a very neat hole in her white sleeve. Beneath the hole blood was beginning to clot on a deep and sore abrasion.

"It took a sample of me!" She was indignant, then something else occurred to her. "What are you three doing in here? You were too scared to come beyond the ramp before. Did you come to help me?"

They did not answer, but the smallest one took her wounded arm, splayed its fingers around the biceps and applied gentle pressure. As it did so, she watched its face. The eyes narrowed as it concentrated on the wound; the face lost its clownlike expression and became still with some kind of knowing. The soreness went away, and as she watched, the discoloration around the wound cleared.

"Hypnosis?" she said as the lumpie released her. "Or are you an empathist? If you can do that . . ." She pointed to her black eye. "That hurts, too."

The trio studied her face, and there was a rapid exchange of finger signaling. The small lumpie pointed to her eye, then to her cheek and lip, and then to the left eye. There was more finger waving.

Lian felt her knees beginning to shake in a delayed reaction from the fear of being trapped by the computer. "If you'll excuse me," she said, staggered a few steps past them, and sat down on the floor.

The consultation ended. All three dropped to their feet and padded over; the self-appointed healer explored the left side of her face with its fingers. It was like being touched by tiny soft erasers. She closed her eyes and took a deep breath. The erasers hesitated, then continued. After a few seconds she tried to open her eyes, and fingers gently pushed the lids down again.

She sat there, not really thinking, yet with a dozen different impressions going through her mind. Why did she trust the lumpies like this when she would not have allowed a similarly strange human to touch her? They needed names; she could not continue thinking of them as big and small and medium. And why did *that thing* want her language if it wasn't going to talk? Perhaps she was going mad and none of this had happened.

"That's enough, thank you," she said, and opened her eyes. "I want to get out of here now. I have had quite

enough for today. I am an astrophysicist, not a guardian. . . ." She paused, wondering why she had used the word "guardian" when *they* were attempting to take care of *her*.

She stood up rather unsteadily and began to walk out. The lumpies followed, still looking anxious. The cameras watched them cross the floor and exit up the ramp. At the gate she paused, then stopped to tug the wedge away from the track. Without a word, a lumpie touched the switch and the gate slid shut behind them.

"Perhaps you already have names," she said as they retraced their route through the ruined hallways. "But I don't know them. So please don't be insulted . . . if you understand. . . . You are Cuddles, because you do that a lot," she told the largest of the three. "You, my small healer, are Poonie. And our switch operator is Naldo."

They padded along beside her, their stubby gray feet almost noiseless compared to her two booted heels, their eyes sure in the dimness that made her stumble. When she repeated their names, touching the shoulder of each one as she did so, they smiled up at her, sweet, vacuous smiles, all the knowing that had briefly appeared before now lacking. Lian felt a great urge to cry without knowing quite why. She decided it was nervous exhaustion from being so frightened.

It felt very good to emerge into the sunlight again. From the bottom of the hill, looking back at the vine-covered cliff, she found it hard to believe what lay behind it. The sun's position told her it was long past noon. She headed back toward the dig, thinking of all she had to report.

"Dr. Farr is going to be so excited!" she said, remembering the undisturbed dust on that floor. Suddenly she noticed there were no footsteps behind her. She turned. The lumpies were nowhere in sight.

"Poonie?" she called. "Naldo?"

"Lian? It's Scotty. Lian? Is that you?" Dr. Scott came hurrying along the path, looking worried. "Who were you calling?"

"Lumpies. They were right behind me. . . ."

"Where did they go?" Then without waiting for an answer, "And where did they get those names?"

Lian shrugged, half embarrassed. "Me."

"Why not?" Dr. Scott was staring at Lian's face. "Forgive me, but you heal very quickly! The swelling's gone from your eye since this morning. There's only a little bruise left on the corner."

"I thought it felt better," Lian said, not wanting to explain it all at the moment, not wanting to betray. "Did you think I was lost? Is that why you were looking for me?"

"Oh, no. It's lunchtime, and we thought maybe your watch was broken in the crash. Did you see anything interesting this morning?"

"I've been . . . all over." Lian hardly knew where to begin, and she no longer was sure she wanted to. It wasn't that she didn't like Dr. Farr or Dr. Scott, but none of this was really her responsibility—not the dig or the lumpies. . . . She would be here less than a week, and then she would never see any of them again. She would go back to the observatory, back to working and studying alone, back to where, if she was late, nobody noticed she was missing. Not even a lumpie.

"Dr. Scott—uh—Scotty, how much do you know about lumpies?"

"Why?"

"I want to know. Actual facts. Not feelings."

"They can weave—I told you that. They seem friendly. None of them bite." She paused to think. "They eat fruits and berries and roots. They are very clean. They go swimming in the river in the morning and again before dark. If they weren't so large, they would make perfect pets. As you probably have decided, judging by the names you've given them."

"Do they hunt?"

"I don't think so. I don't think they like meat. Or perhaps they're afraid to kill things. When the bidernecks—

they're ugly little batlike—"

"I've seen them."

"Well, sometimes they go after a lumpie."

"They eat them?" Lian was horrified.

"No. The odd thing is, they don't. They just seem to like to torment the lumpies. A whole flock will land on one animal, crawl all over it, making a screeching fuss. But they won't bite it more than once, and then only slightly. The other lumpies will drive them off and then stand there with tears running down their faces. It's a very pathetic sight. I saw it happen twice, and I'm not sure, because it's hard for me to tell the animals apart, but I don't believe I've seen either victim of the harassment afterward."

Lian thought that over. "Maybe those two lumpies were dying?"

"Why would you think a thing like that? They died of trauma from being attacked, you mean?" She frowned. "Do you think lumpies are that sensitive?"

"No. Well—maybe? Bidernecks frighten me."

She didn't want to say what she really thought and what suspicions of hers this story might confirm. As scavengers the bidernecks could smell illness in a creature—the scent of a fever, the sweetness of hemorrhage. They were genetically coded to recognize weakness, anticipate death. But they could not digest species alien to their world. If the lumpies knew this . . . it was possible they had come to recognize an attack by bidernecks as a sign of approaching death and wept to see it.

It was also possible that the lumpies were timid and cried because the bidernecks frightened them. Still, the lumpies had come to help her. . . .

"Have you ever heard anything sing around here?"

"Have you?"

"Yes, today," Lian said. "Have you?"

Dr. Scott didn't answer right away, and when she did, her words seemed very deliberate. "There is a place in these woods, beyond the spot where we met back there . . . I was walking alone one evening . . . the first day we were here. I was watching the sky, glad to be out of it . . . glad to be alone for a change. . . ." She stopped and they walked in silence for a bit.

"And?" Lian prompted her after a polite interval.

"I don't know what. A low, mournful song, very long, with infinite variations on a single involved theme. It made sense—mathematically, anyway . . . the moons were up, the shadows were dark. When the wind made the trees move, the shadows changed."

"Were you scared?"

"I was terrified," Dr. Scott said. "And I don't know why, Lian, but it seemed to me then—and it still does now that I think about it—that the song was sung by something at least as intelligent as ourselves. Perhaps that is what frightened me—that idea." She shook her head and smiled apologetically. "I don't like to remember that. Did it affect you the same way?"

"Is that why you came out to find me? Because you were frightened here?"

"No . . . well, maybe a little. But did you hear a song like that?"

"No," Lian said. "But I heard a song. Like a greeting, or maybe just an everyday song. Has anyone else heard singing out here?"

"If they have, no one has mentioned it, and I didn't want to bring it up for fear of scaring people unnecessarily. It's an unknown . . . what do you think it was?"

Lian shrugged. "A lumpie?" Her voice was almost wistful with hope.

Dr. Scott started to laugh and then saw Lian was serious.

"Why?" she said, too gently, a small worry entering her eyes.

"Because." Lian wasn't going to risk being laughed at again. "I . . . just do. Is Dr. Farr still at the dig?"

They arrived back at the dig in time to hear a chorus of "ahs!" Dr. Farr and the others stood on the bank watching two tolats in the pit below. They were trying to cut a hole in the wall of one of the two square structures they had unearthed.

They were using torches designed to cut through the most exotic and resistant of metals or metallic plastics. But whatever this particular substance was, it not only was not cutting, it was deflecting beams so powerful their heat made the exposed red clay boil like magma.

It was hard to tell who was most excited: Dr. Farr, who saw in this indication of an ancient race with a highly advanced technology and possibly a civilization to match; Klat, who immediately wanted the substance analyzed to learn if it was derived from amalfi technology; or the tolats, who looked upon this resistant substance as an engineering problem to be analyzed, solved, and forgotten.

Lian had come back with the full intention of telling Dr. Farr all about her discovery. But now as she stood there listening to all the divergent opinions, she realized that to tell Dr. Farr would be to tell the entire staff. Diplomat that he was, he would include everyone to avoid bitter professional jealousies and general ill feelings among staff members. And that would be not only right but necessary for the harmony of the expedition.

She trusted him but not all the expedition crew. She knew nothing about them. If she talked too much . . . suppose the tolats decided to analyze a lumpie by testing its mental and physical capabilities or even dissecting one or more. This was legally a Class Five world; the lumpies were officially "wildlife," vulnerable animals. They could be hunted, by permit, or collected for zoos.

There was no way she could report what she found without involving the lumpies. If she omitted all mention of them, one look at the interior of the place, with lumpie tracks and finger marks all over, would show they had entered there. The staff might think nothing of that if it were not for the switch plates and, above all, how she had gained access to the dome. These were all educated people; if it was obvious to a complete amateur that the buildings showed a link between lumpie and ruin, it would be more obvious to an expert.

They are going to find out sooner or later, her common sense reminded her, but not because I betrayed the lumpies or their old computer.

"Lian! There you are," Dr. Farr called, and she jumped as if he could read her mind. He came up the walkway to join her. "Did you find the site interesting?"

"Very. I walked quite a distance."

"Find any artifacts on the surface?"

"No," she said honestly.

He nodded. "That's the curious thing about this place. There are no artifacts. No middens. Just structures. It's almost as if it were a model city. As if no one ever lived here. Fascinating, but"—he stared off into the pit—"a bit discouraging at times."

Lian thought how easy it would be to cheer him up and how much of a relief. "Dr. Farr?" she began, then stopped. If the lumpies had wanted to tell somebody else, they would have.

Something in her expression made him regard her more closely. If she told . . . it would be to please him and to ease her own sense of responsibility toward the lumpies—hardly admirable motives. "I—uh—would you please tell Scotty I've gone up to camp to have my lunch?"

One of the man's eyebrows raised questioningly, but all he said was, "Certainly." She had the feeling he was watching her halfway up the road.

Before eating, she went to her quarters to shower and change. Her clothing had become dusty and grass stained during her morning jaunt, and she was unaccustomed to grime of any sort. Observatories were almost surgically clean places. En route to the dining hall, she put the soiled garments into the autocleaner and paused for a moment to watch them writhe.

The dining hall was empty. She took a sandwich and a cube of fruit drink from the dispenser and wandered outside to sit on the grass and eat. That was a mistake. Within seconds a wortle marched around a dome and headed in her direction. Others followed. They formed in review before her, owlish eyes watching each bite she took, wide beaks working over each bite denied them. She went on eating.

Thinking perhaps she wasn't getting the hint, one bird hopped up on her knee and stared from closer range. It was heavy and its claws dug in. She moved to dislodge him, and in that instant another wortle stole her sandwich. The thief in blue feather pants hurried off with its booty, the other wortles giving chase.

"It's not a very good sandwich," Lian called after them. "But compared to the taste of beetles, you may like it."

She sat there to finish the fruit drink, and before long the wortles were straggling back. Liquids apparently held no charms for them. They stared at her awhile, then began to yawn great frog-mouth yawns. One by one they closed their eyes and dozed in the sun. Seeing them was very suggestive. On this revised time schedule an afternoon nap seemed an excellent idea and the lush grass an inviting bed. But remembering the giant beetles she had seen earlier, she went to her room to sleep.

When Dr. Farr woke her, the sun

was low and her room glowed with diffused pink light. "Would you care to walk down to the river and watch the lumpies swim?" he said. "I admit it's not exciting, but we take our entertainment where we can on an expedition."

She glanced at her watch. "Do we have time before dinner?" She was very hungry.

"Dinner is fashionably late here. It fills up a long evening."

They followed a switchback path down through the bushes on the hillside past a series of burrows where the wortle colony lived. Below, some of the staff was already sitting on the rocks. The sound of a miniature landslide from the sandy bluff caused Lian to look back to see a lone tolat coming down the hill. The tolat's eyes were erect to see over the bushes.

"Shall we wait for it?" she asked Dr. Farr. "To be polite? It's all by itself, and it might like company."

"Very well," he said agreeably. "But I doubt if the gesture will be appreciated. Tolats are very different from you and me."

She interpreted the remark as fact. The tolat caught up to them as they stood waiting for it. It swerved past without speaking, without so much as a glance at them, and went on down the path as if they were not there. Seeing her puzzled expression, Dr. Farr said,

"It was a kind thought, Lian. By human standards. But by tolat standards, our colleague was not rude."

"It could at least say good evening."

Dr. Farr smiled. "To a tolat that is an unessential remark and a foolish waste of time. I said good evening to one on a night when it was raining—it promptly went to its superior to question my mental fitness."

The lumpies, some sixty of them, swam from a gravel sandbar a short distance away from the rocks. For the first time Lian saw they came in all ages. She was going to remark aloud on that and stopped herself; of course they had young. But it pleased her to see it nonetheless. The two of them sat down to watch.

"How do you tell male from female?"

"We can't," said Dr. Scott, who sat nearby. "They all look alike. Only another lumpie knows."

Almost the entire expedition crew was watching the creatures, envying them the pleasure of the river. Swimming in untreated water was off limits to the staff. There was always the danger of foreign parasites that might cause exotic illnesses as yet undiagnosed and untreatable by preprogrammed medical computers.

To see a lumpie swim was to see the creature in a different concept. The water turned them into creatures of

grace. They looked like seals in the river, plump and sleek and fast. Heads out and up, rear legs tight together, arms paddling, forelegs balancing and guiding like flippers, they played tag and rolled and arabesqued over and over. And it was an entertaining performance.

When the sun almost touched the horizon, the lumpies began to leave the beach in groups of three or four. The last of the swimmers came ashore and stood looking at the water, as if making sure everyone was safely out. One small lumpie turned to observe the observers, then reached over to touch a friend and pointed toward their audience. Too quickly, as if to cover the gesture, Lian

thought, the friend or parent caught the other's hand and they hurried off together into the woods with the rest of the group.

"Wasn't that cute?" someone said, and there was nervous laughter from the staff; they had not enjoyed being observed.

Why was that funny? Lian wondered, her glance flicking over her companions. Of all the species she might encounter in the twilight, any but the humans would terrify her. And she wasn't sure about the humans.

No matter who or what they were, Lian thought, most sentient creatures felt the need to feel superior to the

others. She never understood why. Her father said it was a question of dominance; her mother said Lian was being unfair and would understand when she was older and had the responsibility of a staff of her own. But this was one of those things Lian did not want to understand because she suspected that when she did, it would make her very sad. Without waiting for the others, she slid off the rock and started up the path.

Dew was rising. Among the shrubs night-blooming flowers were opening and scenting the air. The wortles were muttering in their dark burrows. Insects sang. From across the river something called three flute notes and liked them so well it repeated them over and over.

"There's a big star!" a human voice called, and the hills echoed, "Star—star—star." The line of people ascending the path stopped, and faces turned to the north to look at this beauty, coolly glittering high above the horizon.

"Make a wish."

"It's a good omen."

"It must mean a successful expedition." Dr. Farr's remark was greeted with appreciative murmurings.

Lian looked and with an odd little twinge of pain recognized the beautiful star for what it was—the supernova, the fiery death of a distant sun. She was going to tell them that, then decided not to. People did not always appreciate raw facts—especially when they were engaged in making wishes.

"You must have wished something important," said Scotty. "You look so serious."

"I was wishing I had a telescope," she said, and gave her a lumpie smile.

♦ LIBRARY LINK ♦

Lian discovers some very interesting things about the lumpies. To find out more about them, read The Lost Star *by H. M. Hoover.*

Reader's Response

Do you think Lian should tell the archaeologists about her discovery? Why or why not?

WRITING ABOUT READING

Writing a Research Report

In this unit you discovered how archaeologists help us understand the past. Now you are about to become an amateur archaeologist.

Suppose you are on an archaeological dig and uncover an unusual object. You will try to identify the object and then write a report to support your conclusions.

Prewriting

Below is one archaeologist's report about a jade bead. Notice that the conclusion is given first, followed by the reasons that support it.

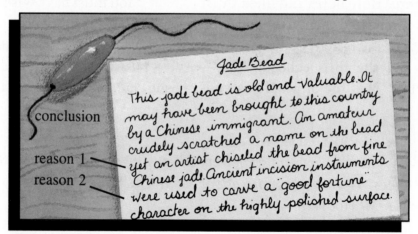

conclusion

reason 1

reason 2

> Jade Bead
>
> This jade bead is old and valuable. It may have been brought to this country by a Chinese immigrant. An amateur crudely scratched a name on the bead yet an artist chiseled the bead from fine Chinese jade. Ancient incision instruments were used to carve a "good fortune" character on the highly polished surface.

Select one object from the picture of ancient tools. (They are carpenter's tools and farm implements that were used in ancient Rome.) Examine the picture of the object closely, and ask yourself, "What does the object remind me of? Why does it have these features? What might it have been used for? Do we use anything like this today?"

Use your imagination and powers of observation in thinking of answers to the questions. In addition, you might want to read about Roman carpentry and farming in an encyclopedia or a book.

Writing

Begin by writing your conclusion about the object and how it was used. Then support your conclusion with facts and evidence. Include at least three reasons to support your conclusion.

Revising

Reread your work to decide which three reasons supporting your conclusion are best. Cross out the remaining reasons. Then arrange your three reasons in ascending order, from least important to most important. Save your most convincing reason for last.

Proofreading

Correct spelling, punctuation, and capitalization errors. Then neatly print your completed report on a file card, or use a clean sheet of paper instead.

Publishing

Make a class archaeologist's catalogue from your reports. You may also want to include advertisements for archaeologists' tools and books.

WORKING TOGETHER

Making a Word Cluster

Archaeologists learn about life in the past by studying the things that people used and produced. What would you like people in the future to know about life today? What objects would best show how we live? Your group will make a word cluster that shows the objects you would like future archaeologists to find. Group members should take responsibility for one or more of these tasks:

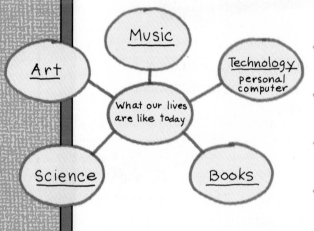

- Checking to make sure people understand what to do

- Encouraging everyone to contribute ideas

- Showing appreciation for people's suggestions

- Keeping a list of people's ideas

Begin by discussing objects that you think would best tell future archaeologists what your lives are like today. Everyone should contribute as many ideas as possible. Keep a list of all suggestions. When you have at least twenty objects on your list, work together to sort them into categories.

Start your cluster by drawing a circle in the center of a sheet of paper and writing the title for your cluster in the circle. Then, draw large category circles around the title circle. Take turns adding objects in the proper circles until you have used all your ideas.

Everyone should be able to explain why you, as a group, chose the particular objects shown in your word cluster.

Discovering Tut-ankh-Amen's Tomb edited by Shirley Glubok *(Macmillan, 1968)* Set in the Valley of the Tombs of the Kings in Egypt, the story is one of suspense and mystery as each clue leads the searchers deeper and deeper into the unknown.

Country of Broken Stone by Nancy Bond *(Atheneum, 1980)* A team of archaeologists is trying to excavate the site of an old Roman fort in northern England. Local residents do not want the archaeologists to disturb the area.

Adam of the Road by Elizabeth J. Gray *(Viking, 1942)* Adam is the son of a minstrel who, with his father, wanders through thirteenth-century England. Adam becomes involved in a series of adventures.

Pyramid by David Macaulay *(Houghton Mifflin, 1975)* This book takes you to Egypt in the twenty-fifth century B.C. Learn why the building of pyramids was important to the Egyptians.

The Root Cellar by Janet Lunn *(Scribner, 1981)* When she discovers an ordinary root cellar, twelve-year-old Rose is transported back in time to the 1860s. She finds that she enjoys living in that era, but when the Civil War touches her life, Rose must make some serious decisions.

BROWSING FOR BOOKS

Your History as a Reader

What is the first book you can remember having someone read to you? What is the first book you read all by yourself? If you had to choose one book that has meant more to you than any other, what would it be? Did you have to think hard to remember these three books? You probably didn't, because books have a way of becoming very important to us.

Try comparing the three books you remembered with your friends' choices. Did anyone else remember the same ones that you did? They may well have, because some books are classics—that is, books that everyone reads and loves. However, there were probably many more differences than similarities in the choices because people have their own tastes in reading.

In fact, what you already have is your own history as a reader—a pattern of reading that is like no one else's. Each person has some favorite authors and one or more series of books that are very special. Each one of us has kinds of books—biographies or history books, sports or horse stories—that we read whenever we have the chance. What kinds of books have you enjoyed most? Which authors and what series have been special favorites of yours? Which books have you read again?

Think about yourself as a reader right now. Have you recently discovered a new kind of book or a new author? It's fun to think about what your history as a reader will be like ten years from now. Perhaps you will still be reading mysteries or science fiction, sports stories or biographies. Or perhaps you will have discovered a completely new kind of book. That's one of the wonderful things about reading books—the possibilities are endless!

NOVELLA

A CROWN OF WILD OLIVE

BY ROSEMARY SUTCLIFF

It was still early in the day, but already it was growing hot; the white dry heat of the Greek summer and the faint off-shore wind that made it bearable had begun to feather the water, breaking and blurring the reflections of the galleys lying at anchor in Pireaus Harbour.[1]

Half Athens, it seemed, had crowded down to the port to watch the *Paralos*, the State Galley, sail for the Isthmus, taking their finest athletes on the first stage of their journey to Olympia.

---

[1]Some words in this selection are spelled in the British style.

Every fourth summer it happened; every fourth summer for more than three hundred years. Nothing was allowed to stand in the way, earthquake or pestilence or even war—even the long and weary war which, after a while of uneasy peace, had broken out again last year between Athens and Sparta.

Back in the spring the Herald had come, proclaiming the Truce of the Games; safe conduct through all lands and across all seas, both for the athletes and those who went to watch them compete. And now, from every Greek state and from colonies and settlements all round the Mediterranean, the athletes would be gathering. . . .

Aboard the *Paralos* was all the ordered bustle of departure, ropes being cast off, rowers in their places at the oars. The Athenian athletes and their trainers with them had gathered on the afterdeck. Amyntas, son of Ariston, had drawn a little apart from the rest. He was the youngest there, still several months from his eighteenth birthday and somewhat conscious that he had not yet sacrificed his boy's long hair to Apollo, while the rest, even of those entered for the boys' events—you counted as a boy at Olympia until you were twenty—were already short-haired and doing their Military Service. A few of them even had scars gained in border clashes with the Spartans, to prove that their real place, whatever it might be on the race track or in the wrestling pit, was with the men. Amyntas envied them. He was proud that he had been picked so young to run for Athens in the Boys' Double Stade,[2] the Four Hundred Yards. But he was lonely. He was bound in with all the others by their shared training; but they were bound together by something else, by another kind of life, other loyalties and shared experiences and private jokes, from which he was still shut out.

The last ropes holding ship to shore were being cast off now. Fathers and brothers and friends on the jetty were calling last moment advice and good luck wishes. Nobody called to Amyntas, but he turned and looked back to where his father stood among the crowd. Ariston had been a runner too in his day, before a Spartan spear wound had stiffened his left knee and spoiled his

---

[2]Stade (stāde): a foot race the length of the stadium

own hopes of an Olympic Olive Crown. Everyone said that he and Amyntas were very alike, and looking back now at the slight dark man who still held himself like a runner, Amyntas hoped with a warm rush of pride, that they were right. He wished he had said so, before he came aboard; there were so many things he would have liked to have said, but he was even more tongue-tied with his father than he was with the rest of the world, when it came to saying the things that mattered. Now, as the last ropes fell away, he flung up his hand in salute, and tried to put them all into one wordless message. "I'll run the best race that's in me, Father—and if the gods let me win it, I'll remember that I'm winning for us both."

Among the waving crowd, his father flung up an answering hand, as though he had somehow received the message. The water was widening between ship and shore; the Bos'n struck up the rowing time on his flute, and the rowers bent to their oars, sending the *Paralos* through the water towards the harbor mouth. Soon the crowd on shore was only a shingle of dark and coloured and white along the waterfront. But far off beyond the roofs of the warehouses and the covered docks, a flake of light showed where high over Athens the sunlight flashed back from the upraised spear-blade of the great Athene of the Citadel, four miles away.

They were out round the mole now, the one sail broke out from the mast, and they headed for the open gulf.

That night they beached the *Paralos* and made camp on the easternmost point of the long island of Salamis; and not long past noon the next day they went ashore at the Isthmus and took horse for Corinth on the far side, where a second galley was waiting to take them down the coast. At evening on the fifth day they rode down into the shallow valley where Olympian Zeus, the father of gods and men, had his sanctuary, and where the Sacred Games were celebrated in his honour.

What with the long journey and the strangeness of everything, Amyntas took in very little of that first evening. They were met and greeted by the Council of the Games, whose president made them a speech of welcome, after which the Chief Herald

read them the rules. And afterwards they ate the evening meal in the athletes' mess; food that seemed to have no more taste nor substance than the food one eats in a dream. Then the dream blended away into a dark nothingness of sleep that took Amyntas almost before he had lain down on the narrow stretcher bed in the athletes' lodging, which would be his for the next month.

e woke to the first dappled fingers of sunlight shafting in through the doorway of his cell. They wavered and danced a little, as though broken by the shadow of tree branches. Somewhere further down the valley a cuckoo was calling, and the world was real again, and his, and new as though it had been born that morning. He rolled over, and lay for a few moments, his hands behind his head, looking up at the bare rafters; then shot off the bed and through the doorway in one swallow-dive of movement, to sluice his head and shoulders in the icy water trickling from the mouth of a stone bull into a basin just outside. He came up for air, spluttering and shaking the water out of his eyes. For a moment he saw the colonnaded court and the plane tree arching over the basin through the splintered brightness of flying droplets. And then suddenly, in the brightness, there stood a boy of about his own age, who must have come out of the lodging close behind him. A boy with a lean angular body, and a dark, bony face under a shock of hair like the crest of an ill-groomed pony. For a long moment they stood looking at each other. Then Amyntas moved aside to let the other come to the conduit.

As the stranger ducked his head and shoulders under the falling water, Amyntas saw his back. From shoulder to flank it was criss-crossed with scars, past the purple stage but not yet faded to the silvery white that they would be in a few years' time; pinkish scars that looked as though the skin was still drawn uncomfortably tight over them.

He must have made some betraying sound or movement, because the other boy ducked out from under the water, thrusting the wet russet hair back out of his eyes, and demanded curtly,

"Have you never seen a Spartan back before?"

So that was it. Amyntas, like everyone else, had heard dark stories of Spartan boys flogged, sometimes to death, in a ritual test of courage, before the shrine of Artemis Orthia, the Lady of the Beasts.

"No," he said, "I am Athenian," and did not add that he hoped to see plenty of Spartan backs when once he had started his military service. It was odd, the cheap jibe came neatly into his head, and yet he did not even want to speak it. It was as though here at Olympia, the Truce of the Games was not just a rule of conduct, but something in one's heart. Instead, he added, "And my name is Amyntas."

They seemed to stand confronting each other for a long time. The Spartan boy had the look of a dog sniffing at a stranger's fist and taking his own time to make sure whether it was friendly. Then he smiled; a slow, rather grave smile, but unexpectedly warm. "And mine is Leon."

"And you're a runner." Amyntas was taking in his build and the way he stood.

"I am entered for the Double Stade."

"Then we race against each other."

Leon said in the same curt tone, "May we both run a good race."

"And meanwhile—when did you arrive, Leon?"

"Last night, the same as you."

Amyntas, who usually found it nearly as difficult to talk to strangers as he did to his own father, was surprised to hear himself saying, "Then you'll have seen no more of Olympia than I have. Shall we go and get some clothes on and have a look around?"

But by that time more men and boys were coming out into the early sunshine, yawning and stretching the sleep out of their muscles. And Amyntas felt a hand clamp down on his shoulder, and heard the voice of Hippias his trainer, "Oh no you don't, my lad! Five days' break in training is long enough, and I've work for you before you do any sightseeing!"

After that, they were kept hard at it, on the practice track

and in the wrestling school that had the names of past Olympic victors carved on the colonnade walls. For the last month's training for the Games had to be done at Olympia itself; and the last month's training was hard, in the old style that did not allow for rest days in the modern fashion that most of the Athenian trainers favoured. Everything at Olympia had to be done the old way, even to clearing the stadium of its four years' growth of grass and weeds and spreading it with fresh sand. At other Crown Games, the work was done by paid labourers, but here, the contending athletes must do it themselves, to the glory of the gods, as they had done it in the far-off days when the Games were new. Some of them grumbled a good deal and thought it was time that the Priests of Zeus and the Council of the Games brought their ideas up to date; but to Amyntas there seemed to be a sort of rightness about the thing as it was.

His training time was passed among boys from Corinth and Epidauros, Rhodes and Samos and Macedon. At first they were just figures in outline, like people seen too far off to have faces, whom he watched with interest at track work, at javelin or discus throwing or in the wrestling pit, trying to judge their form as he knew they were trying to judge his and each other's. But gradually as the early days went by, they changed into people with faces, with personal habits, and likes and dislikes, suffering from all the strains and stresses of the last weeks before the Games. But even before those first few days were over, he and the Spartan boy had drifted into a companionable pattern of doing things together. They would sluice each other down, squatting in the stone hip-baths in the washing room after practice, and scrape the mess of rubbing oil and sand off each other's backs—it took Amyntas a little while to learn to scrape the bronze blade of the strigil straight over the scars on Leon's back as though they were not there—and when they took their turn at scraping up the four years' growth of grass and sun-dried herbs from the stadium, they generally worked together, sharing one of the big rush carrying-baskets between them. And in the evenings, after the day's training was over, or in the hot noonday break when most people stretched themselves out in the shade of the plane trees for sleep or quiet talk, they seemed, more often than not, to drift into each other's company.

Once or twice they went to have a look at the town of tents and booths that was beginning to spring up all round the Sacred Enclosure and the Gymnasium buildings—for a Games Festival drew many people beside those who came to compete or to watch; merchants and wine sellers and fortune tellers, poets determined to get poems heard, horse dealers from Corinth and Cyrene, goldsmiths and leather-workers, philosophers gathering for the pleasure of arguing with each other, sword and fire swallowers, and acrobats who could dance on their hands to the soft notes of Phrygian pipes. But Leon did not much like the crowded noisy tent-ground; and most often they wandered down to the river that flung its loop about the south side of Olympia. It had shrunk now in the summer heat, to little more than a chain of pools in the middle of its pale dried-out pebbly bed; but there was shade under the oleander trees, and generally a whisper of moving air. And lying on the bank in the shade was free. It had dawned on Amyntas quite early that the reason Leon did not like the fairground was that he had no money. The Spartans did not use money, or at least, having decided that it was a bad thing, they had no coinage but iron bars so big and heavy that nobody could carry them about, or even keep a store at home that was worth enough to be any use. They were very proud of their freedom from wealth, but it made life difficult at a gathering such as this, when they had to mix with people from other states. Leon covered up by being extremely scornful of the gay and foolish things for sale in the merchants' booths, and the acrobats who passed the bowl round for contributions after their performance; but he was just that shade too scornful to be convincing. And anyway, Amyntas had none too much money himself, to get him through the month.

So they went to the river. They were down there one hot noontide something over a week after they had first arrived at Olympia; Amyntas lying on his back, his hands behind his head, squinting up into the dark shadow-shapes of the oleander branches against the sky; Leon sitting beside him with his arms round his updrawn knees, staring out in the dazzle of sunlight over the open riverbed. They had been talking runners' talk, and suddenly Amyntas said, "I was watching the Corinthian making his practice run this morning. I don't *think* we have either of us much to fear from him."

"The Rhodian runs well," said Leon, not bringing back his gaze from the white dance of sunlight beyond the oleanders.

"But he uses himself up too quickly. He's the kind that makes all the front running at first, and has nothing left for the home stretch. Myself, I'd say that red-headed barbarian from Macedon had the better chance."

"He's well enough for speed; and he knows how and when to use it. . . . What do you give for Nikomedes' chances?"

"Nikomedes?—The boy from Megara? It's hard to say. Not

much, from the form he's shown so far; but we've only seen him at practice, and he's the sort that sometimes catches fire when it comes to the real thing. . . ."

There was a long silence between them, and they heard the churring of the grasshoppers, like the heat-shimmer turned to sound. And then Amyntas said, "I think you are the one I have most to fear."

And Leon turned his head slowly and looked down at him, and said, "Have you only just woken to that? I knew the same thing of *you*, three days ago."

And they were both silent again, and suddenly a little shocked. You might think that kind of thing, but it was best not to put it into words.

Leon made a quick sign with his fingers to avert ill luck; and Amyntas scrambled to his feet. "Come on, it's time we were getting back." They were both laughing, but a little breathlessly. Leon dived to his feet also, and shot ahead as they went up through the

riverside scrub. But next instant, between one flying leap and the next, he stumbled slightly, and checked; then turned back, stooping to search for something among the dusty root-tangle of dry grass and camomile. Amyntas, swerving just in time to avoid him, checked also.

"What is it?"

"Something sharp. . . ." Leon pulled out from where it had lain half-buried, the broken end of a sickle blade that looked as though it might have lain there since the last Games. "Seems it's not only the Stadium that needs clearing up." He began to walk on, carrying the jagged fragment in his hand. But Amyntas saw the blood on the dry ground where he had been standing.

"You have cut your foot."

"I know," Leon said, and went on walking.

"Yes, I *know* you know. Let me look at it."

"It's only a scratch."

"All the same—show me."

Leon stood on one leg, steadying himself with a hand on Amyntas' shoulder, and turned up the sole of his foot. "Look then. You can hardly see it."

There was a cut on the hard brown sole, not long, but deep, with the blood welling slowly. Amyntas said in sudden exasperation, "Haven't you *any* sense? Oh we all know about the Spartan boy with the fox under his cloak, and nobody but you Spartans thinks it's a particularly clever or praiseworthy story; but if you get dirt into that cut, you'll like enough have to scratch from the race!"

Leon suddenly grinned. "Nobody but we Spartans understand that story. But about the dirt, you could be right."

"I could. And that bit of iron is dirty enough for a start. Best get the wound cleaned up, in the river before we go back to the Gymnasium. Then your trainer can take over."

So with Leon sitting on a boulder at the edge of the shrunken river, Amyntas set to work with ruthless thoroughness to clean the cut. He pulled it open, the cool water running over his hands, and a thin thread of crimson fronded away downstream. It would help clean the wound to let it bleed a little; but after a few moments the bleeding almost stopped. No harm in making sure; he ducked his head to the place, sucked hard and spat crimson into the water. Then he tore a strip from the skirt of his tunic; he would have commandeered Leon's own—after all it was Leon's foot—but he knew that the Spartan boys were only allowed to own one tunic at a time; if he did that, Leon would be left without a respectable tunic to wear at the Sacrifices. He lashed the thin brown foot tightly. "Now—put your arm over my shoulder and try to keep your weight off the cut as much as you can."

"Cluck, cluck, cluck!" said Leon, but he did as Amyntas said.

As they skirted the great open space of the Hippodrome, where the chariot races would be held on the second day of the Games, they came up with a couple of the Athenian contingent, strolling under the plane trees. Eudorus the wrestler looked round and his face quickened with concern, "Run into trouble?"

"Ran into the remains of a sickle blade someone left in the

long grass," Amyntas said, touching the rusty bit of metal he had taken from Leon and stuck in his own belt. "It's near the tendon, but it's all right, so long as there's no dirt left in it."

"Near the tendon, eh? Then we'd best be taking no chances." Eudorus looked at Leon. "You are Spartan, I think?—Amyntas, go and find the Spartan trainer; I'll take over here." And then to Leon again, "Will you allow me to carry you up to the lodging? It seems the simplest way."

Amyntas caught one parting glimpse of Leon's rigid face as Eudorus lifted him, lightly as a ten-year-old, and set off towards the gymnasium buildings; and laughter caught at his stomach; but mixed with the laughter was sympathy. He knew he would have been just as furious in Leon's place. All this fuss and to-do over a cut that would have been nothing in itself—if the Games had not been only three weeks off.

He set off in search of the trainer.

In the middle of that night, Amyntas woke up with a thought already shaped and complete in his mind. It was an ugly thought, and it sat on his chest and mouthed at him slyly. "Leon is the one you have most to fear. If Leon is out of the race. . . ."

He looked at it in the darkness, feeling a little sick. Then he pushed it away, and rolled over on to his face with his head in his arms, and after a while he managed to go back to sleep again.

Next day, as soon as he could slip away between training sessions, he went out into the growing town of tents and booths, and found a seller of images and votive offerings, and bought a little bronze bull with silvered horns. It cost nearly all the money that he had to spare, so that he would not now be able to buy the hunting knife with silver inlay on the hilt that had caught his fancy a day or two since. With the little figure in his hand, he went to the Sacred Enclosure, where, among altars shaded by plane trees, and statues of gods and Olympic heroes, the great Temple of Zeus faced the older and darker house of Hera, his wife.

Before the Temple of Zeus, the ancient wild olive trees from which the victors' crowns were made cast dapple-shade across the lower steps of the vast portico. He spoke to the attendant priest in the deep threshold shadows beyond.

"I ask leave to enter and make an offering."

"Enter then, and make the offering," the man said.

And he went through into the vastness of the Temple itself, where the sunlight sifting through under the acanthus roof tiles made a honeycomb glow that hung high in the upper spaces and flowed down the gigantic columns, but scarcely touched the pavement under foot, so that he seemed to wade in cool shadows. At the far end, sheathed in gold and ivory, his feet half lost in shadows, his head gloried with the dim radiance of the upper air, stern and serene above the affairs of mortal men, stood the mighty statue of the god himself: Olympian Zeus, in whose honour the Sacred Games had been held for more than three hundred years. Three hundred years, such a little while; looking up at the heart-

585

stilling face above him, Amyntas wondered if the god had even noticed, yet, that they were begun. Everything in the god's house was so huge, even time. . . . For a moment his head swam, and he had no means of judging the size of anything, even himself, here where all the known landmarks of the world of men were left behind. Only one thing, when he looked at it, remained constant in size; the tiny bronze bull with the silvered horns that he held in his hand.

He went forward to the first of the Offering Tables before the feet of the gigantic statue, and set it down. Now, the tables were empty and waiting, but by the end of the festival they would be piled with offerings; small humble ones like his own, and silver cups and tripods of gilded bronze to be taken away and housed in the Temple treasury. On the eve of the Games they would begin to fill up, with votive offerings made for the most part by the athletes themselves, for their own victory, or the victory of a friend taking part in a different event. Amyntas was not making the offering for his own victory, nor for Leon's. He was not quite sure why he was making it, but it was for something much more complicated than victory in the Double Stade. With one finger still resting on the back of the little bronze bull, he sent up the best prayer he could sort out from the tangle of thoughts and feelings within himself. "Father of all things, Lord of these Sacred Games, let me keep a clean heart in this, let me run the best race that is in me, and think of nothing more."

Outside again, beyond the dapple-shade of the olive trees, the white sunlight fell dazzling across his eyes, and the world of men, in which things had returned to their normal size, received him back; and he knew that Hippias was going to be loudly angry with him for having missed a training session. But unaccountably, everything, including Hippias' anger, seemed surprisingly small.

Leon had to break training for three days, at least so far as track-work was concerned; and it was several more before he could get back into full training; so for a while it was doubtful whether he would be able to take his place in the race. But with still more than a week to go, both his trainer and the Doctor-Priest of

Asklepius[3] declared him fit, and his name remained on the list of entrants for the Double Stade.

And then it was the first day of the Festival; the day of solemn dedication, when each competitor must go before the Council to be looked over and identified, and take the Oath of the Games before the great bronze statue of Zeus of the Thunderbolts.

The day passed. And next morning before it was light, Amyntas woke to hear the unmistakable, unforgettable voice of the crowds gathering in the Stadium. A shapeless surf of sound, pricked by the sharper cries of the jugglers and acrobats, and the sellers of water and honeycakes, myrtle, and victors' ribbons calling their wares.

This was the day of the Sacred Procession; the Priests and Officials, the beast garlanded for sacrifice, the athletes marching into the waiting Stadium, while the Herald proclaimed the name and state of each one as he passed the rostrum. Amyntas, marching in with the Athenians, heard his own name called, and Leon's, among names from Samos and Cyrene, Crete and Corinth, and Argos and Megara. And he smelled the incense on the morning air, and felt for the first time, under his swelling pride in being Athenian, the thread of his own Greekness interwoven with the Greekness of all those others. This must have been, a little, the thing their Great Grandfathers had felt when they stood together, shield to shield, to hurl back the whole strength of invading Persia, so that they might remain free. That had been in a Games year, too. . . .

The rest of that day was given over to the chariot and horse races; and that night Amyntas went to his sleeping cell with the thunder of hooves and wheels still sounding somewhere behind his ears. He seemed to hear it in his dreams all night, but when he woke in the morning, it had turned into the sound that he had woken to yesterday, the surf-sound of the gathering crowd. But this morning it had a new note for him, for this was the Day, and the crowd that was gathering out there round the Stadium was his crowd, and his belly tightened and the skin prickled at the back of his neck as he heard it.

[3]Asklepius (ăs klē′ pē əs): the Greek god of medicine

He lay for a few moments, listening, then got up and went out to the conduit. Leon came out after him as he had done that first morning of all, and they sluiced down as best they could. The water barely dribbled from the mouth of the stone bull now, for with the vast gathering of people, and the usual end-of-summer drought, the water shortage was getting desperate, as it always did by the time the Festival days arrived.

"How is the foot?" Amyntas asked.

"I can't remember where the cut was, unless I look for it."

They stood looking at each other, the friendship that they had never put into words trying to find some way to reach across from one to the other.

"We cannot even wish each other luck," Amyntas said at last, helplessly.

And Leon said, almost exactly as he had said it at their first meeting, "May both of us run a good race."

They reached out and touched hands quickly and went their separate ways.

The next time they saw each other, they were waiting oiled for the track, with the rest of the Double Stade boys just outside the arched way in the Stadium. The Dolichus, the long-distance race, and the Stade had been run, each with its boys' race immediately after. Now the trumpet was sounding to start the Double Stade. Amyntas' eyes went to meet Leon's, and found the Spartan boy's slightly frowning gaze waiting for him. He heard the sudden roar of the crowd, and his belly lifted and tightened. A little stir ran through the waiting boys; the next time the starting trumpet sounded, the next time the crowd gave that roar, it would be for them. Hippias was murmuring last-minute advice into Amyntas' ear, but he did not hear a word of it. . . . He was going out there before all those thousands upon thousands of staring eyes and yelling mouths, and he was going to fail. Not just fail to win the race, but *fail*. His belly was churning now, his heart banging away right up in his throat so that it almost choked him. His mouth was dry and the palms of his hands were wet; and the beginnings of panic were whimpering up in him. He looked again at Leon, and saw him run the tip of his tongue over his lips as though they were suddenly dry. It was the first time he had ever known the Spartan boy to betray anything of what was going on inside him; and the sight gave him a sense of companionship that somehow steadied him. He began to take deep quiet breaths, as he had been taught, and the rising panic quietened and sank away.

The voice of the crowd was rising, rising to a great roar; the Men's Double Stade was over. He heard the Herald crying the name of the winner, and another roar from the crowd; and then the runners were coming out through the arched entrance; and the boys pressed back to let them past, filthy with sweat and sand and oil. Amyntas looked at the face of the man with the victor's ribbons knotted round his head and arms, and saw that it was grey and spent and oddly peaceful.

"Now it's us!" someone said; and the boys were sprinting down the covered way, out into the open sun-drenched space of the Stadium.

The turf banks on either side of the broad track, and the lower slopes of the Kronon Hill that looked down upon it were packed with a vast multitude of onlookers. Half-way down on the right-hand side, raised above the tawny grass on which everybody else sat, were the benches for the Council, looking across to the white marble seat opposite, where the Priestess of Demeter, the only woman allowed at the Games, sat as still as though she herself were carved from marble, among all the jostling, swaying, noisy throng. Men were raking over the silver sand on the track. The trumpeter stood ready.

They had taken their places now behind the long white limestone curbs of the starting line. The Umpire was calling: "Runners! Feet to the lines!"

Amyntas felt the scorching heat of the limestone as he braced the ball of his right foot into the shaped groove. All the panic of a while back had left him, he felt light, and clear headed, and master of himself. He had drawn the sixth place, with Leon on his left and the boy from Megara on his right. Before him the track stretched white in the sunlight, an infinity of emptiness and distance.

The starting trumpet yelped; and the line of runners sprang forward like a wave of hunting dogs slipped from the leash.

Amyntas was running smoothly and without hurry. Let the green front-runners push on ahead. In this heat they would have burned themselves out before they reached the turning post. He and Leon were running neck and neck with the red-headed Macedonian. The Rhodian had gone ahead now after the front-runners; the rest were still bunched. Then the Corinthian made a sprint and passed the boy from Rhodes, but fell back almost at once. The white track was reeling back underfoot, the turning post racing towards them. The bunch had thinned out, the front-runners beginning to drop back already; and as they came up towards the turning post, first the boy from Macedon, and then Nikomedes catching fire at last, slid into the lead, with Amyntas and Leon close behind them. Rounding the post, Amyntas skidded on the loose sand and Leon went ahead; and it was then, seeing the lean scarred back ahead of him, that Amyntas lengthened his stride, knowing that the time had come to run. They were a quarter of the way down the home lap when they passed Nikomedes; the Megaran boy had taken fire too late. They were beginning to overhaul the redhead; and Amyntas knew in his bursting heart that unless something unexpected happened, the race must be between himself and Leon. Spartan and Macedonian were going neck and neck now; the position held for a few paces, and then the redhead gradually fell behind. Amyntas was going all out, there was pain in his breast and belly and in the backs of his legs, and he did not know where his next breath was coming from; but still the thin scarred back was just ahead. The crowd were beginning to give tongue, seeing the two come through to the front; a solid roar of sound that would go on rising now until they passed the finishing post. And then suddenly Amyntas knew that something was wrong; Leon was labouring a little, beginning to lose the first keen edge of his speed. Snatching a glance downward, he saw a fleck of crimson in the sand. The cut had re-opened.

His body went on running, but for a sort of splinter of time his head seemed quite apart from the rest of him, and filled with

an unmanageable swirl of thoughts and feelings. Leon might have
passed the top of his speed anyway, it might be nothing to do with
his foot—But the cut *had* re-opened. . . . To lose the race because
of a cut foot. . . . It would be so easy not to make that final desperate effort that his whole body was crying out against. Then
Leon would keep his lead. . . . And at the same time another part
of himself was remembering his father standing on the quayside at
Piraeus as the *Paralos* drew away—crying out that he was not run-

592

ning only for himself but for Athens, his City and his people. . . .
A crown of wild olive would be the greatest thing that anyone
could give to his friend. . . . It would be to insult Leon to let him
win . . . you could not do that to your friend. . . . And then, like
a clean cold sword of light cutting through the swirling tangle of
his thoughts, came the knowledge that greater than any of these
things were the gods. These were the Sacred Games, not some
mere struggle between boys in the gymnasium. For one fleeting

instant of time he remembered himself standing in the Temple before the great statue of Zeus, holding the tiny bronze bull with the silvered horns. "Let me run the best race that is in me, and think of nothing more."

He drove himself forward in one last agonizing burst of speed, he was breathing against knives, and the roar of the blood in his ears drowned the roar of the crowd. He was level with Leon—and then there was nothing ahead of him but the winning post.

The onlookers had crowded right down towards it; even above the howl of the blood in his head he heard them now, roar on solid roar of sound, shouting him in to victory. And then Hippias had caught him as he plunged past the post; and he was bending over the trainer's arm, bending over the pain in his belly, snatching at his breath and trying not to be sick. People were throwing sprigs of myrtle, he felt them flicking and falling on his head and shoulders. The sickness eased a little and his head was clearing; he began to hear friendly voices congratulating him; and Eudorus came shouldering through the crowd with a coloured ribbon to tie round his head. But when he looked round for Leon, the Spartan boy had been swept away by his trainer. And a queer desolation rose in Amyntas and robbed his moment of its glory.

A fterwards in the changing room, some of the other boys came up to congratulate him. Leon did not come; but when they had cleaned off the sand and oil and sweat, and sluiced down with the little water that was allowed them, Amyntas hung about, sitting on the well kerb outside while the trainer finished seeing to his friend's foot. And when Leon came out at last, he came straight across to the well, as though they had arranged to meet there. His face was as unreadable as usual.

"You will have cooled off enough by now, do you want to drink?" Amyntas said, mainly because somebody had to say something; and dipped the bronze cup that also stood on the well kerb in the pail that he had drawn.

Leon took the cup from him and drank, and sat down on the

well kerb beside him. As Amyntas dipped the cup again and bent his head to drink in his turn, the ends of the victor's ribbon fell forward against his cheek, and he pulled it off impatiently, and dropped it beside the well.

"Why did you do that?" Leon said.

"I shall never be sure whether I won that race."

"The judges are not often mistaken, and I never heard yet of folk tying victors' ribbons on the wrong man."

Amyntas flicked a thumb at Leon's bandaged foot. "You know well enough what I mean. I'll never be sure whether I'd have come first past the post, if that hadn't opened up again."

Leon looked at him a moment in silence, then flung up his head and laughed. "Do you really think that could make any difference? It would take more than a cut foot to slow me up, Athenian!—You ran the better race, that's all."

It was said on such a harsh, bragging note that in the first moment Amyntas felt as though he had been struck in the face. Then he wondered if it was the overwhelming Spartan pride giving tongue, or simply Leon, hurt and angry and speaking the truth. Either way, he was too tired to be angry back again. And whichever it was, it seemed that Leon had shaken it off already. The noon break was over, and the trumpets were sounding for the Pentathlon.

"Up!" Leon said, when Amyntas did not move at once. "Are you going to let it be said that your own event is the only one that interests you?"

They went, quickly and together, while the trainer's eye was off them, for Leon was under order to keep off his foot. And the people cheered them both when they appeared in the Stadium. They seldom cared much for a good loser, but Leon had come in a close second, and they had seen the blood in the sand.

The next day the heavyweight events were held; and then it was the last day of all, the Crowning Day. Ever after, Amyntas remembered that day as a quietness after great stress and turmoil. It was not, in truth, much less noisy than the days that had gone before. The roaring of the Stadium crowds was gone; but in the town of tents the crowds milled to and fro. The jugglers with knives and the eaters of fire shouted for an audience and the merchants cried their wares; and within the Sacred Enclosure where the winners received their crowns and made their sacrifices before the Temples of Zeus and Hera, there were the flutes and the songs in praise of the victors, and the deep-voiced invocations to the gods.

But in Amyntas himself, there was the quiet. He remembered the Herald crying his name, and the light springy coolness of the wild olive crown as it was pressed down on his head; and later, the spitting light of pine torches under the plane trees, where the officials and athletes were feasting. And he remembered most, looking up out of the torchlight, and seeing, high and remote above it all, the winged tripods on the roof of the great Temple, outlined against the light of a moon two days past the full.

The boys left before the feasting was over; and in his sleeping cell Amyntas heard the poets singing in praise of some chariot team, and the applause, while he gathered his few belongings together, ready for tomorrow's early start, and stowed his olive crown among them. Already the leaves were beginning to wilt after the heat of the day. The room that had seemed so strange the first night was familiar now; part of himself; and after tonight it would not know him anymore.

Next morning in all the hustle of departure, he and Leon contrived to meet and slip off for a little on their own.

The whole valley of Olympia was a chaos of tents and booths being taken down, merchants as well as athletes and onlookers making ready for the road. But the Sacred Enclosure itself was quiet, and the gates stood open. They went through, into the shade of the olive trees before the Temple of Zeus. A priest making the morning offering at a side altar looked at them; but they seemed to be doing no harm, and to want nothing, so he let them alone. There was a smell of frankincense in the air, and the early morning smell of last night's heavy dew on parched ground. They stood among the twisted trunks and low-hanging branches, and looked at each other and did not know what to say. Already they were remembering that there was war between Athens and Sparta, that the Truce of the Games would last them back to their own states, but no further; and the longer the silence lasted, the more they remembered.

From beyond the quiet of the Enclosure came all the sounds of the great concourse breaking up; voices calling, the stamping of impatient horses. "By this time tomorrow everyone will be gone," Amyntas said at last. "It will be just as it was before we came, for another four years."

"The Corinthians are off already."

"Catching the cool of the morning for those fine chariot horses," Amyntas said, and thought, There's so little time, why do we have to waste it like this?

"One of the charioteers had that hunting knife with the silver inlay. The one you took a fancy to. Why didn't you buy it after all?"

"I spent the money on something else." For a moment Amyntas was afraid that Leon would ask what. But the other boy only nodded and let it go.

He wished suddenly that he could give Leon something, but there was nothing among his few belongings that would make sense in the Spartan's world. It was a world so far off from his own. Too far to reach out, too far to call. Already they seemed to be drifting away from each other, drifting back to a month ago, before they had even met. He put out a hand quickly, as though to hold the other boy back for one more moment, and Leon's hand came to meet it.

"It has been good. All this month it has been good," Leon said.

"It has been good," Amyntas agreed. He wanted to say, "Until the next Games, then." But manhood and military service were only a few months away for both of them; if they did meet at another Games, there would be the faces of dead comrades, Spartan and Athenian, between them; and like enough, for one of them or both, there might be no other Games. Far more likely, if they ever saw each other again, it would be over the tops of their shields.

He had noticed before how, despite their different worlds, he

and Leon sometimes thought the same thing at the same time, and answered each other as though the thought had been spoken. Leon said in his abrupt, dead-level voice, "The gods be with you Amyntas, and grant that we never meet again."

They put their arms round each other's necks and strained fiercely close for a moment, hard cheekbone against hard cheekbone.

"The gods be with you, Leon."

And then Eudorus was calling, "Amyntas! Amyntas! We're all waiting!"

And Amyntas turned and ran—out through the gateway of the Sacred Enclosure, towards where the Athenian party were ready to start, and Eudorus was already coming back to look for him.

As they rode up from the Valley of Olympia and took the tracks towards the coast, Amyntas did not look back. The horses' legs brushed the dry dust-grey scrub beside the track, and loosed the hot aromatic scents of wild lavender and camomile and lentisk upon the air. A yellow butterfly hovered past, and watching it out of sight, it came to him suddenly, that he and Leon had exchanged gifts of a sort, after all. It was hard to give them a name, but they were real enough. And the outward and visible sign of his gift to Leon was in the little bronze bull with the silvered horns that he had left on the Offering Table before the feet of Olympian Zeus. And Leon's gift to him. . . . That had been made with the Spartan's boast that it would take more than a cut foot to slow him up. He had thought at the time that it was either the harsh Spartan pride, or the truth spoken in anger. But he understood now, quite suddenly, that it had been Leon giving up his own private and inward claim to the olive crown, so that he, Amyntas, might believe that he had rightfully won it. Amyntas knew that he would never be sure of that, never in all his life. But it made no difference to the gift.

The track had begun to run downhill, and the pale dust-cloud was rising behind them. He knew that if he looked back now, there would be nothing to see.

GLOSSARY

Full pronunciation key* The pronunciation of each word is shown just after the word, in this way:
abbreviate (ə brē′vē āt).

The letters and signs used are pronounced as in the words below.

The mark ′ is placed after a syllable with a primary or heavy accent as in the example above.

The mark ′ after a syllable shows a secondary or lighter accent, as in **abbreviation** (ə brē′vē ā′shən).

SYMBOL	KEY WORDS	SYMBOL	KEY WORDS
a	ask, fat	b	bed, dub
ā	ape, date	d	did, had
ä	car, father	f	fall, off
		g	get, dog
e	elf, ten	h	he, ahead
er	berry, care	j	joy, jump
ē	even, meet	k	kill, bake
		l	let, ball
i	is, hit	m	met, trim
ir	mirror, here	n	not, ton
ī	ice, fire	p	put, tap
		r	red, dear
o	lot, pond	s	sell, pass
ō	open, go	t	top, hat
ô	law, horn	v	vat, have
oi	oil, point	w	will, always
oo	look, pull	y	yet, yard
o͞o	ooze, tool	z	zebra, haze
yoo	unite, cure		
yo͞o	cute, few	ch	chin, arch
ou	out, crowd	ŋ	ring, singer
		sh	she, dash
u	up, cut	th	thin, truth
ʉr	fur, fern	*th*	then, father
		zh	s in pleasure
ə	a in ago		
	e in agent	′	as in (ā′b′l)
	e in father		
	i in unity		
	o in collect		
	u in focus		

*Pronunciation key and respellings adapted from *Webster's New World Dictionary, Basic School Edition,*
Copyright © 1983 by Simon & Schuster, Inc. Reprinted by permission.

A

ab·hor·rence (əb hôr′əns) *noun.* a feeling of hatred: He felt an *abhorrence* of the angry crowd.

ab·stract (ab strakt′ *or* ab′strakt) *adjective.* **1.** a quality considered apart from an actual person or thing that possesses it. **2.** hard to understand. **3.** ideal, as opposed to practical. **4.** in art, tending away from the realistic or representational.

ac·cen·tu·ate (ak sen′choo wāt) *verb.* **1.** to emphasize or heighten the effect of: The room was very pretty, with red pillows *accentuating* the red in the wallpaper. **2.** to pronounce or mark by accenting or stressing. **accentuating.**

ac·quaint (ə kwānt′) *verb.* **1.** to inform. **2.** to cause to know; to make familiar with. **acquainted.**

ac·rid (ak′rid) *adjective.* **1.** sharp or bitter to taste or smell: The *acrid* smoke made them gasp for air. **2.** sharp, sarcastic in speech.

ac·ro·stat·ic (ak′rō stat′ik) *adjective.* coined word describing large hot-air balloons tied to the ground.

aer·i·al (er′ē əl) *adjective.* **1.** of or relating to the air. **2.** relating to aircraft or flying.

aer·o·dy·nam·ics (er′ō dī nam′iks) *noun.* the branch of mechanics that studies the relationship of atmospheric conditions, gravity, and flight.

aer·o·naut (er′ə nôt′) *noun.* one who navigates in the air, especially in a balloon.

aes·thet·ic (es thet′ik) *adjective.* relating to beauty and what is beautiful; artistic: The *aesthetic* quality of the scene inspired the painter.

a·gen·da (ə jen′də) *noun.* a list of things to be done; especially business to be conducted at a meeting.

a·gent (ā′jənt) *noun.* **1.** a person or thing that brings about a result. **2.** person or firm empowered to act for others: Some writers have *agents* to handle their business. **agents.**

ag·gres·sive (ə gres′iv) *adjective.* **1.** showing readiness to start fights or trouble: He was too *aggressive* to be an effective leader. **2.** bold, forceful, sometimes pushy.

a·gil·i·ty (ə jil′ə tē) *noun.* the ability to move with quickness and ease.

ag·ri·cul·tur·ist (ag′ri kul′chər ist) *noun.* one who grows crops or livestock. **agriculturists.**

air·borne (er′bôrn) *adjective.* **1.** supported by or carried through the air. **2.** in flight; flying.

al·a·bas·ter (al′ə bas′tər) *noun.* a smooth, usually white stone used for statues, vases, and ornaments. —*adjective.* any substance that is like alabaster in color or texture.

al·le·giance (ə lē′jəns) *noun.* **1.** loyalty to a country or ruler. **2.** loyalty or devotion given to a friend or idea.

al·pha (al′fə) *noun.* **1.** the first letter of the Greek alphabet. **2.** the first or the beginning of anything. —*adjective.* first in order of importance.

al·tim·e·ter (al tim′ə tər) *noun.* any instrument used for determining altitude, especially in an aircraft.

al·ti·tude (al′tə tood *or* al′tə tyood) *noun.* **1.** height, especially above the earth's surface, or above sea level. **2.** in geometry, the vertical distance from the base of a figure to its highest point.

al·tru·is·tic (al′troo is′tik) *adjective.* unselfishly interested in the good of others: She was well loved for her *altruistic* acts.

am·a·teur (am′ə chər *or* am′ə toor) *noun.* **1.** a person who takes part in something for pleasure only, and not as a profession. **2.** someone who does something unskillfully. —*adjective.* of, relating to, or done by amateurs. **amateurs.**

am·big·u·ous (am big′yoo wəs) *adjective.* **1.** something that can be understood in more than one way; having two or more possible meanings. **2.** uncertain or indistinct.

am·i·ca·ble (am′i kə b'l) *adjective.* friendly; peaceable: They had an *amicable* discussion about dividing the work.

abstract art

altimeter

am·pli·fi·er (am'plə fī'ər) *noun.* **1.** a person or thing that makes something larger, stronger, louder, etc. **2.** a device that magnifies sound or electric waves, as in a radio or stereo system.

a·nach·ro·nism (ə nak'rə niz'm) *noun.* **1.** something not belonging to a particular time. **2.** something out of its proper place in time.

an·te·cham·ber (an'ti chām'bər) *noun.* a small room serving as an entrance way to a larger, more important room.

ap·pre·hen·sion (ap'rə hen'shən) *noun.* **1.** the arrest or capture of someone such as a criminal. **2.** the power of understanding. **3.** a feeling of fear or anxiety about the future: The thought of going to the doctor filled him with *apprehension.*

ar·chae·ol·o·gy or **ar·che·ol·o·gy** (är'kē ol'ə jē) *noun.* the science or study of history by excavating the remains of ancient civilizations. **archaeologist** or **archeologist.**

ar·ti·fact (är'tə fakt) *noun.* any object produced by human art or skill. **artifacts.**

as·cen·sion (ə sen'shən) *noun.* the process of going up or rising. **ascensions.**

as·phyx·i·ate (as fik'sē āt) *verb.* to cause a person or animal to lose consciousness or die by cutting off the normal intake of oxygen. **asphyxiated.**

as·tro·naut (as'trə nôt) *noun.* a person who is trained for flight into space. **astronauts.**

at·trib·ute (ə trib'yoot) *verb.* to consider that something comes from, or belongs to, or is caused by a particular person or thing: The scientist was *attributing* human intelligence to the animals she worked with. **attributing.**

au·di·tion (ô dish'ən) *noun.* a trial performance by which an actor, musician, singer, or dancer may be chosen for a job. —*verb.* to test or try out in an audition.

aus·ter·i·ty (ô ster'ə tē) *noun.* **1.** a harsh or stern action or manner. **2.** plainness; lack of luxury.

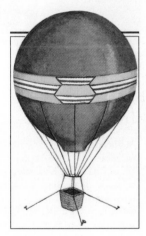

balloon

B

bal·loon (bə loon') *noun.* **1.** a large bag that rises into the air when it is filled with hot air or with a gas that is lighter than air. **2.** a small rubber bag that can be filled with air or gas, used as a toy. **ballooning, balloonists.** —*verb.* **1.** to ascend or travel in a balloon. **2.** to swell; expand.

ba·rom·e·ter (bə rom'ə tər) *noun.* **1.** an instrument that measures air pressure and is useful for predicting changes in the weather. **2.** anything that indicates or predicts changes.

ba·zaar (bə zär') *noun.* **1.** an outdoor market or a street of shops. **2.** a sale of miscellaneous items in which the profits benefit a club, church, or charity. **bazaars.**

be·drag·gled (bi drag''ld) *adjective.* wet, dirty, messy, as something that has been dragged through the mud: She came in from the storm, *bedraggled* and miserable.

bell (bel) *noun.* **1.** a hollow object, usually cuplike, made of metal or other hard material that makes a ringing sound when it is struck. **2.** the sound made by a bell. **3.** on shipboard, the stroke or strokes of a bell marking every half-hour. —*verb.* to cry out, as an animal in fear or flight. **bells.**

bi·as (bī'əs) *noun.* **1.** a line running diagonally across the weave of a fabric. **2.** a tendency to feel favorably or unfavorably about someone or something; partiality; prejudice. —*adjective.* on or related to the bias of a fabric: The pattern called for a *bias* fold.

black·out (blak'out) *noun.* **1.** the act of putting out lights and covering windows at night, especially as protection against enemy air raids. **2.** loss of consciousness or vision. **3.** loss of electric power for a certain time.

blight (blīt) *noun.* **1.** a plant disease that causes plants to wither and die. **2.** anything that injures, withers, or destroys.

bliss (blis) *noun.* supreme happiness or delight. —**blissful** *adjective.* —**blissfully** *adverb.*

boom (bōōm) *noun.* **1.** a long pole extending from the mast of a sailboat, used to keep the sail stretched out and to move the sail to catch the wind. **2.** a beam sticking out from the mast of a derrick, for lifting and guiding a load. **3.** a rapid and large increase in use, growth, or popularity. **4.** a deep, hollow sound.

bow (bou) *noun.* the front part of a ship or boat.

brit·tle (brit″l) *adjective.* **1.** hard, but easy to snap or break; inflexible. **2.** having a sharp, hard quality.

broach (brōch) *verb.* **1.** to introduce a subject for conversation. **2.** to make a hole in.

bro·gan (brō′g'n) *noun.* a coarse, heavy work shoe.

brusque (brusk) *adjective.* rude or abrupt in speaking; reticent or cool in manner: He liked his teacher, in spite of her *brusque* personality.

bul·ly (bŏŏl′ē) *noun.* an aggressive person who teases or hurts weaker people. —*verb.* **1.** to act like a bully toward; to intimidate. **2.** to force someone to do something by using threats. **bullied.**

C

cache (kash) *noun.* **1.** a place used for hiding, storing, or preserving treasure or supplies. **2.** something hidden or stored in a cache.

ca·ma·ra·de·rie (käm′ə räd′ər ē) *noun.* warm feeling of friendship between two people or among members of a group: A feeling of *camaraderie* developed between the two girls as they worked together.

cam·e·o (kam′ē ō) *noun.* a carved gem or shell with differently colored layers. The top layer may have a portrait or other figure carved into it.

ca·pit·u·la·tion (kə pich′ə lā′shən) *noun.* a surrender or giving up on certain conditions; yielding: The commander's *capitulation* before the battle was lost angered the surviving soldiers.

ca·pri·cious (kə prish′əs) *adjective.* fickle; likely to change without warning.

cap·u·chin (kap′yŏŏ chin) *noun.* **1.** a woman's hooded cloak. **2.** a genus of long-tailed South American monkey.

cat·a·log or **cat·a·logue** (kat″l ôg) *noun.* **1.** a list of names, titles, or items listed by some system, especially alphabetical. **2.** a book or file containing systematic listings. —*verb.* to enter an item into such a list. **cataloged** or **catalogued, cataloging** or **cataloguing.**

cav·ern·ous (kav′ər nəs) *adjective.* **1.** full of caves or caverns. **2.** something that is like a cave, in that it is large and hollow.

ce·leb·ri·ty (sə leb′rə tē) *noun.* **1.** a famous or celebrated person. **2.** fame.

cen·ter·board (sen′tər bôrd′) *noun.* in small sailboats, a board that can be lowered into the water from the center of the boat, to keep the boat from drifting sideways.

cha·ot·ic (kā ot′ik) *adjective.* disordered and confused.

char·ac·ter (kar′ik tər) *noun.* **1.** the combination of traits that make one personality different from another; personality. **2.** goodness; moral strength; integrity. **3.** a distinguishing attribute. **4.** a person in a story or play. **5.** a symbol used in writing or printing; mark; letter.

check·ered (chek′ərd) *adjective.* **1.** divided into squares. **2.** having light and dark patches. **3.** full of ups and downs, some unpleasant or unsavory.

Chi·ca·no (chi kä′nō) *noun.* U.S. citizen or inhabitant of Mexican descent.

chore (chôr) *noun.* **1.** any routine task that must be performed regularly, especially in a house or on a farm. **2.** any unpleasant task. **chores.**

cir·cum·spect (sur′kəm spekt) *adjective.* cautious; wary; very careful before acting or making a decision.

cir·cum·vent (sur′kəm vent′) *verb.* **1.** to get the better of; avoid; outwit. **2.** to go around. **circumvented.**

a fat	oi oil	ch chin
ā ape	ŏŏ look	sh she
ä car, father	ōō tool	th thin
e ten	ou out	*th* then
er care	u up	zh leisure
ē even	ur fur	ŋ ring
i hit		
ir here	ə = a *in* ago	
ī bite, fire	e *in* agent	
o lot	i *in* unity	
ō go	o *in* collect	
ô law, horn	u *in* focus	

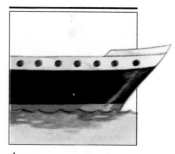

bow

cameo

contraption

Cool in its slang use has been with us since about 1950. It originated with jazz musicians who developed a style of music that they labeled *cool jazz*. Cool jazz was considered unemotional and intellectual in contrast with the bop music that came before it.

Decibel is made up of two parts; *deci* means "one tenth" and *bel* is a unit of measure of the loudness of electrical signals. *Bel* came from the Old English *bellan* meaning "to roar."

clime (klīm) *noun.* a region, country, or climate. **climes.**

coax (kōks) *verb.* to persuade or influence by flattery, tact, or gentle persistence. **coaxed.**

co·coon (kə kōon′) *noun.* the case that certain worms and caterpillars spin around themselves for protection as they change into moths or butterflies.

col·league (kol′ēg) *noun.* a fellow worker; a person who is in the same profession or endeavor. **colleagues.**

com·pas·sion·ate (kəm pash′ən it) *adjective.* feeling pity or a desire to help another; sympathetic.

com·pli·ment (kom′plə mənt) *noun.* an expression of admiration or praise. —*verb.* to say something in praise or admiration.

com·pu·ta·tion (kom′pyōo tā′shən) *noun.* **1.** the act or method of figuring something by arithmetic. **2.** the results obtained by computing. **computations.**

com·rade (kom′rad) *noun.* a companion or friend.

con·de·scend (kon də send′) *verb.* **1.** to lower oneself. **2.** to grant a favor while making it clear that one is better than others; to patronize. —**condescension** *noun.* actions in a snobbish or superior manner: Although he was polite to us, his *condescension* was obvious and insulting.

con·fla·gra·tion (kon′flə grā′shən) *noun.* a huge and disastrous fire.

con·fron·ta·tion (kon′frən tā′shən) *noun.* **1.** a face-to-face meeting. **2.** a crisis or conflict between two opposing groups.

con·spic·u·ous (kən spik′yōo wəs) *adjective.* **1.** easily seen. **2.** attracting attention.

con·spir·a·tor (kən spir′ə tər) *noun.* a person who is involved in a conspiracy, or secret plan; plotter. —**conspiratorially** *adverb.* in a secretive manner: He glanced at me *conspiratorially* as we tiptoed out of the house.

con·tem·plate (kon′təm plāt) *verb.* **1.** to look at carefully. **2.** to consider thoughtfully. **3.** to intend or plan.

con·trap·tion (kən trap′shən) *noun.* a gadget or strange-looking mechanical device. **contraptions.**

con·trive (kən trīv′) *verb.* **1.** to plot or plan. **2.** to build or make in a clever or skillful manner. **3.** to manage to bring about, as with a clever plan. **contrived.**

con·viv·i·al (kən viv′ē əl) *adjective.* fond of people and socializing; fun-loving: People liked him because he was so *convivial.*

con·vul·sion (kən vul′shən) *noun.* **1.** an attack of sudden, involuntary tightening or twitching of the muscles. **2.** any strong or violent disturbance, such as an earthquake. **convulsions.**

cool (kōol) *adjective.* **1.** somewhat cold. **2.** not too hot; comfortable. **3.** calm and deliberate in action. **4.** lacking enthusiasm or interest. **5.** *(slang)* very good.

cor·rupt (kə rupt′) *verb.* **1.** to cause to change from good to bad: The dream of easy money had *corrupted* the young man. **2.** to influence something in an improper way. **corrupted.**

coun·sel (koun′s'l) *noun.* **1.** an exchange of opinions. **2.** advice or opinion given. —*verb.* **1.** to advise. **2.** to recommend. **counsels.**

cringe (krinj) *verb.* **1.** to shrink back in fear. **2.** to behave in a very humble way. **cringed.**

cull (kul) *verb.* **1.** to pick over; select; choose. **2.** to look over in order to find what is wanted. **culling.**

cyn·i·cal (sin′i k'l) *adjective.* **1.** doubting that anyone can be sincere, good, or trustworthy. **2.** sarcastic; bitter; gloomy.

D

death·watch (deth′woch *or* deth′wôch) *noun.* a vigil or a watching at the side of one who is dying or has recently died.

de·bris *or* **dé·bris** (də brē′ *or* dā′brē) *noun.* scattered fragments of something that has been destroyed.

de·ceased (di sēst′) *adjective.* dead. —**the deceased** *noun.* the dead person or persons.

dec·i·bel (des′ə bel) *noun.* a unit of power used to express the intensity, or loudness, of sound.

de·ci·pher (di sī′fər) *verb*. **1.** to translate from code or secret writing; decode. **2.** to interpret or determine the meaning of: We tried to *decipher* the complicated map.

de·file (di fīl′) *verb*. **1.** to make dirty or foul. **2.** to corrupt. **3.** to violate the purity of. —**defiled** *adjective*. made impure; corrupted.

de·par·ture (di pär′chər) *noun*. **1.** the act of going away. **2.** a turning away from the usual way, or a changing to something new.

des·o·late (des′ə lit) *adjective*. **1.** deserted; abandoned; lonely. **2.** ruined or destroyed. **3.** gloomy; dreary; miserable.

de·te·ri·o·rate (di tir′ē ə rāt′) *verb*. to make or become worse; become less valuable.

di·a·met·ri·cal (dī′ə met′ri k'l) *adjective*. **1.** having to do with a diameter. **2.** directly opposite. —**diametrically** *adverb*.

di·he·dral (dī hē′drəl) *adjective*. **1.** two-sided. **2.** in aeronautics, the upward or downward slope of an airplane's supporting surfaces.

din·ette (dī net′) *noun*. **1.** an alcove or small room used for dining. **2.** a set of table and chairs for such a room.

dir·i·gi·ble (dir′i jə b'l) *noun*. a lighter-than-air aircraft that can be steered.

dis·creet (dis krēt′) *adjective*. careful not to say or do the wrong thing; prudent.

dis·may (dis mā′) *verb*. to make unable to act because of fear or confusion. —*noun*. a sudden feeling of fear or loss of courage; discouragement.

drench (drench) *verb*. to make thoroughly wet; soak. **drenched.**

dwin·dle (dwin′d'l) *verb*. to make or become less or smaller. **dwindled.**

dy·nas·ty (dī′nəs tē) *noun*. **1.** a series of rulers from the same family or group. **2.** period of time during which a family or group reigns.

E

eaves (ēvz) *plural noun*. the lower part of a sloped roof that hangs over the edge of a building.

ec·stat·ic (ek stat′ik) *adjective*. showing very great happiness; extreme delight.

ef·face (i fās′) *verb*. **1.** to rub out; erase. **2.** to obliterate or destroy. **3.** to make (oneself) less important.

e·la·tion (i lā′shən) *noun*. triumphant joy; pride; high spirits.

e·lim·in·ate (i lim′ə nāt) *verb*. **1.** to get rid of; to do away with. **2.** to ignore. **3.** to remove from further competition by defeating. —**elimination** *noun*. the act of removing.

em·bod·y (im bod′ē) *verb*. **1.** to represent an idea or a quality in a definite or visible form: The fur-draped actress *embodied* the glamour of Hollywood. **2.** to collect into an organized whole. **embodied.**

em·i·grate (em′ə grāt) *verb*. to move from one country or part of a country to another. **emigrated.**

e·mit (i mit′) *verb*. to send forth or give out: The radio *emitted* some very strange sounds. **emitted.**

e·nig·ma (ə nig′mə) *noun*. anything or anyone that is puzzling or hard to understand.

en·thu·si·asm (in thōō′zē az′m) *noun*. strong interest in or devotion to something; ardor; zeal.

ep·i·lep·sy (ep′ə lep′sē) *noun*. a disorder of the central nervous system that can cause fainting and convulsions.

ep·och (ep′ək) *noun*. **1.** a period of time marked by the beginning of important events or changes: The televising of athletic events introduced a new *epoch* in sports history. **2.** a period in the history of the earth.

e·ques·tri·enne (i kews′trē en′) *noun*. a female horseback rider.

e·rup·tion (i rup′shən) *noun*. **1.** a breaking or bursting forth with violent force. **2.** a throwing forth of lava, water, etc. **3.** a breaking out, as in a rash. **eruptions.**

a fat	oi oil	ch chin
ā ape	ŏŏ look	sh she
ä car, father	ōō tool	th thin
e ten	ou out	*th* then
er care	u up	zh leisure
ē even	ur fur	ng ring
i hit		
ir here	ə = a *in* ago	
ī bite, fire	e *in* agent	
o lot	i *in* unity	
ō go	o *in* collect	
ô law, horn	u *in* focus	

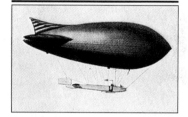

dirigible

equestrienne

excavation

Extraterrestrial is a combination of two words that have come into English from Latin. *Extra*, in this case, means "outside, from without." *Terrestris* is a Latin word meaning "of the earth." So, a good description of a creature from another planet is *extraterrestrial*.

forge

---

etch (ech) *verb*. **1.** to produce a figure or design on metal or glass by means of lines eaten into the surface by acid. **2.** to outline. **etched.**

eth·nic (eth′nik) *adjective*. of or related to a distinctive racial, cultural, or language group.

ex·ca·va·tion (eks′kə vā′shən) *noun*. **1.** a hole or hollow made by digging. **2.** something brought into view by digging, such as ruins. **excavations.**

ex·cru·ci·at·ing (iks krōō′shē āt′ing) *adjective*. causing or inflicting great pain; agonizing.

ex·cur·sion (ik skur′zhən) *noun*. **1.** a short pleasure trip. **2.** a round trip that is available at a lower fare.

ex·ert (ig zurt′) *verb*. **1.** to put forth or put into action: He tried to *exert* his authority over me, but I resisted. **2.** to put (oneself) into action or tiring effort.

ex·ile (eg′zīl *or* ek′sīl) *verb*. to cause a person or persons to leave their homeland or country and live somewhere else. **exiled.** —*noun*. **1.** the condition of being exiled. **2.** a person who has been banished.

ex·tra·ter·res·tri·al (eks′trə tə res′trē əl) *adjective*. outside of or beyond the earth. —*noun*. in fantasy or science fiction, a being or creature whose origins are from somewhere other than earth.

ex·trav·a·gant (ik strav′ə gənt) *adjective*. **1.** wasteful, especially of money; spending too much. **2.** going beyond what is reasonable or suitable.

ex·trem·i·ty (ik strem′ə tē) *noun*. **1.** the farthest point, end, or edge. **2.** an extreme condition of distress, need or danger. —**extremities** *plural noun*. the hands and feet.

ex·ult·ant (ig zult″nt) *adjective*. full of triumph; expressing great joy. —**exultantly** *adverb*.

F

fac·sim·i·le (fak sim′ə lē) *noun*. an exact copy or reproduction.

fas·tid·i·ous (fas tid′ē əs) *adjective*. hard to please; delicate or refined; squeamish.

fault (fôlt) *noun*. **1.** a blemish; flaw; whatever keeps something from being perfect. **2.** a mistake or blunder. **3.** responsibility for a mistake or blunder. **4.** a break in the earth's crust along which movement (earthquakes) can occur.

fet·id (fet′id *or* fēt′id) *adjective*. smelling of decay; stinking: A dead raccoon in the well had made the water *fetid*.

flat·ter·y (flat′ər ē) *noun*. praise or a compliment that is too much or that is not really meant.

flot·sam (flot′səm) *noun*. **1.** goods or pieces of a wrecked ship, found floating on the sea. **2.** any objects floating on a body of water. **3.** any discarded odds and ends.

floun·der (floun′dər) *verb*. **1.** to struggle to move, through mud, snow, etc. **2.** to speak or act in a clumsy, awkward, or confused manner. **floundered.**

fo·li·age (fō′lē ij) *noun*. the growth of leaves on a tree or plant, or the growth of many trees and plants.

fore·run·ner (fôr′run′ər) *noun*. **1.** a person or thing that precedes someone or something. **2.** an advance sign of something or someone to follow.

forge (fôrj) *noun*. a furnace where metal is shaped and worked. —*verb*. **1.** to produce an imitation of something for the purpose of deceiving. **2.** to move slowly, but steadily forward. **forged.**

for·lorn (fər lôrn′) *adjective*. sad; cheerless; lonely; left alone. —**forlornly** *adverb*.

for·mi·da·ble (fôr′mə də b'l) *adjective*. **1.** causing fear or dread by reason of size or strength. **2.** extremely difficult.

fraught (frôt) *adjective*. filled or loaded: Her journey was *fraught* with danger.

friv·o·lous (friv′ə ləs) *adjective*. not important; not serious; silly.

fu·ner·ar·y (fyoo′nə rer′ē) *adjective.* designed for, or part of, a funeral.

fu·tile (fyoot′'l) *adjective.* having no result or effect; done in vain; useless.

G

glid·er (glīd′ər) *noun.* **1.** an airplane without an engine, that glides on air currents. **2.** a porch chair built onto a frame so that it glides back and forth.

glyph (glif) *noun.* a raised or carved figure or form that represents an idea or word; hieroglyph. **glyphs.**

gnash (nash) *verb.* to strike or grind the teeth together, as in a rage: It is frightening when he's so angry that he *gnashes* his teeth. **gnashes.**

gorge (gôrj) *noun.* a narrow, deep valley, often with a river running through it. —*verb.* to overeat or stuff greedily with food. **gorges.**

gross (grōs) *adjective.* **1.** very bad or wrong. **2.** fat, large, or hulking. **3.** a total, without any deductions. **4.** vulgar. —*noun.* **1.** the entire amount. **2.** twelve dozen; 144. —*verb.* to earn a certain amount without considering expenses or deductions. **grosses.**

H

hal·low (hal′ō) *verb.* to treat as sacred; to make or keep holy. —**hallowed** *adjective.* sacred; holy; revered.

hap·haz·ard (hap′haz′ərd) *adjective.* happening by chance; without a plan; accidental. —**haphazardly** *adverb.*

he·ral·dic (hə ral′dik) *adjective.* having to do with heraldry, or the symbolism of royalty.

he·red·i·tar·y (hə red′ə ter′ē) *adjective.* **1.** derived from ancestors; inherited. **2.** of something that can be passed on from a plant or animal to its offspring.

here·to·fore (hir′tə fôr′) *adverb.* before now.

hi·er·o·glyph·ic (hī′ər ə glif′ik) *noun.* a picture or symbol representing a sound, word, object, or idea, as in the writing of the ancient Egyptians. —**hieroglyphics** *plural noun.* **1.** a system of writing, using such pictures. **2.** any writing that is very difficult to read.

hin·drance (hin′drəns) *noun.* something that hinders, or gets in the way of; obstacle: The flat tire was a *hindrance* to their enjoyment of the bicycle trip.

hos·pi·tal·i·ty (hos′pə tal′ə tē) *noun.* friendly and generous treatment of guests.

hus·band·man (huz′bənd mən) *noun.* a farmer; one who grows crops, raises livestock.

hy·dro·gen (hī′drə jən) *noun.* an odorless, colorless gas that is lighter than other gases and burns very easily.

a fat	oi oil	ch chin
ā ape	oo look	sh she
ä car, father	oo tool	th thin
e ten	ou out	*th* then
er care	u up	zh leisure
ē even	ur fur	ng ring
i hit		
ir here	ə = a *in* ago	
ī bite, fire	e *in* agent	
o lot	i *in* unity	
ō go	o *in* collect	
ô law, horn	u *in* focus	

hieroglyphics

I

i·dol·ize (ī′d'l īz) *verb.* **1.** to love or admire very much or too much. **2.** to make an idol of. **idolized.**

ig·no·min·i·ous (ig′nə min′ē əs) *adjective.* **1.** indicating disgrace; dishonorable. **2.** humiliating. —**ignominiously** *adverb.*

im·i·ta·tion (im′ə tā′shən) *noun.* **1.** the act of copying. **2.** a likeness or resemblance of something else.

im·per·a·tive (im per′ə tiv) *adjective.* **1.** absolutely necessary. **2.** expressing a command or strong desire.

im·per·cep·ti·ble (im′pər sep′tə b'l) *adjective.* so small as not to be able to be perceived or noticed. —**imperceptibly** *adverb.*

Hieroglyphics comes from two Greek words *hieros* or "holy" and *glyphein*, "to carve." Together they mean "holy or sacred carvings."

in·con·gru·ous (in koṅg′grōō wəs) *adjective.* out of place; not suitable or reasonable: The pretty daisies were *incongruous* growing in the junkyard.

in·cor·po·rate (in kôr′pə rāt) *verb.* **1.** to combine or merge one thing with another. **2.** to form into a legal corporation. **incorporated.**

in·cred·u·lous (in krej′ōō ləs) *adjective.* not willing to believe; doubtful that something is true.

in·dis·crim·i·nate (in′dis krim′ə nit) *adjective.* **1.** showing no awareness of differences; careless in choosing. **2.** confused; chaotic. **indiscriminately** *adverb.*

in·dis·pen·sa·ble (in′dis pen′sə b′l) *adjective.* essential; that which cannot be done without: When she was ill, her friend's help was *indispensabie.*

in·ef·fec·tu·al (in′i fek′chōō wəl) *adjective.* not able to produce the expected or usual effect. —**ineffectually** *adverb.*

in·fe·ri·or·i·ty (in fir′ē ôr′ə tē) *noun.* **1.** the condition of being lower in worth or quality. **2.** the state of being lower in position or rank.

in·fil·trate (in fil′trāt *or* in′fil trāt) *verb.* **1.** to filter into or move through. **2.** to join a group or organization for the secret purpose of spying, or to gain control.

in·gen·ious (in jēn′yəs) *adjective.* **1.** showing cleverness or skill. **2.** doing something in an especially original or clever way.

in·her·ent (in hir′ənt *or* in her′ənt) *adjective.* being a permanent part of the nature of a person or thing.

in·her·it (in her′it) *verb.* **1.** to receive something from someone when that person dies. **2.** to have or get certain personal traits from one's parents or ancestors. **inherited.**

in·oc·u·late (i nok′yōō lāt) *verb.* to inject into a person or animal a serum or vaccine containing a weakened form of a disease, causing the body to produce antibodies that help it fight the disease later. **inoculating.**

in·scrip·tion (in skrip′shən) *noun.* something that is printed, written, or engraved as a lasting record.

in·stinct (in′stiṅgkt) *noun.* **1.** a tendency or response of an animal or person to a given situation, which is natural and inborn: A mother bear's *instinct* is to protect her cubs from danger. **2.** a natural talent, aptitude, or knack.

in·su·la·tion (in′sə lā′shən) *noun.* **1.** keeping apart; protection. **2.** any material used for preventing electricity, heat, or sound from escaping.

in·sur·mount·a·ble (in′sər moun′tə b′l) *adjective.* impossible to overcome.

in·tan·gi·ble (in tan′jə b′l) *adjective.* **1.** not possible to touch; lacking a physical presence. **2.** vague or indefinite.

in·ter·act (in tər akt′) *verb.* to act upon one another. —**interaction** *noun.* action on each other.

in·ter·gen·er·a·tion·al (in′tər jen′ə rā′shən əl) *adjective.* between generations.

in·tri·cate (in′tri kit) *adjective.* **1.** complicated; involved. **2.** difficult to understand.

in·vec·tive (in vek′tiv) *noun.* violent attack in words; strong criticism; abuse; insults.

in·ven·tive (in ven′tiv) *adjective.* **1.** creative. **2.** skillful at invention.

in·vol·un·tar·y (in vol′ən ter′ē) *adjective.* **1.** not made or done willingly or by one's choice: The beating of our hearts is an *involuntary* action. **2.** not controlled by will; without thinking.

ir·rev·o·ca·ble (i rev′ə kə b′l) *adjective.* **1.** impossible to undo or take away. **2.** incapable of being brought back or changed. —**irrevocably** *adverb.*

Inoculate comes from a Latin word, *inoculare*, that meant "to graft a bud from one tree to another." The word was first used in its modern sense around 1700, when people were intentionally exposed to the smallpox virus to build an immunity to the disease. This method of disease prevention was called *inoculation.*

jade

J

jade (jād) *noun.* a hard stone, which is usually green, used for making jewelry and sculpture.

jet (jet) *noun.* **1.** a sudden rush of liquid or gas through a narrow opening or nozzle. **2.** liquid or gas that spurts from a nozzle. **3.** a jet-propelled aircraft.

jim·my (jim'ē) *noun.* a burglar's crowbar.
—*verb.* to break or pry open a lock, door, or window: They had lost their key, so she *jimmied* the lock. **jimmied.**

K

keen (kēn) *noun.* a wailing cry for someone who has died. **keening** —*verb.* to wail loudly.

kin·ship (kin'ship') *noun.* the state of being closely related, especially as in a family.

knell (nel) *noun.* **1.** the slow tolling of a bell, especially one announcing death. **2.** a warning of the end or failure of something. **3.** any sad or doleful sound.

knoll (nōl) *noun.* a small, round hill.

knot (not) *noun.* **1.** an intertwining of string, ribbon, etc. **2.** a small group or cluster of people or things. **3.** the hard lump on a tree where a branch joins the trunk. **4.** a difficulty; problem. **5.** a nautical mile.

L

lab·y·rinth (lab'ə rinth) *noun.* **1.** a place that consists of winding passages and dead ends, designed to confuse whoever tries to go through; maze. **2.** any intricate, confusing set of difficulties.

la·con·ic (lə kon'ik) *adjective.* not talkative; brief; concise.

la·ser (lā'zər) *noun.* a device that produces a narrow, powerful beam of light in which all the waves are vibrating in the same direction at the same time.

lat·er·al (lat'ər əl) *adjective.* being on or directed toward the side.

leave·tak·ing (lēv'tāk'ing) *noun.* an act of departure; farewell.

lib·er·ate (lib'ə rāt) *verb.* to set free; release, as from captivity or slavery. **liberated.**

lithe (līth) *adjective.* bending easily or gracefully; limber; supple: The *lithe* bodies of the dancers were beautiful to see.

loathe (lōth) *verb.* to feel great hatred or disgust for; to detest.

loot (lōōt) *verb.* to rob or carry off as plunder. —*noun.* goods that have been stolen or taken by force. —**looter** *noun.* a person who steals. **looters.**

lo·tus (lōt'əs) *noun.* a kind of waterlily noted for its large leaves and showy, often fragrant, flowers.

M

ma·che·te (mə shet'ē *or* mə chet'ē) *noun.* a large, heavy knife used for cutting vegetation and also as a weapon. **machetes.**

mag·ne·to (mag nēt'ō) *noun.* a small electric generator, often used to produce the ignition spark for certain kinds of gasoline engines. **magnetos.**

ma·nip·u·late (mə nip'yə lāt) *verb.* **1.** to control or move with the hands, especially to handle skillfully. **2.** to manage shrewdly and especially with the intent to deceive. —**manipulation** *noun.* **1.** act of skilled use of the hands. **2.** management for one's own advantage.

man·ta (man'tə) *noun.* **1.** coarse cotton cloth used for shawls, capes, etc., in Spanish America. **2.** a shawl, cape, etc., made of this. **3.** a devilfish, the largest kind of ray, with a broad flat body and a long tail. *also* **manta ray.**

ma·te·ri·al·ize (mə tir'ē ə līz) *verb.* **1.** to become actual fact. **2.** to assume material or visible form; to appear: He was afraid the ghost was going to *materialize* right there in his room. **3.** to appear suddenly or unexpectedly.

a fat	oi oil	ch chin
ā ape	oo look	sh she
ä car, father	ōō tool	th thin
e ten	ou out	th then
er care	u up	zh leisure
ē even	ur fur	ng ring
i hit		
ir here	ə = a *in* ago	
ī bite, fire	e *in* agent	
o lot	i *in* unity	
ō go	o *in* collect	
ô law, horn	u *in* focus	

jimmy

Laconic came from Latin, but originated in Laconia, Greece, during an ancient war. The Athenians sent a message to the Laconians saying, "If we enter Laconia, we will destroy your city." The Laconians sent back a one-word reply, "If." *Laconic* became descriptive of a person of few words.

Mercurial is derived from Mercury, who was the fast messenger of the gods in Roman mythology. The planet Mercury was named for this god. Early astrologers believed that people ruled by the planet Mercury were subject to quick changes of mood and temper.

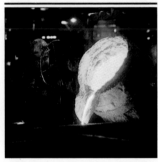

molten

mosaic

me·di·o·cre (mē′dē ō′kər) *adjective*. **1.** of only average quality, neither good nor bad. **2.** not good enough. —**mediocrity** *noun*. the quality of being ordinary.

med·i·tate (med′ə tāt) *verb*. **1.** to spend time in continuous quiet thinking; to reflect. **2.** to think about doing; plan. —**meditation** *noun*. act of being in deep thought.

mer·cu·ri·al (mər kyoor′ē əl) *adjective*. **1.** lively, clever, changeable. **2.** of or having to do with the metal mercury.

met·a·mor·pho·sis (met′ə môr′fə sis) *noun*. **1.** change from one form, shape, or substance into another. **2.** complete change of character. **3.** in biology, an animal's change in form in its development from embryo to adult.

me·thod·i·cal (mə thod′i k'l) *adjective*. **1.** arranged in or proceeding in a regular order. **2.** having orderly or systematic habits. —**methodically** *adverb*.

me·tic·u·lous (mə tik′yoo ləs) *adjective*. very or overly precise about details; painstaking; fussy.

mi·gra·to·ry (mī′grə tôr′ē) *adjective*. having a way of life that includes moving from one place to another: *Migratory* birds may travel thousands of miles every fall and spring.

min·is·tra·tion (min′is trā′shən) *noun*. the act of helping or serving. **ministrations.**

mis·in·ter·pret (mis′in tur′prit) *verb*. to give a wrong meaning to; misunderstand: They said we got lost because we *misinterpreted* their directions. **misinterpreted.**

mol·ten (mōl′t'n) *adjective*. **1.** made liquid, especially by heat. **2.** formed by casting in a mold.

mo·men·tum (mō men′təm) *noun*. **1.** in physics, the force with which a body moves, which is the product of its mass multiplied by its speed. **2.** a strength or force that keeps growing.

mon·i·tor (mon′ə tər) *noun*. **1.** in school, a person chosen to help the teacher with certain tasks. **2.** a person or device that warns or reminds. **3.** a radio or TV set adapted for use in a studio. **4.** a unit that displays computer readouts.

mon·soon (mon soon′) *noun*. **1.** a seasonal wind that blows in the Indian Ocean and southern Asia, in the winter from the northeast and the summer from the southwest. **2.** the rains which are brought by the summer wind.

mor·tal (môr′t'l) *adjective*. **1.** sure to die at some time. **2.** relating to this life before death. **3.** likely to cause death. **4.** ending in death. **5.** very great; extreme.

mo·sa·ic (mō zā′ik) *noun*. a picture or design made from bits of stone or glass that have been inlaid on a surface. **mosaics.**

mo·tive (mō′tiv) *noun*. a need or drive that causes a person to behave in a certain way. —*adjective*. causing, or having the power to cause, motion.

mu·le·teer (myoo lə tir′) *noun*. one who drives mules.

N

nav·i·ga·tion (nav′ə ga′shən) *noun*. **1.** the act or practice of navigating. **2.** the art or science of planning the direction or course of an airplane or ship.

ne·crop·o·lis (nə krop′ə lis) *noun*. a large burial area for the dead, especially in ancient times.

ne·go·ti·ate (ni gō′shē āt) *verb*. **1.** to discuss with another for the purpose of reaching an agreement. **2.** to arrange for something, by discussion. **3.** to manage to get around, through, or over something: I can *negotiate* the muddy path if you help me.

niche (nich) *noun*. **1.** a recessed space or hollow, usually in a wall, for the placement of an object. **2.** a place or position that is perfectly suited to a person. **niches.**

no·mad (nō′mad) *noun*. **1.** one of a group of people who constantly move from one place to another in search of food, water, or pasture for its animals. **2.** a wanderer. **nomads.**

nu·ance (nōō′äns *or* nyōō′äns) *noun.* a slight variation in color, tone, or meaning.

numb·ness (num′nis) *noun.* loss of the power of feeling or moving.

O

ob·sess (əb ses′) *verb.* to occupy the mind completely, to an excessive degree; to haunt one's thoughts. **obsessed.**

ob·so·lete (ob′sə lēt′ *or* ob′sə lēt) *adjective.* **1.** gone out of fashion. **2.** no longer in use.

op·pres·sive (ə pres′iv) *adjective.* **1.** cruel, harsh, or difficult to endure: We found the heat in the desert to be *oppressive.* **2.** causing to feel worried or weighed down.

or·phan (ôr′fən) *noun.* a child or animal whose parents are dead. —**orphaned** *adjective.* was an orphan: The *orphaned* pony had lost its mother and father.

P

pa·go·da (pə gō′də) *noun.* a temple in the form of a tower, several stories high: In China the towering *pagodas* are very beautiful. **pagodas.**

pam·per (pam′pər) *verb.* to be overly kind, generous, and gentle. **pampered.**

pan·de·mo·ni·um (pan′də mō′nē əm) *noun.* wild disorder, noise, uproar, or confusion.

pan·to·mime (pan′tē mīm) *noun.* **1.** a show in which the actors use only physical gestures and do not speak. **2.** the indication of something by use of gestures. —*verb.* to express something without using the voice.

par·a·lyze (par′ə līz) *verb.* **1.** to cause the loss of power to move or feel in any part of the body. **2.** to make powerless or inactive. **paralyzed.**

pas·sive (pas′iv) *adjective.* **1.** acted upon by something external. **2.** submitting or yielding without resistance. **3.** in grammar, having the verb in the form that shows that the subject was acted upon, rather than acting.

pass·port (pas′pôrt) *noun.* **1.** a government document that states the nationality of the person who carries it. **2.** anything that allows a person to go or get in somewhere, or do something.

pa·ter·nal (pə tur′n'l) *adjective.* **1.** of or like a father: His *paternal* embrace made the boy feel safe and secure. **2.** received from or connected with one's father.

pa·thol·o·gist (pə thol′ə jist) *noun.* an expert in the origins, causes, and development of disease.

pent (pent) *adjective.* penned in or shut in.

per·fo·rate (pur′fə rāt) *verb.* **1.** to make a hole through. **2.** to make many small holes in a row. —**perforations** *plural noun.* the holes used to make something easy to tear.

per·me·ate (pur′mē āt) *verb.* to spread throughout; pervade. **permeated.**

per·spire (pər spīr′) *verb.* to sweat. **perspired.**

per·sua·sive (pər swā′siv) *adjective.* able or likely to get someone to do or believe something.

per·verse (pər vurs′) *adjective.* **1.** purposely behaving in a way that is unacceptable or unconventional. **2.** morally wrong or wicked. —**perversity** *noun.* the state of behaving in a perverse way.

pil·grim·age (pil′grəm ij) *noun.* **1.** a journey to a holy place or shrine, made by a pilgrim. **2.** any long or difficult journey.

pin·na·cle (pin′ə k'l) *noun.* **1.** a high, pointed peak. **2.** the highest point of achievement. **3.** a small turret or slender tower.

plain·tive (plān′tiv) *adjective.* expressing sadness; mournful.

plea (plē) *noun.* **1.** an appeal or request for help. **2.** an argument in defense of oneself. **3.** the legal response of a defendant in a law case.

poign·ant (poin′yənt) *adjective.* **1.** deeply affecting; moving. **2.** piercing and sharp.

a fat	oi oil	ch chin
ā ape	oo look	sh she
ä car, father	ōō tool	th thin
e ten	ou out	th then
er care	u up	zh leisure
ē even	ur fur	ŋ ring
i hit		
ir here	ə = a *in* ago	
ī bite, fire	e *in* agent	
o lot	i *in* unity	
ō go	o *in* collect	
ô law, horn	u *in* focus	

Pandemonium was coined by poet John Milton in 1667 in his poem "Paradise Lost" to describe the capital of hell. He created it from two Greek words, *pan*, which means "all," and *daimōn*, which means "demon."

pantomime

portly

pyramid

pon·der (pon'dər) *verb.* to think over or consider carefully. —**pondering** *noun.* state of being in deep thought.

port·ly (pôrt'lē) *adjective.* large and overweight, but with a dignified carriage and manner.

pred·e·ces·sor (pred'ə ses'ər) *noun.* **1.** one who has gone before another in time, as in a job or position. **2.** a thing followed by something else. **predecessors.**

pre·mo·ni·tion (prē'mə nish'ən) *noun.* a forewarning; a feeling that something will happen, especially something bad.

pres·ti·gious (pres tij'əs *or* pres tē'jəs) *adjective.* having fame or respect as a result of good character, success, wealth, or great works.

probe (prōb) *noun.* **1.** an instrument used by a doctor to examine the inside of a wound. **2.** a careful investigation. —*verb.* **1.** to examine with a probe. **2.** to investigate thoroughly. **probed.**

prom·e·nade (prom'ə nād' *or* prom'ə näd') *noun.* **1.** a walk taken for pleasure, exercise, or to be seen. **2.** a public place for walking: The *promenade* along the beach was crowded with people. —*verb.* to take a promenade.

pro·pel (prə pel') *verb.* to cause to go forward or ahead. **propelled.**

pros·per·ous (pros'pər əs) *adjective.* successful; thriving; wealthy; favorable.

prov·erb (prov'ərb) *noun.* **1.** a short saying, especially one that contains a wise thought. **2.** something that has become a typical example.

pum·ice (pum'is) *noun.* a light, porous volcanic rock, used in powder form as an abrasive or polishing agent. *Also called* **pumice stones.**

pu·ny (pyōo'nē) *adjective.* weak and feeble in importance; small in size and power.

pyr·a·mid (pir'ə mid) *noun.* **1.** in geometry, a solid shape with a square base and triangular sides that meet in a point at the top. **2.** a structure built in the shape of a pyramid, as in ancient Egypt. **pyramids.**

Q

quad·ri·ple·gic (kwod'rə plē'jik) *noun.* a person who is paralyzed from the neck down.

quar·rel (kwôr'əl) *noun.* **1.** an unfriendly or violent disagreement; dispute. **2.** the cause of the dispute. —*verb.* **1.** to argue or disagree. **2.** to find fault; complain. **3.** to end a friendship. **quarreled.**

R

rap·ture (rap'chər) *noun.* an intense feeling of joy, love, happiness, etc. —**rapturously** *adverb.* with deep emotion: He was *rapturously* enthusiastic about the opera.

ra·tion (rash'ən *or* rā'shən) *noun.* **1.** a portion or share. **2.** in times of scarcity, the amount of food, fuel, etc., each person is allowed to have. —*verb.* to divide into portions, for the purpose of distributing evenly.

ra·tion·al·ize (rash'ən ə līz') *verb.* to make excuses for something, usually one's conduct.

re·af·firm (rē'ə furm') *verb.* to declare again, as for emphasis: He wanted to *reaffirm* that he would never cheat on a test.

re·cede (ri sēd') *verb.* **1.** to move back; withdraw. **2.** to move or fade away. **receded.**

reek (rēk) *verb.* to give off a strong, unpleasant odor. —*noun.* a strong, bad smell; stench.

re·flex·ive (ri flek'siv) *adjective.* **1.** in grammar: a. kind of verb having an object that is the same as the subject. b. kind of pronoun that is the object of a reflexive verb. **2.** occurring automatically, as if controlled by the reflexes.

ref·uge (ref'yōoj) *noun.* **1.** shelter or protection from danger. **2.** a safe, protected place.

re·ha·bil·i·tate (rē′hə bil′ə tāt) *verb.* **1.** to make good or whole again. **2.** to restore to a former, better condition. —**rehabilitation** *noun.* the state of being brought back to good condition.

re·hearse (ri hurs′) *verb.* **1.** to prepare for a public performance by practicing beforehand. **2.** to repeat over and over again. **3.** to tell or relate. **rehearsing.**

re·it·er·ate (rē it′ə rāt) *verb.* to say or do again. **reiterated.**

re·luc·tant (ri luk′tənt) *adjective.* showing unwillingness to do something. —**reluctantly** *adverb.* with hesitation.

re·morse (ri môrs′) *noun.* a hopeless feeling of guilt or sorrow over a wrong one has done: She felt great *remorse* after she stole the money.

re·nown (ri noun′) *noun.* great fame; celebrity. —**renowned** *adjective.* well known.

rep·er·toire (rep′ər twär) *noun.* all the plays, songs, operas, etc., that a company or person knows and is prepared to perform.

re·plen·ish (ri plen′ish) *verb.* **1.** to refill something that has been at least partially emptied. **2.** to bring back to completeness.

re·put·ed (ri pyoot′id) *adjective.* supposed; usually thought of. —**reputedly** *adverb.* according to popular belief.

re·sound (ri zound′) *verb.* **1.** to cause to be filled with sound; echo. **2.** to sound loudly. —**resounding** *adjective.* making a loud echoing sound.

re·tract (ri trakt′) *verb.* **1.** to withdraw. **2.** to take back. —**retractable** *adjective.* able to be pulled in or drawn back: This knife has a *retractable* blade.

rig (rig) *verb.* **1.** to fit out a ship with ropes and braces. **2.** to equip or supply. **3.** to make or construct quickly. **4.** to arrange for dishonest purposes. **rigged.**

rip·cord (rip′kôrd) *noun.* **1.** the cord that, when pulled, releases gas from a balloon, allowing the balloon to descend. **2.** the cord that releases a parachute from its pack.

rite (rīt) *noun.* **1.** a ceremony that is performed in an established manner. **2.** any formal ceremony or act.

rit·u·al (rich′oo wəl) *noun.* **1.** an established form for a solemn rite or ceremony. **2.** anything performed at regular intervals. —**ritualistic** *adjective.* of, like, or done as a rite.

ru·di·men·ta·ry (roo′də men′tər ē) *adjective.* **1.** elementary; simple. **2.** not fully developed.

S

sac·ri·lege (sak′rə lij) *noun.* an action showing disrespect for something sacred.

sal·vage (sal′vij) *noun.* **1.** the saving of a ship from wreck or capture. **2.** any action of saving property. **3.** that which is saved, as from a wreck. —*verb.* to recover something usable from wrecked or damaged goods.

sanc·tu·ar·y (saŋk′choo wer′ē) *noun.* **1.** a holy or sacred place. **2.** a place of refuge or shelter; also, the safety found there. **3.** the state of being protected.

sap·ling (sap′liŋ) *noun.* a young tree.

sar·coph·a·gus (sär kof′ə gəs) *noun.* **1.** any stone coffin or tomb. **2.** an ornamental, carved stone coffin, usually exposed to view.

sa·rong (sə rôŋ′) *noun.* a skirtlike garment made of silk or cotton. **sarongs.**

sa·vor (sā′vər) *noun.* **1.** the special taste, odor, or flavor of a thing. **2.** relish; zest. —*verb.* **1.** to have a special flavor or taste. **2.** to taste or enjoy with great pleasure.

scant (skant) *adjective.* **1.** barely enough: They tried to feed all the men from their *scant* supplies. **2.** just short of full.

schol·ar·ship (skol′ər ship) *noun.* **1.** the knowledge of one who studies; learning. **2.** money given to help a student to continue his or her education.

scribe (skrīb) *noun.* **1.** one who writes out or copies books, or documents, usually before the invention of printing. **2.** a writer. **3.** a teacher of Jewish law. **scribes.**

sapling

Sarcophagus is made up of two Greek words, which translate as "flesh eating." It originally meant a kind of stone that the Greeks thought consumed the flesh of the dead, thereby making it a good material for coffins.

scrim·mage (skrim′ij) *noun.* **1.** a rough-and-tumble struggle. **2.** a game played among members of the same team for practice.

scru·ti·ny (skr͞oōt″n ē) *noun.* a close examination: His *scrutiny* did not reveal any new problems.

seep (sēp) *verb.* to soak slowly through tiny openings. **seeping.**

se·mes·ter (sə mes′tər) *noun.* one of the two terms, or instructional periods, that make up a school year.

sham (sham) *noun.* an imitation, fake, or counterfeit. —*adjective.* not real; false. —*verb.* to act in a deceptive way; to fake.

shard (shärd) *noun.* a broken piece or fragment of a brittle substance such as pottery or glass. **shards.**

shred (shred) *noun.* **1.** a small, narrow strip that has been torn or cut off. **2.** a bit; fragment; particle. **shreds.** —*verb.* to cut or tear into small pieces.

sieve (siv) *noun.* a utensil used for separating finer particles from larger ones or solids from liquids; strainer. —*verb.* to cause to pass through a sieve.

sig·na·ture (sig′nə chər) *noun.* **1.** the name of a person, written by that person: I needed my mother's *signature* on my report card. **2.** in music, the symbol used at the beginning of a piece that gives the key or the time.

sim·i·an (sim′ē ən) *adjective.* of or like apes and monkeys. —*noun.* an ape or monkey.

skep·ti·cal (skep′ti k′l) *adjective.* doubting; questioning.

smoke·house (smōk′hous) *noun.* a building or closed room in which meat or fish is cured by smoke.

sound·proof (sound′pr͞oōf) *adjective.* capable of keeping sound from entering or spreading. —**soundproofing** *noun.* material used to deaden or reduce sound.

sou·ve·nir (s͞oō və nir′) *noun.* an object that is kept as a reminder of something.

spasm (spaz″m) *noun.* **1.** a sudden, involuntary contraction of muscles. **2.** any sudden, short burst of activity or feeling.

sta·lac·tite (stə lak′tīt) *noun.* a lime deposit, shaped like an icicle, hanging down from the roof of a cave. **stalactites.**

stealth·y (stel′thē) *adjective.* moving or acting quietly, secretly, and furtively.

—**stealthily** *adverb.* in a manner not seen or heard: She was sneaking *stealthily* along behind the bushes.

stern (sturn) *noun.* the back end of a boat or ship.

stodg·y (stoj′ē) *adjective.* dull; stuffy; uninteresting: He felt bored while spending the day with his *stodgy* uncle.

sto·ic (stō′ik) *noun.* a person who remains calm and self-controlled and does not appear to respond to pleasure or pain. —*adjective.* not responsive to pleasure or pain.

stren·u·ous (stren′yoo wəs) *adjective.* **1.** requiring much energy or effort. **2.** very active or energetic.

sub·merge (səb murj′) *verb.* **1.** to put or go under water. **2.** to cover or hide. **submerged.**

sub·mis·sion (səb mish′ən) *noun.* **1.** the act of submitting to the power or authority of another. **2.** the state of being humble or obedient. **3.** the act of giving, or submitting, something to someone for decision or consideration.

sub·ti·tle (sub′tīt″l) *noun.* in movies, words that appear at the bottom of the screen, translating the words the actors speak into another language. **subtitles.**

sub·tle (sut″l) *adjective.* **1.** having a keen awareness of small differences in effect or meaning. **2.** hard to understand or recognize. **3.** crafty; clever; sly. **4.** having or showing delicate skill.

suc·cumb (sə kum′) *verb.* **1.** to give in or yield to: He *succumbed* to the temptation to eat a hot-fudge sundae. **2.** to die. **succumbed.**

suf·fo·cate (suf′ə kāt) *verb.* **1.** to kill by depriving of air; smother. **2.** to die from lack of oxygen. **3.** to have a feeling of smothering. **4.** to have difficulty breathing. **suffocating.**

sump·tu·ous (sump′choo wəs) *adjective.* lavish; expensive. —**sumptuously** *adverb.* in a splendid manner, at great cost.

sur·re·al·is·tic (sə rē′ə lis′tik) *adjective.* **1.** having to do with a movement in 20th-century art and literature that tried to express things that were hidden in the unconscious. **2.** bizarre; dreamlike; outside of everyday reality.

Skeptical comes to us from the ancient Greek word *skeptikos*, meaning "thoughtful or inquiring." When followers of one school of Greek philosophy began questioning all assumptions, they found they could not arrive at any real knowledge. These philosophers were called *Skeptics*.

stalactites

stern

sus·cep·ti·ble (sə sep'tə b'l) *adjective.* easily influenced by; open to; sensitive: He is very *susceptible* to catching cold.

sus·pense (sə spens') *noun.* **1.** the condition of being anxious, uncertain, or undecided. **2.** the pleasant excitement experienced as a plot unfolds.

sus·tain (sə stān') *verb.* **1.** to hold up the weight of. **2.** to keep up. **3.** to keep up the courage or spirits of. **4.** to undergo or endure. **sustaining.**

T

ta·ble (tā b'l) *noun.* **1.** a piece of furniture with a flat top and supporting legs. **2.** food being served. **3.** the people seated at a table. **4.** a short list. **5.** a systematic arrangement of information, often involving numbers, usually arranged in parallel columns. **tables.**

tact (takt) *noun.* the ability to say or do the right thing, especially without causing anger or hurt feelings.

tar·pau·lin (tär pô'lin *or* tär'pə lin) *noun.* waterproof canvas, used to cover merchandise, protect a field, etc.

tax·i (tak'sē) *noun.* an automobile that carries passengers for payment; taxicab. —*verb.* **1.** to ride in a taxicab. **2.** in aviation, to move slowly along the ground or water before takeoff or after landing. **taxied.**

tech·ni·cian (tek nish'ən) *noun.* a person who is skilled in performing the tasks in a particular field of art or science. **technicians.**

te·di·ous (tē'dē əs *or* tē'jəs) *adjective.* long and boring: Pulling weeds is *tedious* work.

ter·ra·pin (ter'ə pin) *noun.* an edible North American turtle that lives in or near water.

terse (tʉrs) *adjective.* short and to the point; concise. —**tersely** *adverb.* in a clear manner using few words.

teth·er (te*th*'ər) *noun.* a line used to confine or limit the movement of something, often an animal. —*verb.* to fasten or confine with a tether. **tethered.**

the·sis (thē'sis) *noun.* **1.** a statement or an idea to be defended in an argument. **2.** a long piece of writing based on research done to fulfill the requirements for a university degree.

thim·ble (thim'b'l) *noun.* a plastic, metal, or wooden cap worn over the finger, to protect it while sewing. —**thimbleful. 1.** an amount that would fit into a thimble. **2.** a very small quantity.

ti·tan·ic (tī tan'ik) *adjective.* enormous in size and power.

tod·dle (tod''l) *verb.* to walk with unsteady, small steps as a small child does. **toddled.**

to·ga (to'gə) *noun.* a loose garment worn in public by the citizens of ancient Rome.

trans·lu·cent (trans loo's'nt) *adjective.* allowing light to pass through, but not allowing a clear view of what is on the other side, such as frosted glass.

treach·er·ous (trech'ər əs) *adjective.* **1.** disloyal. **2.** appearing safe or trustworthy, but not being so: Our canoe approached the *treacherous* rapids.

trea·dle (tred''l) *noun.* a lever worked by the foot to drive a machine. —*verb.* to work with a treadle. **treadles.**

trek (trek) *verb.* **1.** to make one's way slowly and with difficulty. **2.** to go on foot. —*noun.* a long, difficult trip: Jon and Tracy like to go on *treks* in the Himalayas. **treks.**

trench (trench) *noun.* a long, narrow ditch.

trep·i·da·tion (trep'ə dā'shən) *noun.* **1.** a state of alarm or fear. **2.** a trembling.

tri·fle (tri'f'l) *noun.* **1.** anything of little value or importance. **2.** a small amount, especially of money.

tril·o·gy (tril'ə jē) *noun.* a set of three plays, books, movies, etc., which form a related group, although each is a complete work in itself.

trow·el (trou'əl) *noun.* **1.** a small, flat-bladed tool, used for smoothing plaster, mortar, etc. **2.** a small hand tool used by gardeners for digging.

trun·dle (trun'd'l) *verb.* **1.** to transport in a wheeled vehicle. **2.** to roll along. **trundled.**

ty·phoon (tī foon') *noun.* a violent tropical cyclone that starts near the Philippines or the China Sea.

terrapin

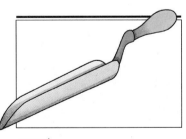

trowel

u

un·a·bashed (un ə basht′) *adjective*. not embarrassed; unashamed: He cried with *unabashed* emotion when his dog died.

un·bid·den (un bid′n) *adjective*.
1. uninvited; without having been asked. **2.** spontaneous.

un·cer·e·mo·ni·ous (un ser′ə mō′nē əs) *adjective*. informal; sudden; discourteous. —**unceremoniously** *adverb*.

un·heed·ing (un hēd′iṅg) *adjective*. without paying attention.

un·re·lent·ing (un′ri len′tiṅg) *adjective*.
1. not relenting or giving in. **2.** not letting up; unchanging.

un·scru·pu·lous (un skrōo′pyə ləs) *adjective*. without regard for what is the right or moral thing to do; not honest.

un·stint·ed (un stint′əd) *adjective*. unlimited; generous.

Vandalize is taken from the ancient Germanic tribes of Vandals who ransacked Rome in the year A.D. 455. They destroyed many precious cultural objects as they destroyed the city. It is probably from that event that the word derives its current meaning, although it wasn't used in this sense until the end of the eighteenth century.

veranda

v

vac·u·um (vak′yōo wəm *or* vak′yōom) *noun*.
1. space that is absolutely free of matter. **2.** a contained space from which almost all air and gas has been removed. —*verb*. to clean with a vacuum cleaner.

van·dal·ize (van′d'l īz) *verb*. to destroy or deface property maliciously, especially anything artistic or beautiful.

van·tage (van′tij) *noun*. **1.** advantage or superiority over a competitor. **2.** a position that gives one a clear view, *also called* **vantage point.**

ve·ran·da (və ran′də) *noun*. an open porch, usually roofed, along the outside of a building.

ver·dict (vur′dikt) *noun*. **1.** a decision reached by a jury in a trial. **2.** conclusion; judgment; decision: The *verdict* was that the meal was a huge success.

veterinarian

ver·ti·cal (vur′ti k′l) *adjective*. straight up and down; perpendicular to the horizontal. —**vertically** *adverb*.

vet·er·i·nar·i·an (vet′ər ə ner′ē ən) *noun*. a doctor who specializes in the treatment of animals. **veterinarians.**

vil·la (vil′ə) *noun*. a large, impressive house in the country or outside a city.

vis·i·bil·i·ty (viz′ə bil′ə tē) *adjective*. **1.** the quality of being visible or able to be seen. **2.** the degree of clearness in the atmosphere.

vi·sion·ar·y (vizh′ən er′ē) *adjective*. **1.** not based on fact. **2.** dreamy, impractical. **3.** idealistic. —*noun*. **1.** a person who has visions. **2.** a person who attempts to reach visionary goals; idealist.

voice (vois) *noun*. **1.** sound made through the mouth, especially by people. **2.** the ability to make such sounds. **3.** expressed choice, opinion, or wish: The *voice* of the people was heard at the election.

vul·ner·a·ble (vul′nər ə b'l) *adjective*.
1. capable of being wounded or hurt.
2. likely to be hurt.

w

wind·lass (wind′ləs) *noun*. a winch for hauling and lifting, especially one that has a core or drum around which the hoisting rope winds and that is turned by a crank.

wrench (rench) *noun*. **1.** a violent twist to one side. **2.** an injury caused by twisting. **3.** sudden strong emotion. **4.** a small tool, used for turning nuts and bolts. —*verb*. **1.** to twist or pull violently. **2.** to injure by a sudden sharp twisting. **3.** to strain meaning. **4.** to force a reply or expression of feelings: His hidden rage was *wrenched* from him by the skillful lawyer. **wrenched.**

Z

zo•di•ac (zō′də ak′) *noun.* an imaginary belt that goes across the sky and that includes the paths of most of the planets. It is divided into twelve constellations or signs. In astrology, the sign under which one is born is believed to affect one's personality and fate.

a fat	oi oil	ch chin
ā ape	o͝o look	sh she
ä car, father	o͞o tool	th thin
e ten	ou out	*th* then
er care	u up	zh leisure
ē even	ur fur	ng̑ ring
i hit		
ir here	ə = a *in* ago	
ī bite, fire	e *in* agent	
o lot	i *in* unity	
ō go	o *in* collect	
ô law, horn	u *in* focus	

Zodiac is from Greek. The literal translation is "the circle containing animals." This refers to the imaginary belt in the sky circling the earth, which contains constellations in the shapes of animals and humans.

ABOUT THE AUTHORS

The authors listed below have written some of the selections that appear in this book. The content of the notes was determined by a survey of what readers wanted to know about authors.

JUDIE ANGELL

JUDIE ANGELL

Judie Angell, who was born in New York City, has been an elementary school teacher, an associate editor for *TV Guide,* and a television writer. She thinks that "growing up heads the list of The Hardest Things To Do In Life. It's so hard, in fact, that some of us never get there. But even if the world changes as rapidly as it does, the feelings that we have while we're coping with those changes don't. I take a lot of those feelings, hug them, wrap them carefully in some words, and present them in a book with an invisible card that says, maybe this'll help a little—make you laugh—make you feel you're not alone." *(Born 1937)*

PATRICIA BEATTY

PATRICIA BEATTY

Patricia Beatty began her career as a librarian and high school teacher of English and history. Her father was a Coast Guard officer and commanded Coast Guard stations located on Native American reservations in Oregon and Washington. She says, "My early childhood was interesting, for I spent much of my youth living in a series of Indian villages up and down the northwest United States." She has turned her memories of those places and people into novels, and she tries to bring worthwhile facts about the past to the awareness of young people. Among the literary awards she has won is the Golden Kite Award. *(Born 1922)*

HILARY BECKETT

Hilary Beckett, who lives in New York City, has written short stories, poems, articles, and reviews of books by other authors. She has also written books of her own. One of her books, *Street Fair Summer,* reflects her love of street fairs. Two other books she has written are *My Brother, Angel* and *Rafael and the Raiders.*

WENDELL BERRY

Wendell Berry was born in Henry County, Kentucky, and has spent most of his life in Kentucky. He has taught English at the University of Kentucky for many years. A poet, novelist, and essayist, Wendell Berry's work expresses his concern for his native Kentucky. He has received the National Institute of Arts and Letters Literary Award of the Bess Hokin Prize for poetry. He has also received grants from both the Guggenheim and Rockefeller foundations. *(Born 1934)*

WENDELL BERRY

RAY BRADBURY

When Ray Bradbury was in high school, he founded and edited a mimeographed quarterly called *Futurai Fantasia.* He has published more than 400 short stories and his work appears in over 700 anthologies. He has also written and adapted several movies, including *It Came from Outer Space* and *The Beast from 20,000 Fathoms,* and has written television plays, including eight shows for "Alfred Hitchcock Presents." Ray Bradbury has won many literary honors and awards. His short film "Icarus Montgolfier Wright" was nominated for an Academy Award. *(Born 1920)*

RAY BRADBURY

SHEILA BURNFORD

SHEILA BURNFORD

Sheila Burnford was born in Scotland. In 1951, she emigrated to Canada with her husband, her children, and her dog, an English bull terrier named Bill. In Canada, Sheila Burnford acquired Simon, a Siamese kitten. Bill and Simon became very good friends. Her husband got a Labrador who became good friends with Bill and Simon. When Bill's sight began to fail, the Labrador helped him get around by showing him the way to go. Sheila Burnford said, "Communication between animals has always fascinated me, not just instinctive means, but day to day, individual and original communication. There were endless examples of this with our animal trio." For her book *The Incredible Journey,* she won the Canadian Library Association Book of the Year medal and the American Library Association Aurianne Award. The book has been translated into 16 languages and made into a movie. *(1918–1984)*

ARTHUR C. CLARKE

ARTHUR C. CLARKE

Arthur C. Clarke was born in England. He became interested in astronomy when he was about eleven, and he spent many nights mapping the moon. "Before long," he says, "I knew the lunar landscape much better than my native Somerset." He became a science-fiction fan when he was a teenager, and in the 1950s he developed a keen interest in skin-diving. Many of his novels and short stories reflect his interest in science fiction and the sea. *(Born 1917)*

ROBIN COOK

Robin Cook is a physician. He is also the author of several very popular novels. He has said that it is "a lot more difficult to write a book than you think it will be when you first start out. You look at a book with a glossy cover and you read a few pages and you say to yourself, 'I could do this.' There is, obviously, a lot more involved." When his first book, *The Year of the Intern,* did not make the best-seller lists, Robin Cook set out to learn why. He read best-selling books and paid careful attention to how to create suspense in a novel. His next book, *Coma,* not only was a best-selling novel, but was also made into a popular movie. *(Born 1940)*

ROBIN COOK

BILL COSBY

William Henry Cosby, Jr., was born in Philadelphia. Bill Cosby, who earned a Ph.D. from the University of Massachusetts, has written several popular books. He is best known, however, as an entertainer. He has won three Emmy awards for his television acting and received critical recognition for his movie roles. He has been called "one of the funniest men in entertainment." Bill Cosby has said that becoming a successful entertainer is a difficult task. "If you want to make the old school try," he says, "you'd better have plenty of grits and determination 'cause you'll need all you can muster." *(Born 1937)*

BILL COSBY

PATRICIA DEMUTH

Patricia Demuth and her husband both grew up in small towns in Iowa where they had friends who were part of a family farm team. When they decided to write a book about rural America and illustrate it with pictures, they found a farm in Wisconsin to serve as the setting for their story. They took their two young sons with them and lived in Wisconsin while Patricia Demuth wrote the text and Jack Demuth did the photography. *Joel: Growing Up a Farm Man* was awarded Best Children's Book of 1982 by the Society of Midland Authors. *City Horse,* also written by Patricia Demuth and illustrated with photographs by her husband, was chosen as a Junior Literary Guild selection.

WILLIAM PÈNE du BOIS

WILLIAM PÈNE du BOIS

William Pène du Bois, who is an author and illustrator, was born in New Jersey, but he attended school in France from the time he was eight until he was fourteen. The son of a painter and art critic, he has always been interested in the illustrations in books. "I did some scattered reading of a peculiar type in adventure books," he said. "If, for instance, I read a caption under a thrilling frontispiece which said, 'Bill Ballantine slipped from his trapeze and fell into the lion cage below (see page 178),' I would quickly turn to page 178 to find out whether he was chewed up." William Pène du Bois won the John Newbery Medal for his book *The Twenty-one Balloons. (Born 1916)*

T. S. ELIOT

T. S. (Thomas Stearns) Eliot was born and grew up in
St. Louis, Missouri. After he graduated from Harvard, he
went to England to attend Oxford University. He became
a British citizen and never returned to the United States to
live. Considered one of the major poets of the twentieth
century, he was also a well-known critic and playwright. He
won many awards and honors, including the prestigious
Nobel Prize in literature. And he is one of the two
Americans honored by being recognized in Westminster
Abbey: a memorial stone was placed on the floor of
the Poet's Corner, near the bust of Henry Wadsworth
Longfellow. The popular Broadway musical, *Cats*, was
adapted from T. S. Eliot's book of whimsical poems, *Old
Possum's Book of Practical Cats*. *(1888–1965)*

T. S. ELIOT

WALTER FARLEY

Walter Farley began writing *The Black Stallion* when he
was still a student in high school and finished it when he
was in college. He says that his great love was, and still is,
horses. When Walter Farley was young, he wanted a pony,
but never owned one. "I tried selling subscriptions to win a
pony. Then my uncle with show horses and jumpers moved
from the West Coast to Syracuse, and I was deliriously
happy. I was at the stables every chance I could get." Most
of his books have something to do with horses, including a
series of books about the Black and the fillies and colts that
the great horse sired. *(Born 1920)*

WALTER FARLEY

PENELOPE FARMER

PENELOPE FARMER

Penelope Farmer was born in England. As a child she enjoyed reading and writing stories. She said, "I don't write for any particular age group. I don't write a book for children. I write a book; and this is a big distinction, I think." She also said, "When you are a writer, you work very much by yourself, shut up in a little room. Being a writer can be incredibly lonely sometimes." Her book *The Summer Birds* received a Carnegie Medal commendation.
(Born 1939)

JEAN CRAIGHEAD GEORGE

JEAN CRAIGHEAD GEORGE

Jean Craighead George has written many books for young people, including the Newbery Medal winner *Julie of the Wolves* and *My Side of the Mountain,* which was made into a movie. She says she writes "about children in nature and their relationship to the complex web of life. I call my books 'documentary novels,' for the investigations into nature are scientific and carefully researched. Today a work for children must be accurate and faithful to the truth."
(Born 1919)

BIL GILBERT

Bil Gilbert was born in Washington, D.C. He says about his writing career: "As a reporter and author I have written on a wide range of subjects, including urban problems, sports, and police and fire stories. I began my career as a sportswriter for the *Washington Post* at the age of 16. I retained an interest in athletics after transferring to the newsroom, and I continue that interest today as a baseball coach." He is a co-author of *All These Mornings, Keep Off My Turf,* and *High School Basketball* among other books.
(Born 1931)

FRANCES GOODRICH

Frances Goodrich and her husband, Albert Hackett, worked as a writing team. They were both interested in acting and met when they were acting in different plays. They have written a number of Broadway plays and screenplays. Among their screenplays are *Easter Parade* and *The Virginian*. They also worked together on the dramatization of *The Diary of Anne Frank*. *(1891–1984)*

FRANCES GOODRICH

NANCY GOOR

Besides being a writer, Nancy Goor has taught art in a public high school in Bethesda, Maryland, and was the director of the Insect Zoo at the Smithsonian Institution, Natural History Museum, Washington, D.C. She is married to Ron Goor, who has done the photography for all her books and is listed as co-author. She says, "I have always considered myself an artist. It was not until the publication in several newspapers of my article 'Traveling in Italy with Children' that I seriously considered writing as a vocation. We [she and her husband] are often asked where we get the ideas for our books. Our ideas arise from our everyday experiences. For example, when my son was in the first grade he told me, 'Mommy, I like to read signs.' Ron and I set to work and *Signs* was published." *(Born 1944)*

NANCY GOOR

RON GOOR

Ron Goor says, "Ever since I can remember I have been interested in biology. While at the Smithsonian Institution developing biological exhibits for the lay public, I began to take photographs and discovered that photography opened up new avenues of self-expression as well as exploring and documenting the world." He and his wife, Nancy, have won several awards for their books. *Shadows: Here, There, and Everywhere* was selected as one of the Library of Congress's best books of the year. *(Born 1940)*

RON GOOR

ELOISE GREENFIELD

ELOISE GREENFIELD

Eloise Greenfield has been a clerk-typist, a secretary, and co-director of adult fiction for the District of Columbia Black Writer's Workshop. She said, "Writing was the farthest thing from my mind when I was growing up. I loved words, but I loved to read them, not write them. I loved their sounds and rhythms, and even some of their aberrations, such as homonyms and silent letters, though the pluralizing of 'leaf' as 'leaves' annoyed me. I could think of no good reason for getting rid of that *f.*" She now considers writing "an important and enriching part" of her life. Eloise Greenfield has received the American Library Association Notable Book Award, as well as citations from the Council on Interracial Books for Children, the District of Columbia Association of School Librarians, and Celebrations in Learning. *(Born 1929)*

ALBERT HACKETT

ALBERT HACKETT

Albert Hackett was born of theatrical parents. He appeared on the stage when he was only six years old and studied at the Professional Children's School. He met his wife, Frances Goodrich, when they were acting in different plays. Together he and his wife have written a number of successful Broadway plays and screenplays. Among the screenplays are *Seven Brides for Seven Brothers* and *The Virginian.* Together they dramatized *The Diary of Anne Frank.*

JAMES HERRIOT

James Herriot, whose real name is James Alfred Wight, was born in Scotland. He was a veterinary surgeon in Yorkshire, England, for nearly 30 years before he wrote his first book at the age of 50. The town of Darrowby, the setting for his books, is a made-up town that has features of two towns in the area. Herriot says about being a veterinarian: "It can be rough and dirty and the accident rate is high. If a horse kicks you, it can mean a broken leg. My daughter Rosemary was mad keen to be a country vet, but I talked her out of it, so she's a doctor instead, which is the next best thing." *(Born 1916)*

JAMES HERRIOT

MINFONG HO

Minfong Ho was born in Rangoon, Burma and grew up in Thailand. She now lives in Ithaca, New York. Her novel *Sing to the Dawn,* which was illustrated by her brother, won first prize from the Council of Interracial Books for Children. Minfong Ho said, "When I wrote *Sing to the Dawn,* it was in a moment of homesickness during the thick of winter in upstate New York, when Thailand seemed incredibly far away. Writing about the dappled sunlight and school children of home brought them closer to me; it aired on paper that part of me which couldn't find any place in America." *Sing to the Dawn* is now being made into a TV movie in Singapore. Her new book is entitled *Rice Without Rain.* She says, "I write to bring back what is gone, to relive what is lost, to make a mosaic out of fragments." *(Born 1951)*

MINFONG HO

H. M. Hoover

H. M. Hoover

H. M. Hoover, whose full name is Helen Mary Hoover, says she "grew up in an old country house in northeastern Ohio with orchards, ponds, creeks, fields, and woods for roaming. Pets and children were left unleashed." She said that for her the high spot in the school week was Wednesday morning when the county library truck arrived. "I read anything, juvenile or adult, junk or classic. Junk books affected me like junk food, when my stomach turned I switched to more solid stuff." One of her books was selected as a Children's Book of the Year by the Child Study Association of America. Another was chosen as one of the American Library Association's "Best Books for Young Adults." *(Born 1935)*

Lee Bennett Hopkins

Lee Bennett Hopkins

In addition to interviewing authors and illustrators, Lee Bennett Hopkins also compiles poetry anthologies and writes poetry himself. He says, "I love doing children's books. Each one is a new challenge, a new day, a new spring for me. It is exciting to see each unfold, going from my typewritten copy to the joy of holding the finished book in my hand. Opening the bound copy for the first time is like seeing the big curtains being raised in a darkened theatre. It's magical, fun, scary. I'm not too interested in what adults think of my books for children because they are not for adults. I respect their opinions but get greater satisfaction when I receive a note from a child. That makes it all worthwhile." *(Born 1938)*

ANNE MORROW LINDBERGH

Anne Morrow met the famous aviator Charles Lindbergh at the U.S. Embassy in Mexico, where her father was ambassador. Charles Lindbergh was the first person to fly solo from New York to Paris. The night after she met him, Anne Morrow wrote in her diary: "He is great not because he crossed the ocean alone. He might have shown his genius some other way. The flight gave him to the world." After she and Charles married, Anne Lindbergh acquired her pilot's license and her radio operator's license. "Flying," she said, "was a normal life for us." She accompanied her husband as co-pilot and radio operator on many flights, including a flight of 40,000 miles that crossed five continents. Her first book, *North to the Orient,* was written after this flight. Her writings include books of poetry and essays, as well as her diaries, in which she wrote every night for many years. *(Born 1906)*

ANNE MORROW LINDBERGH

MYRA COHN LIVINGSTON

Myra Cohn Livingston, who was born and reared in Nebraska, now lives with her husband and three children in California. She has written many books of poetry. Among the literary honors she has received are the Southern California Council on Literature for Children and Young People Award and the New York Herald Tribune honor award. Her first book, a collection of poems for young children, was written when she was a freshman in college. When the book was published, a reviewer chided her for writing about "simple things — merely everyday experiences." She says: "Although intended as a rebuke, I accept it now as a compliment for what more can one offer to the young than a touchstone to deal with the early daily experiences of feelings, sights, and sounds around them?" *(Born 1926)*

MYRA COHN LIVINGSTON

JACK LONDON

JACK LONDON

Jack London was born in San Francisco. As a very young man he was first a sailor and then a hobo. When he was in his early twenties, he spent a year in the Klondike region of Alaska. Many of his stories are set in this rugged, starkly beautiful country. After his return to San Francisco, he devoted himself to his writing and was quite successful. He believed three things were necessary to be a writer: "First, a study and knowledge of literature as it is commercially produced today. Second, a knowledge of life, and third, a working philosophy of life." During his lifetime, London wrote numerous short stories and more than forty books. *(1876–1916)*

DAVID MACAULAY

DAVID MACAULAY

David Macaulay moved to the U.S. from England when he was eleven years old. An author and illustrator, David Macaulay said he spent much time in high school drawing. "I must have copied every photograph ever taken of the Beatles." After high school he studied architecture at the Rhode Island School of Design. He liked illustrating books and began to ask his friends to write books so that he could illustrate them. Then he realized that the building of a cathedral could be made into a story, so he wrote his own book and illustrated it. He said his first book "was difficult in the beginning since I am not a 'natural' writer." Now he finds that "writing is as much fun and as much of a challenge as making the pictures for the book." He has won numerous awards for his books. *Cathedral: The Story of Its Construction* was named one of the Ten Best Illustrated Books by the *New York Times,* and *Motel of the Mysteries* was the American Library Association's Best Book for Young Adults in 1979. *Cathedral* was adapted for television as "Castle." *(Born 1946)*

BERYL MARKHAM

Beryl Markham was born in England, but was taken to North Africa by her father when she was four years old. She spent her childhood playing with native Murani children. She spoke Swahili, Nandi, and Massai, as well as English. For several years, she trained and bred race horses, then she became an aviatrix. She carried mail, passengers, and supplies to remote corners of the Sudan, Tanzania, Kenya, Zambia, and Zimbabwe. Beryl Markham started a business spotting big game from the air for land-based safaris. In 1936, she became the first woman to fly solo across the Atlantic from east to west. She took off from England and crash-landed in Nova Scotia. Her book *West with the Night* was first published in 1942. It was republished in 1987 and has been a bestseller since its republication. *(1902–1986)*

BERYL MARKHAM

ROBERT NATHAN

Robert Nathan wrote over fifty books. He was also a screenwriter for Metro-Goldwyn-Mayer. Two of his best-known books, which were made into movies, are *Portrait of Jennie* and *One More Spring*. Robert Nathan was awarded the U.S. Treasury Department Silver Medal for his work in World War II. He also earned the California Writer's Guild Award of Honor. In addition to being a writer, Robert Nathan loved music. He once said, "I have been devoted to music all my life. If I had my 'druthers,' I'd have been a great opera singer." He also studied fencing and belonged to a fencing club. *(1894–1985)*

ROBERT NATHAN

CARL SANDBURG

CARL SANDBURG

Carl Sandburg, the son of Swedish immigrants, is considered one of the major writers of the twentieth century. Few writers have received, during their own lifetime, as many honors and as much recognition as Sandburg did. The cottage in which he was born in Galesburg, Illinois, was dedicated as a literary shrine in 1946. Even his goat farm in North Carolina was among the best known in the country. His books on the life of Abraham Lincoln are regarded as one of the monumental works of this century. Carl Sandburg once wrote: "My father couldn't sign his name. He made his 'mark' on the company's payroll sheet. My mother was able to read the Scriptures in her native language, but she could not write, and I wrote about Abraham Lincoln whose own mother could not read or write! I guess that somewhere along in this you'll find a story of America." *(1878–1967)*

MAY SARTON

MAY SARTON

May Sarton, who was born in Belgium, moved to Cambridge, Massachusetts, when she was four years old. She said that she began to write poetry in the ninth grade. When she finished high school, she wanted to become an actress so she went to New York City. After a few years she gave up acting and concentrated on writing. She won many awards for her poetry. She also wrote fiction and nonfiction. She said: "Everything I've written is, first of all, to understand something—some idea, some emotion. By putting a group of characters in a series of crucial situations, I come to understand something I hadn't before. I have a very great compulsion to find out where I am, and so I write." *(Born 1917)*

BYRD BAYLOR SCHWEITZER

Byrd Baylor Schweitzer was born in Texas and grew up in the deserts of the Southwest. She spent many of her childhood summers in Mexico. Many of her stories and poems are set in these familiar surroundings. *Before You Came This Way* describes what life might have been like in the southwestern canyons in the prehistoric ages. Several of her books have been named Caldecott Honor Books, and she has received the Catlin Peace Pipe Award and the Brooklyn Art Books for Children Citation. She also writes under the names of Byrd Baylor and B. B. Schweitzer. *(Born 1924)*

BYRD BAYLOR SCHWEITZER

KARL SHAPIRO

Karl Shapiro is both a poet and a literary critic. He won many awards for his early poetry, including the Pulitzer Prize for poetry. These poems, which were influenced by the work of the poet W. H. Auden, were of a traditional nature. Later, Karl Shapiro began to be more experimental in his poetry. He said he felt that the restrictions of traditional poetry stifled the poet's creativity. Many of his later poems are free verse, based on the style of poetry made famous by Walt Whitman. *(Born 1913)*

KARL SHAPIRO

PERCY BYSSHE SHELLEY

Percy Bysshe Shelley is generally considered one of the great lyric poets of the English language. He was born in England but left there when he was twenty-four. He spent the last six years of his life in Italy. He was drowned while sailing off the coast of Naples. Among his best known poems are "To a Skylark" and "Ozymandias." His wife, Mary Wollstonecroft Shelley, is the author of *Frankenstein*. *(1792–1822)*

PERCY BYSSHE SHELLEY

JESSE STUART

JESSE STUART

Jesse Stuart, the son of a tenant farmer, was born in a small town near Reverton, Kentucky. He made these comments about himself and his writing: "I live on a farm, I have lived here all my life. I am interested in conservation of land and people too; I am interested in teaching. About my writing, I do the writing and let others make the comments." His works have been translated into all the major European and East European languages and several African languages, as well as Japanese, Persian, and Pashto. Jesse Stuart received a number of awards for both his poetry and his prose. *(1907–1984)*

ROSEMARY SUTCLIFF

ROSEMARY SUTCLIFF

Rosemary Sutcliff was born in Surrey, England. Her father was a naval officer, and during her first ten years of life she did not live in one place for more than two years. When she was ten years old, she entered an art school. She said that painting was her first love, "but writing has come to mean more to me than painting ever did." Her interest in writing began when her mother read aloud to her *Peter Rabbit, Winnie-the-Pooh,* and the books of Charles Dickens and Anthony Trollope. She has won numerous awards for her writing, including the Boston Globe–Horn Book Award and the Carnegie Medal Award. *(Born 1920)*

LOUIS UNTERMEYER

LOUIS UNTERMEYER

Louis Untermeyer was born in New York City. As the oldest of three children, it was often his job to entertain the younger children. Mr. Untermeyer wrote in his autobiography, "Fantasy was the most important part of my boyhood." He says he read all the poems and tales he could find. Many of these stories he then retold to his brother and sister. When he was grown, he continued to entertain young people by writing and editing books of stories and poetry. *(1885–1977)*

WALT WHITMAN

Walt Whitman is now considered one of the outstanding American poets, and *Leaves of Grass* is recognized as a great literary achievement. When *Leaves of Grass* was first published, it received unfavorable critical attention. In fact, Walt Whitman once was fired from a job because it was said that he wrote "immoral" verse. During the War Between the States, Walt Whitman worked as a hospital nurse with the sick and wounded. *(1819–1892)*

WALT WHITMAN

JAY WILLIAMS

Jay Williams wrote many books, both fiction and nonfiction, for young people. He said, "At the age of twelve I won a prize (it was a book) for the best original ghost story told round the campfire in a boys' camp. The experience went to my head and I have been telling stories to children ever since. Even my nonfiction has grown out of subjects which attracted me because they were good stories. And what is a good story? I have no universal definition, but for me it is one which binds teller as much as reader in a web of surprise, tension, and wonderment." *(1914–1978)*

JAY WILLIAMS

CHARLOTTE ZOLOTOW

Charlotte Zolotow has been quoted as saying, "Even at the age of three I had decided on my future. Whenever anyone asked me what I was going to be, I would answer, 'I'm going to be an author and illustrate my own books.' Only part of this came true. I have written books, but I have not illustrated them. While in the fourth grade, I composed my first essay. In it I pretended I was a Boston bull terrier wondering what school was. My teacher read the piece aloud to the class and made me feel like a writer." Her books have received many awards, including recognition as Caldecott Honor Books and Newbery Honor Books. *(Born 1915)*

CHARLOTTE ZOLOTOW

AUTHOR INDEX

W. Lawson Collection/© Susan Van Etten; 314–319, Royal Library, Turin, courtesy, Art Resource; 324, (t) John F. O'Conner, M.D./Photo Nats, (b) Margot Conte/Animals, Animals; 326, G. I. Bernhard/Oxford Scientific Films/Animals, Animals; 332–338, The Granger Collection; 368–380, from *West with the Night* by Beryl Markham, published in 1983 by North Point Press; 385, NASA; 386, Wendell Metzen/Bruce Coleman, Inc.; 389, Wayne Lankinen/Bruce Coleman, Inc.; 406, (t) from *The Universe: Past, Present and Future,* photo: Carlos Vergara, (bl) Vassar College Library, (br) National Optical Astronomy Observatories & Lowell Observatory, The Granger Collection; 407, (tl) Royal Observatory, Edinburgh, (tc & tr) James A. Sugar/Black Star, (b) Carlos Vergara; 433, (t) from *The Edge of the Cloud* by K. M. Peyton, illustrated by Victor G. Ambrus, published in 1969 by World, (c) from *Dragonflight* by Anne McCaffrey, published in 1978 by Ballantine, (b) from *Enchantress from the Stars* by Sylvia Engdahl, published in 1970 by Atheneum; 434, 25.3.182, The Metropolitan Museum of Art, New York; 450, Art Resource; 455–456, Art Resource; 458, Art Resource; 480, Robert E. Pelham/Bruce Coleman, Inc.; 482, D. Donne Bryant; 485–487, Art Resource; 488, D. Donne Bryant; 490, *Woman weaver,* Mayan, 700–900 A.D., photo by Laurie Platt Winfrey, Inc.; 506, Lee Boltin; 511, Culver Pictures; 513, Metropolitan Museum of Art; 516, (t) copyright © The British Museum; 517, (b) Robert Caputo, Stock Boston; 567, (t) from *Discovering Tut-ankh-Amen's Tomb* edited by Shirley Glubok, published in 1968 by Macmillan, (c) jacket illustration by Robert Lawson from *Adam of the Road* by Elizabeth Gray, illustrations copyright © 1942 by Robert Lawson, illustrations copyright renewed © 1970 by John Boyd, executor of the estate of Robert Lawson, all rights reserved, reprinted by permission of Viking Penguin, Inc., (b) from *Pyramid* by David Macaulay, published in 1981 by Houghton Mifflin Company; 601, Stuart Cohen/Stock Boston; 603, © Frank Siteman 1988; 604, North Wind Archive; 605, North Wind Archive; 606, © Frank Siteman 1988, Tom Pantages; 607, North Wind Archive; 608, Tom Pantages; 610, Ruth Lacey, Donald Dietz/Stock Boston; 611, Owen Franken/Stock Boston; 612, © Frank Siteman 1988; 614, Peter Laytin; 616, Richard Pasley/Stock Boston, Mike Malyszko/Stock Boston; 618, (b) H.W. Wilson Company; 619, (t) Tony Hauser, (b) Debra Cook; 620, (t) H.W. Wilson Company, (b) Charles Adams; 621, Barbara Walz; 622, Arni; 623, (t) Wide World, (b) © Tim Farley, Random House; 624, (t) H.W. Wilson Company; 625, (t) Wide World, (c) Ron Goor, (b) provided by author; 626, (b) Wide World; 627, (t) Associated Press, (b) provided by author; 628 (t) Viking Penguin, (b) provided by author; 629, (t) Richard W. Brown, (b) H.W. Wilson Company; 630, (t) Bettmann Archive, (b) H.W. Wilson Company; 632, (t) Bettmann Archive, (b) The Granger Collection; 633, (c) Rollie McKenna, (b) Bettmann Archive; 634, (t) Mark Morrow, (c) Dial Dutton, (b) Bettmann Archive; 635, (t) Bettmann Archive, (c) H.W. Wilson Company, (b) Harper & Row.

E F G H I J—VHP—96 95 94 93 92 91 90 89